W9-AYW-382

SRA

Connecting Math Concepts

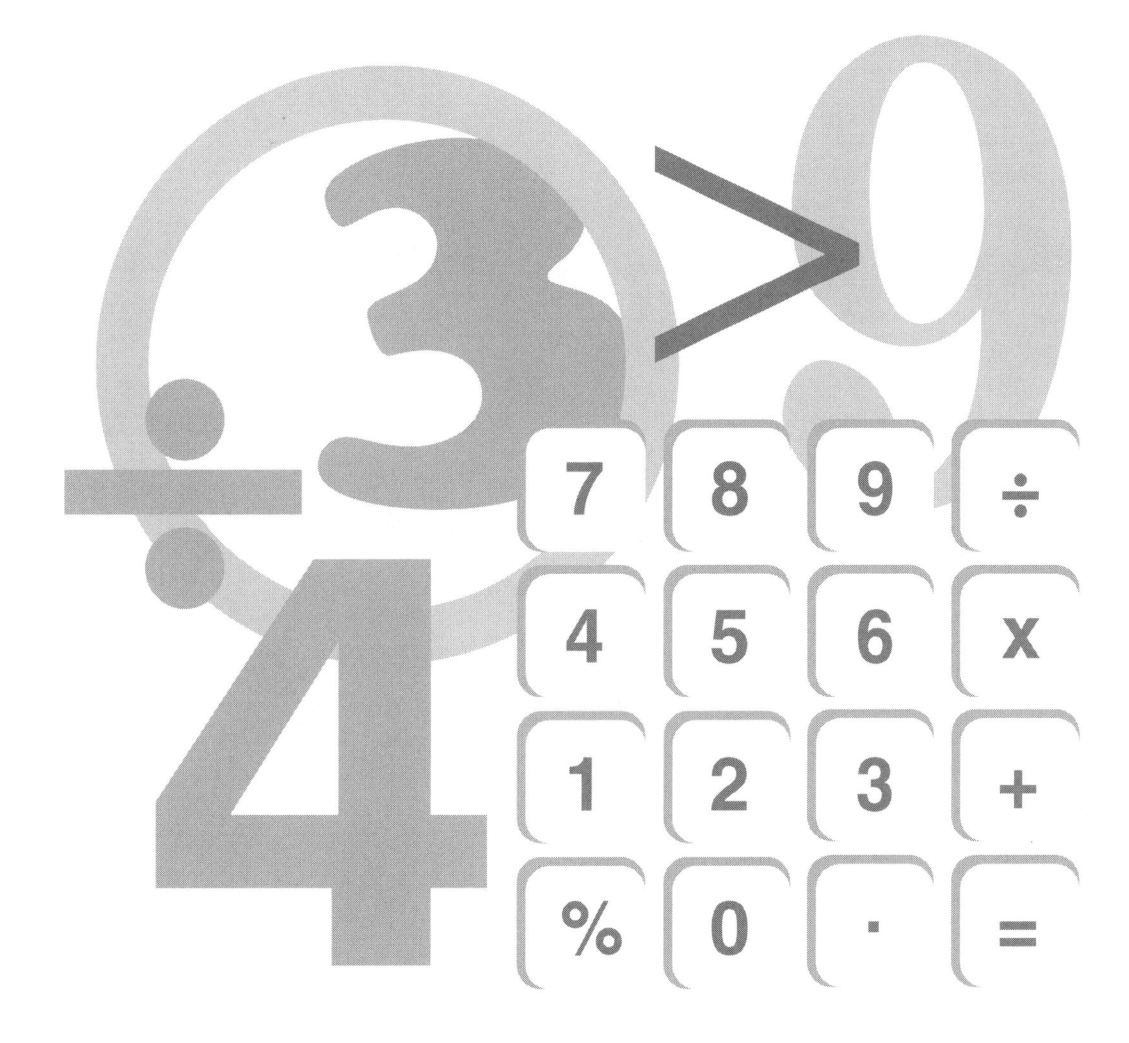

Columbus, Ohio

The McGraw-Hill Companies

Acknowledgments

The authors are grateful to the following people for their input in the field-testing and preparation of *Connecting Math Concepts,* Level E:

Lou Bradley
Bernadette Gilman
Debbi Kleppen
Lori McGinty
Juan Carlos Nolasco
Laurie Nowak-Crawford
Nelda Owsiak
Mary Rosenbaum
Christine Thurmond
Linda Van Hook
Roberta Weisberg
Tina Wells
Bryan Wickman

www.sra4kids.com

Copyright © 2003 by SRA/McGraw-Hill.

All rights reserved. Except as permitted under the United States Copyright Act, no part of this publication may be reproduced or distributed in any form or by any means, or stored in a database or retrieval system, without the prior written permission of the publisher, unless otherwise indicated.

Send all inquiries to:
SRA/McGraw-Hill
8787 Orion Place
Columbus, OH 43240-4027

Printed in the United States of America.

ISBN 0-02-684687-X

1 2 3 4 5 6 7 8 9 VHG 08 07 06 05 04 03 02

Contents

Program Summary

Facts about *Connecting Math Concepts, Level E*

Students who are appropriately placed in Level E	Students who have completed Level D or who pass placement test
Placement criterion	Pass placement test (see page 10)
Format of lessons	Scripted presentations for all activities Program designed for presentation to entire class
Number of lessons	Maximum 125 (including 12 test lessons)
Content	Lessons 1–15: Review of Level D Lessons 16–125: New teaching, extensions of earlier-taught concepts, and projects
Scheduled time for math period	50–55 minutes per period for teacher-directed activities Additional 15–25 minutes for independent work (homework)
Weekly schedule	5 periods per week
Teacher material	*Teacher's Guide* *Presentation Book 1* (Lesson 1–test 6) *Presentation Book 2* (Lesson 61–end of program) *Answer Key*
Student material	Program material: *Workbook* (Lessons 1–125) *Textbook* (Lessons 1–125) Additional materials: calculator ruler coins scissors tape measure or yardstick protractor colored pencils construction paper masking tape or thumbtacks
In-program tests	Tests 1–12 (tests follow every 10th regular lesson, i.e., Lesson 10, 20, 30, through 120) Final Test (follows Lesson 125)
Remedies	See page 37, Test Remedies

Scope and Sequence for

Connecting Math Concepts, Level E

Lessons

	1	5	10	15	20	25	30	35	40	45
TOOL SKILLS										
WHOLE NUMBER OPERATIONS										
Column Multiplication										
Division										
CALCULATOR SKILLS										
NUMBER RELATIONSHIPS										
Fractions/Whole Numbers										
Fractions/Decimals/Mixed Numbers										
Fractions/Decimals/Percents										
OPERATIONAL RELATIONSHIPS										
Inverse Operations										
Fractions/Division/Multiplication										
PLACE VALUE AND ROUNDING										
Whole Numbers										
Decimals										
FRACTIONS										
Analysis										
Addition/Subtraction										
Multiplication										
Equivalence										
Comparison										
Simplification										
WHOLE NUMBER PROPERTIES										
Prime Numbers										
Odd/Even Numbers										
MENTAL ARITHMETIC										
MIXED NUMBER OPERATIONS										
NUMBER FAMILIES AND EXTENSIONS										
Whole Number Operations										
Number-Family Tables										
Fraction Number Families										
DECIMAL OPERATIONS										
Addition/Subtraction										
Multiplication/Division										
COORDINATE SYSTEM										
Points and Lines										
Functions										
APPLICATIONS **PROBLEM SOLVING**										
Addition/Subtraction										
Number-Family Tables										
Multistep Problems										
Fraction Number Families										
Ratios and Proportions										
Multiplication/Division										
Inverse Operations										
Measurement										
PROBABILITY										
GEOMETRY										
Perimeter and Area										
Circles										
Surface Area										
Volume										
Angles and Lines										
PROJECTS										

The Scope and Sequence Chart shows where each track or major topic begins and where it ends. The chart does not show various lessons on which activities are presented. For more details on the lessons in which particular skills are taught, see pages 187–198.

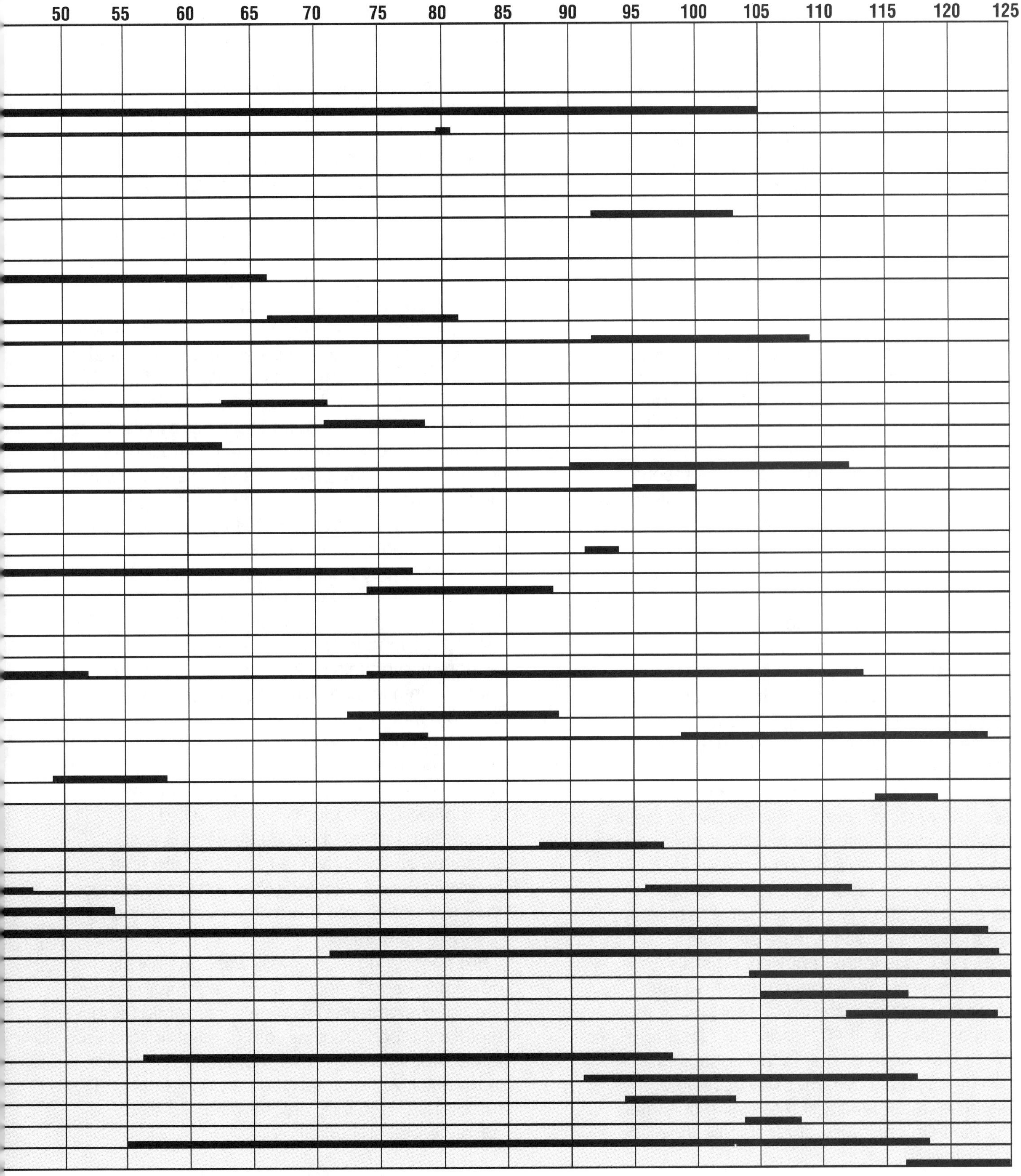

50 55 60 65 70 75 80 85 90 95 100 105 110 115 120 125

How the Program Is Different

Connecting Math Concepts differs from traditional approaches in the following ways:

Field Tested

Connecting Math Concepts has been shaped through extensive field testing and revision based on difficulties students and teachers encountered. This work was completed before the program was published. The field-test philosophy of *Connecting Math Concepts* is that, if teachers or students have trouble with material presented, the program is at fault. Revisions are made to correct the problems.

Organization

The organization of how skills are introduced, developed, and reviewed is unique. In traditional programs, the curriculum is called a spiral. The students work exclusively on a particular topic for several lessons. Then a new topic (often unrelated to the preceding topic) is presented. *Connecting Math Concepts* does not follow this format for the following reasons:

a) During a period, it is not productive to work only on a single topic. If new information is being presented, it is very easy for students to become overwhelmed with the information. A more sensible procedure, and one that has been demonstrated to be superior in studies of learning and memory, is to distribute the practice, so that, instead of working for 50 minutes on a single topic, students work each day for possibly 10 minutes on each of four or five topics.

b) When full-period topics are presented, it becomes very difficult for the teacher to provide review on the latest skills that have been taught. If the skills that have been taught are not used and reviewed, students' performance will deteriorate, and the skills will have to be retaught when they reappear. A more sensible organization is to present work on skills continuously (not discontinuously), so that students work on a particular topic (such as division) for part of 40 lessons, not for 5 or 6 entire lessons at a time. In this context of continuous development of skills, review becomes automatic and reteaching becomes unnecessary because students use the skills in every lesson.

c) When skills are not developed continuously, students are required to learn a lot of new concepts during a short period and are also expected to become "automatic" in applying the new concepts and skills. For most students, adequate learning will not occur. A better method is to develop skills and concepts in small steps so that students are not required to learn as much new material at a time, and so they receive a sufficient amount of practice to become facile or automatic in applying it.

d) When skills are not developed continuously, students and teachers may develop very negative attitudes about mastery. Students may think that they are not expected to "learn" the new material, because it will go away in a few days. Teachers become frustrated because they often understand that students need much more practice, but they are unable to provide it if they are to move through the program at a reasonable rate. Again, the continuous development of skills solves this problem because students learn very quickly that what is presented is used in this lesson, the next lesson, and many subsequent lessons. When the practice is sufficient, students develop the mind-set needed for learning to mastery because the skill is something they will need in the immediate future.

e) When lessons are not clearly related to periods of time, the teacher has no precise way to gauge the performance of the students or to judge how long to spend on a particular lesson. A more reasonable procedure is to organize material into lessons that require approximately 50–55 minutes to teach.

In *Connecting Math Concepts*, skills are organized in **tracks.** A track is an ongoing development of a particular topic. Within each lesson, work from four to seven tracks is presented. The teaching presentations are designed so it is possible to present the entire lesson in 50–55 minutes (although some lessons may run longer, and more time may be needed for lower performers).

From lesson to lesson, the work on new skills develops a small step at a time, so that students are not overwhelmed with new information and receive enough practice both to master skills and to become facile with them. Students, therefore, learn quickly about learning new concepts and realize that what they are learning has value because they will use it.

Connections

The teaching and the design of the tracks in Level E permit all students to learn connections that are typically presented but not mastered by students in traditional programs.

For the teacher and the student, the track design and the development of problem-solving skills means that anything introduced in one lesson will appear in later lessons. It will be further developed and integrated into a full range of problem types. It will later become a component skill in sophisticated applications.

An example of the connections and problem-solving applications is the work with whole numbers and fractions, proportions, percents, and probability. The flow chart specifies the major connections.

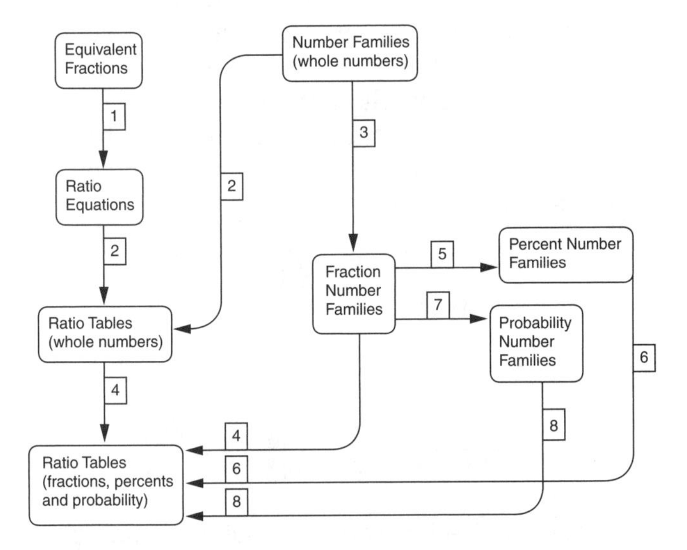

• **Link 1** shown on the chart relates equivalent fractions and ratio equations.

The solution to ratio problems is presented as an extension of equivalent-fraction problems in which a value is missing.

Here's an example of an equivalent-fraction problem:

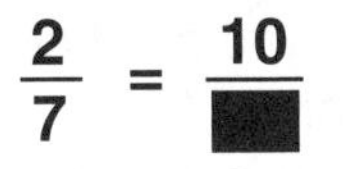

Students learn that if the fractions are equal, the first fraction can be multiplied by 1 to yield the fraction after the equals sign.

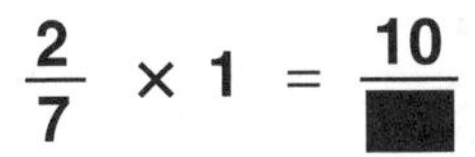

The solution to the problem requires students to identify the fraction that equals 1.

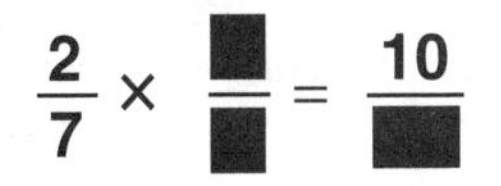

Students first determine whether they can work the problem on top or on the bottom. For this pair of fractions, they work on top because two numbers are given. The problem they work is: 2 times some value equals 10. The answer is 5. The missing fraction is 5-fifths, so the missing denominator is 35.

$$\frac{2}{7} \times \frac{5}{5} = \frac{10}{\boxed{35}}$$

Students use the same strategy to work basic ratio and proportion problems. For example:

There are 8 bees for every 5 flowers. If there are 72 bees, how many flowers are there?

The first sentence gives the names for the fraction and the numbers for the first fraction. The next sentence indicates that 72 is the number for bees after the equals sign.

Students apply what they know about equivalent fractions to figure out the fraction that equals 1. First they work the problem on top (8 times some value equals 72). Students write the fraction that equals 1 (9/9), and work the problem for the bottom numbers (5 times 9). The answer is 45 flowers.

$$\frac{\textbf{bees}}{\textbf{flowers}} \quad \frac{8}{5}\left(\frac{9}{9}\right) = \frac{72}{\boxed{45}}$$

Students practice problems that provide information about ratio numbers (The ratio of goats to sheep is 9 to 8) and problems that describe proportional relationships (There are 3 cups of flower for every 2 cups of milk).

• **Link 2** connects number families and ratio equations to a more complicated problem type.

A number family shows the relationship between three values that are related by addition and subtraction. The number family also serves as a template for showing the relationship between a class and subclasses—such as the class of children, which is divided into boys and girls, or the class of cars, which may be divided into cars that are new and those that are not new.

Here's how a simple word problem would be represented with a number family:

There are 56 children on the playground. 25 of them are boys. How many are girls?

Here's the family:

The "big" number is at the end of the arrow. That's the number for children. The other numbers are "small" numbers. To find the missing value for this family, students work the problem: 56 minus 25.

Here's another example:

There are 56 unripe apples and 42 ripe apples in a barrel. How many apples are in the barrel?

Here's the family:

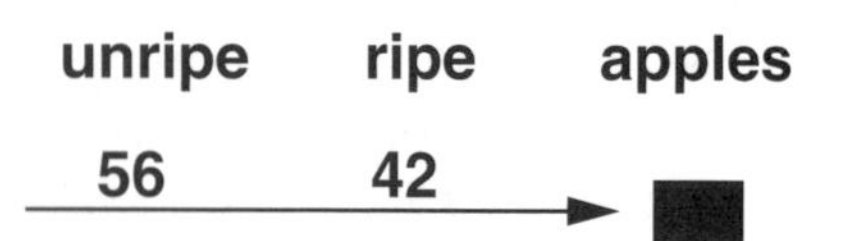

To find the missing value for this family, students work the problem: 56 plus 42.

The link between number families and ratios occurs because some ratio relationships involve the same categories that are represented with number families. Problems that express these relationships are different from simple ratio problems because they refer to three categories, not two.

Here's an example:

The ratio of boys to girls is 5 to 4. If there are 63 children in all, how many boys are there? How many girls are there?

Ratio numbers can be added. Therefore, the ratio numbers for **boys, girls,** and **children** can be represented with a number family:

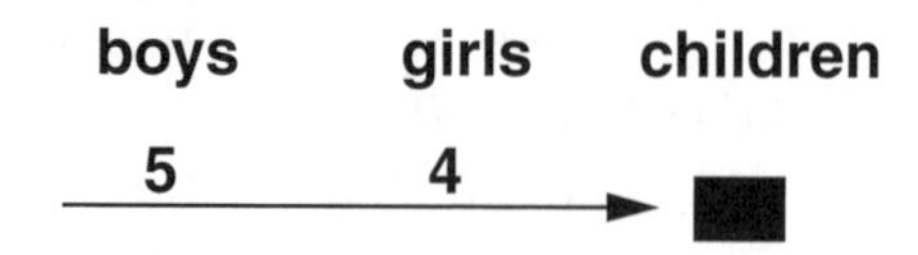

These values can also be represented with a "ratio table" that shows the ratio numbers in the first column and the actual number of children in the second column.

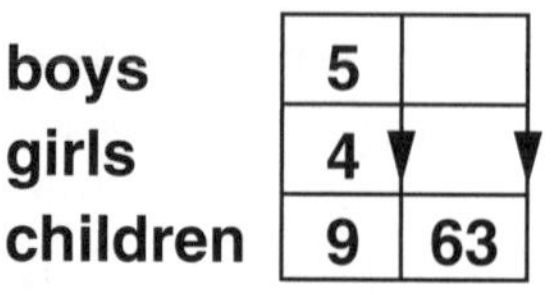

boys	5	
girls	4	
children	9	63

Each row of the table shows a multiplication relationship. Therefore, any two rows of the table can be pulled out and expressed as a pair of equivalent fractions. Students solve the ratio-table problem by constructing an equation that involves the row with two numbers and any other row. Either this equation:

$$\frac{\textbf{boys}}{\textbf{children}} \quad \frac{5}{9}\left(\blacksquare\right) = \frac{\blacksquare}{63}$$

Or this one:

$$\frac{\textbf{girls}}{\textbf{children}} \quad \frac{4}{9}\left(\blacksquare\right) = \frac{\blacksquare}{63}$$

Students solve the equation, put the missing value in the table, and figure out the other missing number by adding or subtracting. For example:

$$\frac{\textbf{girls}}{\textbf{children}} \quad \frac{4}{9}\left(\frac{7}{7}\right) = \frac{\boxed{28}}{63}$$

boys	5	■
girls	4	28
children	9	63

To figure out the number of boys, students work the problem: 63 minus 28.

- **Link 3** relates number families to fractions.

Fraction number families show fractions with the same denominator.

For example:

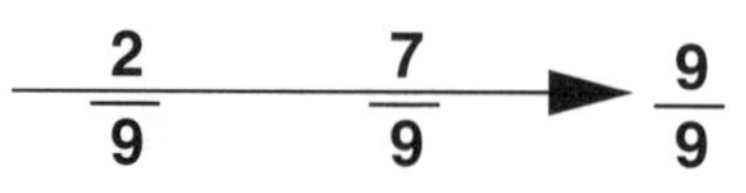

These families are used to solve word problems involving addition and subtraction.
For example:

4/7 of the children are girls. What fraction of the children are boys?

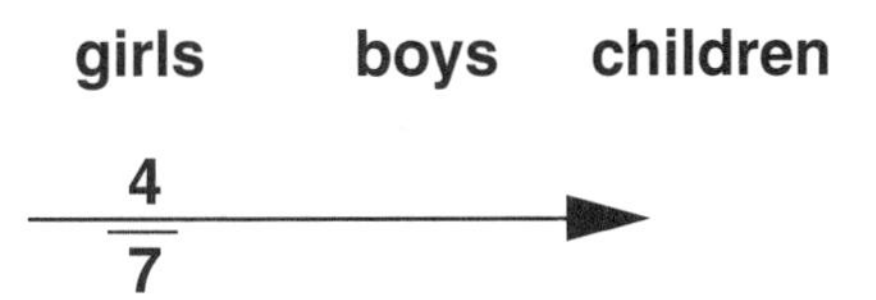

Students complete the number family. The fraction for the whole group (children) equals 1. That's 7/7.

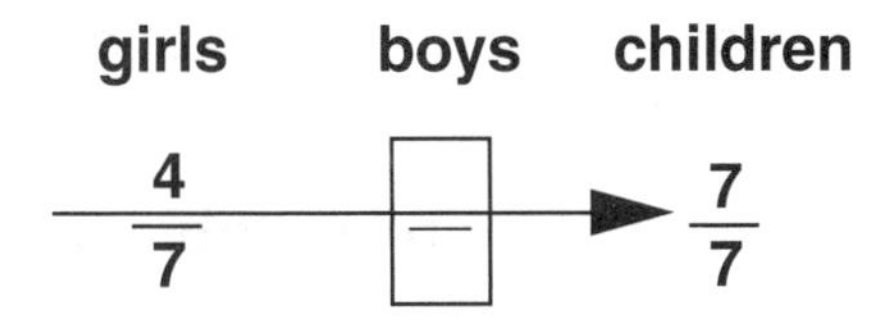

The fraction for boys is 3/7.

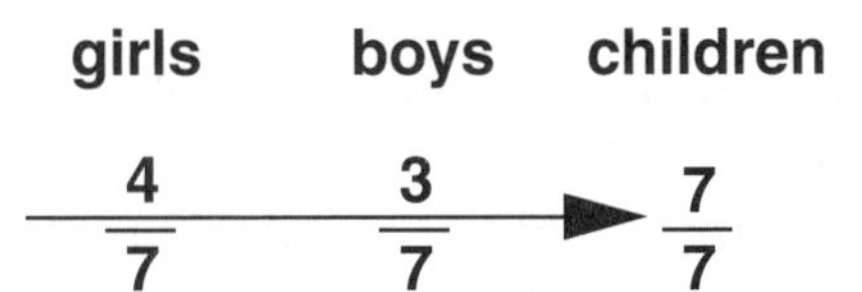

• **Link 4** extends fraction number families to ratio tables.
The extension is a ratio table that processes the information from fraction number families.
For example:

7/10 of the cars on Joe's lot are new. If there are 66 used cars, how many new cars are there? How many total cars are there on the lot?

Students first make the number family.

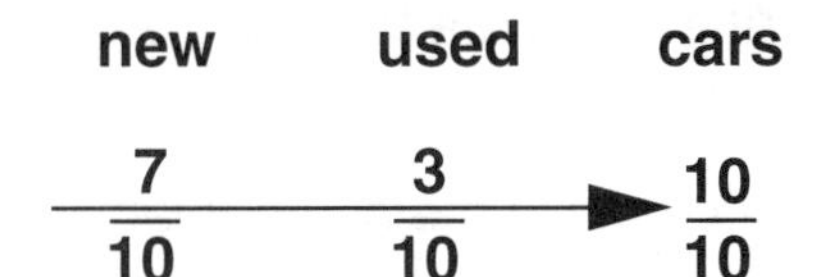

The numerators of the fractions are ratio numbers that go in the first column of the table.

new	7	
used	3	
(total) cars	10	

The problem gives a number for used cars. It goes in the second column of the table.

new	7	
used	3	66
(total) cars	10	

Students use what they know about ratio tables to solve the problem. They use the row with two numbers and one of the other rows.

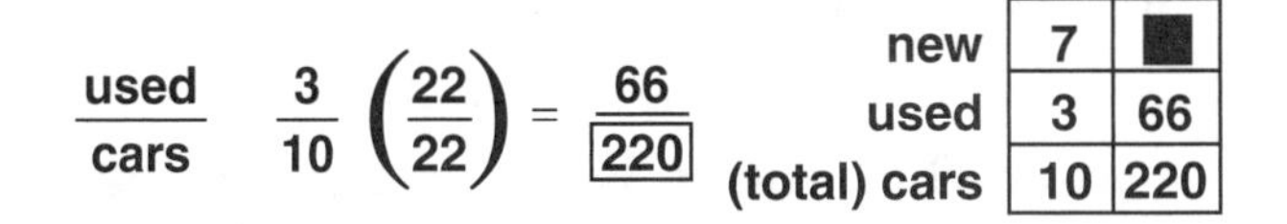

There are 220 cars in all. There are 154 new cars.

• **Link 5** extends fraction number families to percents.
Percents are fractions with a denominator of 100. There are two main problem types. One provides classification information. The other expresses comparison information.
Examples:

1) Classification

25 percent of the nails are rusty.

rusty	not rusty	nails
25/100	75/100	→ 100/100

2) Comparison

The regular price was 20 percent more than the sale price.

dif	SP	RP
20/100	100/100	→ 120/100

3) Comparison

There was 30 percent less rainfall in February than in March.

dif	F	M
30/100	70/100	→ 100/100

Note: Comparisons involve one whole—100 percent. The name that something is compared to is 100 percent. In the sentence, **The regular price is 20 percent more than the sale price,** the sale price is the basis for comparison. It is 100 percent. In the sentence, **There was 30 percent less rainfall in February than in March,** March is the basis for comparison. It is 100 percent.

• **Link 6** extends percent relationships to ratio tables.

Here's an example of a ratio-table problem:

Train A is 60 percent longer than train B. If train A is 360 meters longer than train B, how long is train B? How long is train A?

Students make the fraction number family.

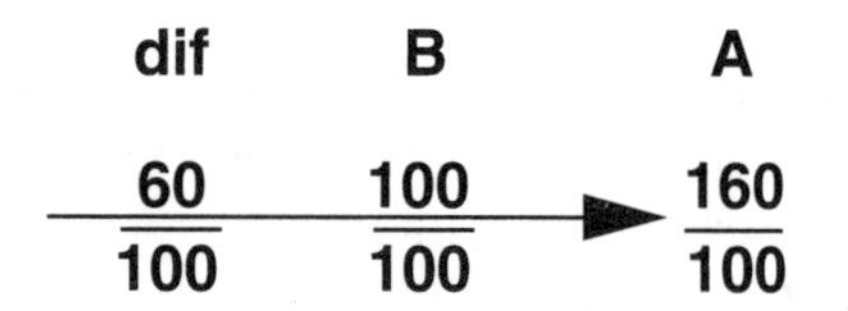

They make the ratio table with the numerators in the first column.

dif	60	
B	100	
A	160	

The problem gives a number for the difference. It goes in the second column.

dif	60	360
B	100	■
A	160	■

Students complete a ratio equation to figure out the length of train B or the length of train A.

Example:

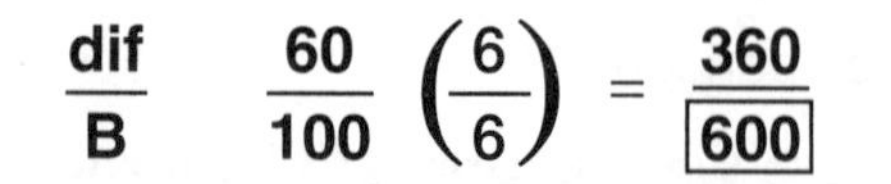

Train B is 600 meters long. So Train A is 960 meters long.

• **Link 7** extends fraction number families to situations involving probability.

All possibilities are represented by one whole, which is expressed as a fraction that equals 1.

Example:

In a bag there are 5 objects. 2 of them are circles.

The fraction for circles expresses the probability of pulling a circle from the bag (2/5). The fraction implies the fraction number family for **circles, not circles,** and the **total number of things** in the bag.

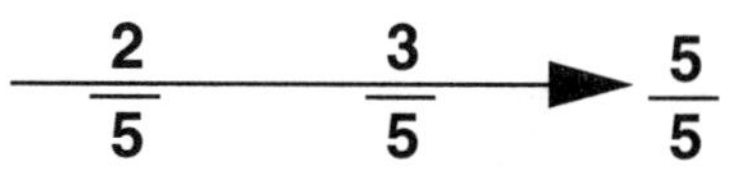

The fraction number family also shows the proportion of circles to not-circles. The proportion suggests what would happen if different numbers of trials were taken. If 5 trials were taken, the expected number of circles pulled from the bag would be 2. The expected number of objects that are not circles would be 3.

• **Link 8** extends probability relationships to ratio tables. By using a fraction number family, students can work problems that involve different numbers of trials. Example:

A bag has 8 objects in it. 3 of those objects are blue. If you took 56 trials, how many blue objects would you expect to pull out? How many objects that are not blue would you expect to pull out?

Students first make the number family.

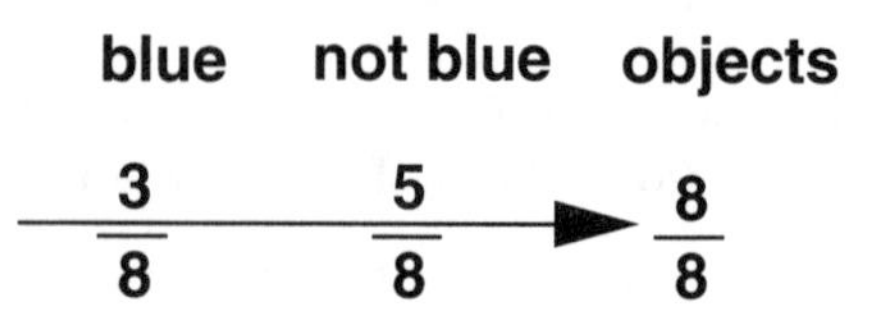

They put the numbers in the ratio table and figure out the missing values.

blue	**3**	■
not blue	**5**	■
objects	**8**	**56**

You would expect to pull out 21 blue objects and 35 objects that are not blue.

SUMMARY

The connections shown for equivalent fractions in Level E address the various problem types that are logically connected. The teaching for the links is provided. This same operational format applies to the other skills and problem types that are taught in Level E. The key concepts are identified and prioritized through exercises that provide students with the tool skills that are needed to work basic problems. More elaborate problems and extensions then connect the basic problems to conceptually-related problems and operations.

Placement

There are two placement tests. Placement Test A is for students who have not gone through Level D of *Connecting Math Concepts*. Placement Test B is for students who have completed Level D. Reproducible copies of the tests appear on pages 11–13.

Administering the Placement Test

Administer the placement test that is appropriate for the class. If none of the students went through Level D, administer Placement Test A. If some of the students went through Level D, administer Placement Test A. If all or nearly all of the students when through Level D, administer Placement Test B. If possible, complete the testing on the first day of instruction.

Pass out a test form to each student. Present the wording in the test administration script.

Note: What you say is shown in blue type.

When observing the students, make sure that they are working on the correct part or correct item of the test. Do not prompt them in a way that would let them know the answer to the item.

TEST A ADMINISTRATION SCRIPT:
FOR NEW STUDENTS ONLY

- Find part 1.
  You're going to write numerals that I dictate. You're going to line them up the same way you would if you were adding them. You can see 7 thousand, 3 hundred 24 is already written. That shows where you'd begin a thousands numeral.
  Numeral A. 2 thousand, 6 hundred 50. Write it.
  Numeral B. 11 thousand, 9 hundred 3. Write it.
  Numeral C. 7 hundred 9. Write it.
  Numeral D. 20 thousand, 45. Write it.
- You'll work the rest of the parts on your own. For part 3, read each problem. Write the number problem and the answer.
- For the rest of the parts, just follow the directions for working each item. Raise your hand when you're finished.
- (Collect test forms.)

TEST B ADMINISTRATION SCRIPT:
FOR CONTINUING STUDENTS ONLY

- This is a test. Follow the directions for working each part. Raise your hand when you're finished.
- (Collect test forms.)

Placement Criteria

The criteria for passing Test A are:

	Pass	Fail
Part 1	0–1 errors	2 or more errors
Part 2	0–1 errors	2 or more errors
Part 3	0–1 errors	2 or more errors
Part 4	0 errors	1 or more errors
Part 5	0–2 errors	3 or more errors
OVERALL	8 or fewer errors	9 or more errors
PLACEMENT	CMC Level E Lesson 1	CMC Level D Administer placement test

Is Level E appropriate for your classroom? A rule of thumb is that three-fourths or more of the students in the class should pass the placement test. If more than one-fourth of the students fail the placement test, it may be difficult to present Level E to the entire class. A recommendation is to place the lower performers in Level D.

The criteria for passing Test B are:

	Pass	Fail
Part 1	0 errors	1 or more errors
Part 2	0–1 errors	2 or more errors
Part 3	0 errors	1 or more errors
Part 4	0–1 errors	2 or more errors
Part 5	0 errors	1 or more errors
Part 6	0–2 errors	3 or more errors
Part 7	0 errors	1 or more errors
OVERALL	5 or fewer errors	6 or more errors
PLACEMENT	CMC Level E Lesson 16	CMC Level E Lesson 1

If more than one quarter of the students fail test B, begin instruction at Lesson 1 of Level E.

If three-fourths or more of the students pass the placement test, begin instruction at Lesson 16 of Level E.

Note: Students who failed the test need additional teaching and practice if they are to keep pace with classmates who start at Lesson 16. Try to provide that additional work, or place these students in a group that is working on material that is appropriate for these students (possibly at Lesson 1 of Level E).

Placement Test A (for new students)

Name ____________________ Score ______

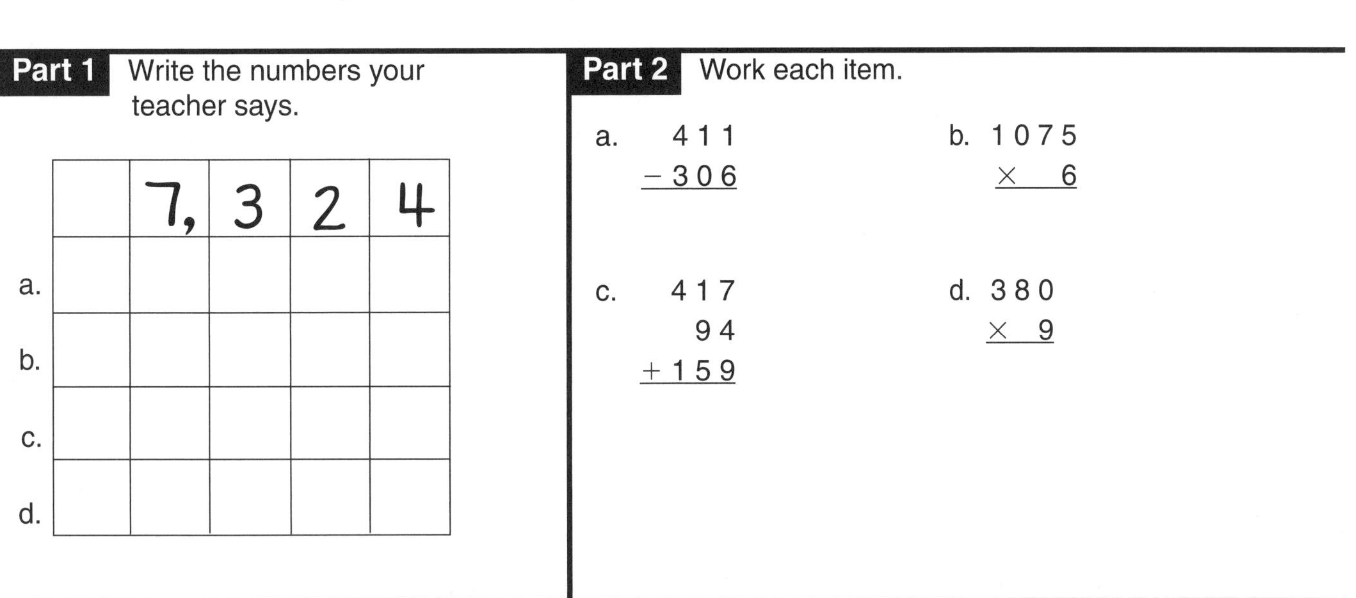

Part 1 Write the numbers your teacher says.

	7,	3	2	4
a.				
b.				
c.				
d.				

Part 2 Work each item.

a. $\begin{array}{r} 411 \\ -\ 306 \\ \hline \end{array}$

b. $\begin{array}{r} 1075 \\ \times\ \ \ 6 \\ \hline \end{array}$

c. $\begin{array}{r} 417 \\ 94 \\ +\ 159 \\ \hline \end{array}$

d. $\begin{array}{r} 380 \\ \times\ \ 9 \\ \hline \end{array}$

Part 3 Figure out the answer to each question. Show your work.

a. There are 37 students on the playground. 16 of the students are boys. How many girls are on the playground?

b. Phyllis had 48 dogs. She bought another 103 dogs. How many dogs does Phyllis have now?

c. A man had 59 stamps in his collection. He traded some stamps for coins. Now he has 45 stamps. How many stamps did he trade?

d. A truck started out with 2190 pounds of gravel. It delivered 2000 pounds of gravel. How many pounds of gravel were still on the truck?

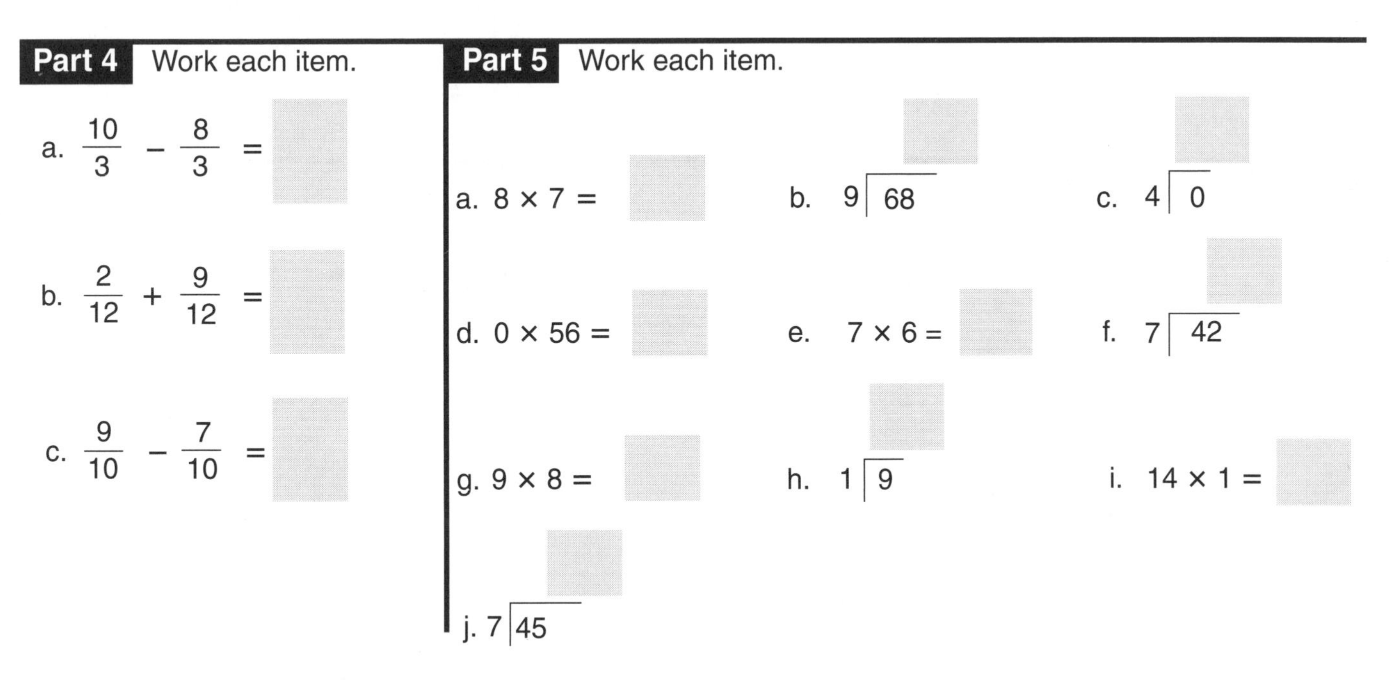

Part 4 Work each item.

a. $\frac{10}{3} - \frac{8}{3} =$

b. $\frac{2}{12} + \frac{9}{12} =$

c. $\frac{9}{10} - \frac{7}{10} =$

Part 5 Work each item.

a. $8 \times 7 =$

b. $9\overline{)68}$

c. $4\overline{)0}$

d. $0 \times 56 =$

e. $7 \times 6 =$

f. $7\overline{)42}$

g. $9 \times 8 =$

h. $1\overline{)9}$

i. $14 \times 1 =$

j. $7\overline{)45}$

Copyright © SRA/McGraw-Hill. Permission is granted to reproduce for school use.

Placement Test B (for students continuing from Level D) Name ______________ Score ______

Part 1 Work each item

a. $\begin{array}{r} 88 \\ \times 47 \\ \hline \end{array}$

b. $\begin{array}{r} 156 \\ \times 42 \\ \hline \end{array}$

Part 2 Complete the table.

Multiplication	Division
a. 4 × ☐ = 12	
b. 9 × ☐ = 54	

Part 3 Answer each question.

This table shows the number of deer and squirrels that live in Hill Park and River Park.

a. How many deer live in River Park? ________

b. What's the total number of squirrels for both parks? ________

c. In which park do fewer squirrels live? ________

d. What is the total number for both animals in both parks? ________

	Deer	Squirrels	Total for both animals
Hill Park	23	19	42
River Park	40	86	126
Total for both parks	63	105	168

Part 4 Write the fraction for each lettered arrow.

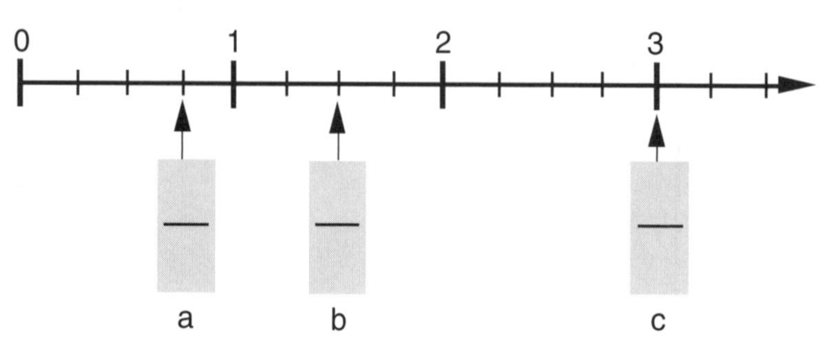

Copyright © SRA/McGraw-Hill. Permission is granted to reproduce for school use.

Part 5 Complete the table.

	Fraction Equation	Division
a.	$\frac{24}{3} = \square$	$3\overline{)24}$
b.	$\frac{28}{7} = \square$	$\overline{)\quad}$

Part 6 Complete the table.

			Total
		47	98
	28	72	
Total			

Part 7 Figure out the answer to each question. Show your work.

a. Robert is 25 pounds heavier than Adam. Robert weighs 96 pounds. How many pounds does Adam weigh?

b. The chess club has 31 fewer members than the band. There are 68 people in the chess club. How many people are in the band?

Copyright © SRA/McGraw-Hill. Permission is granted to reproduce for school use.

Placement Test A Answer Key

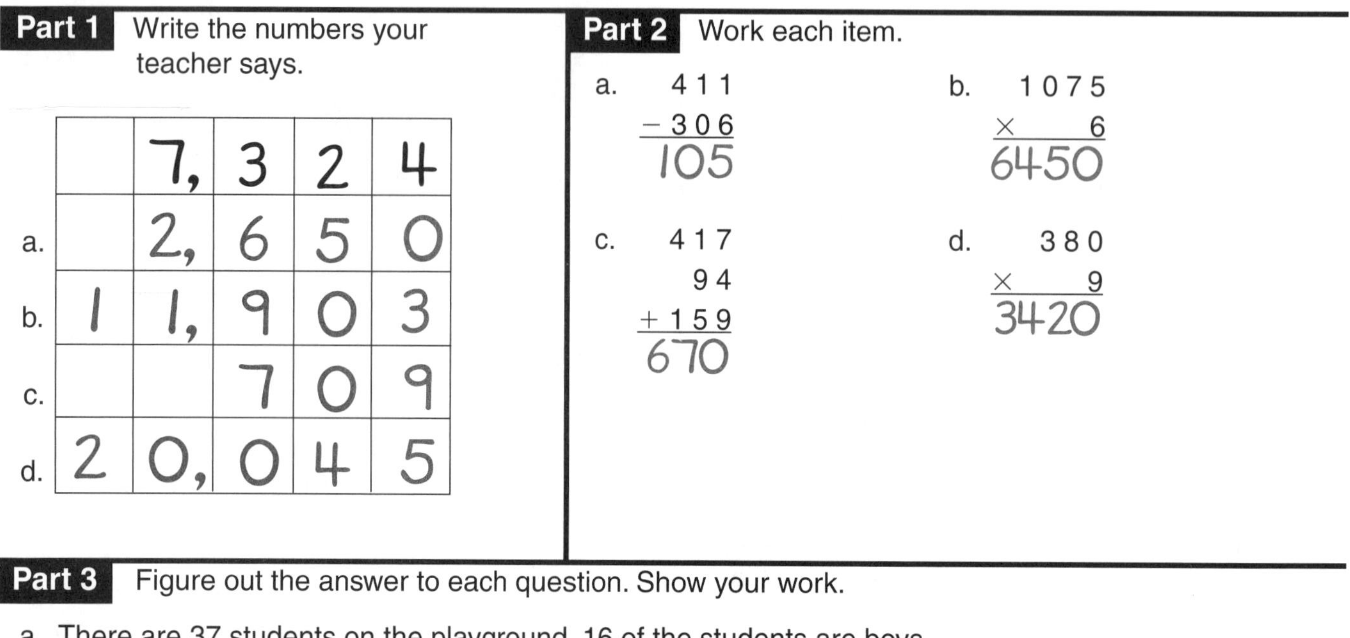

Part 1 Write the numbers your teacher says.

		7,	3	2	4
a.		2,	6	5	0
b.	1	1,	9	0	3
c.			7	0	9
d.	2	0,	0	4	5

Part 2 Work each item.

a. $411 - 306 = 105$

b. $1075 \times 6 = 6450$

c. $417 + 94 + 159 = 670$

d. $380 \times 9 = 3420$

Part 3 Figure out the answer to each question. Show your work.

a. There are 37 students on the playground. 16 of the students are boys. How many girls are on the playground? **21 girls**

b. Phyllis had 48 dogs. She bought another 103 dogs. How many dogs does Phyllis have now? **151 dogs**

c. A man had 59 stamps in his collection. He traded some stamps for coins. Now he has 45 stamps. How many stamps did he trade? **14 stamps**

d. A truck started out with 2190 pounds of gravel. It delivered 2000 pounds of gravel. How many pounds of gravel were still on the truck? **190 pounds**

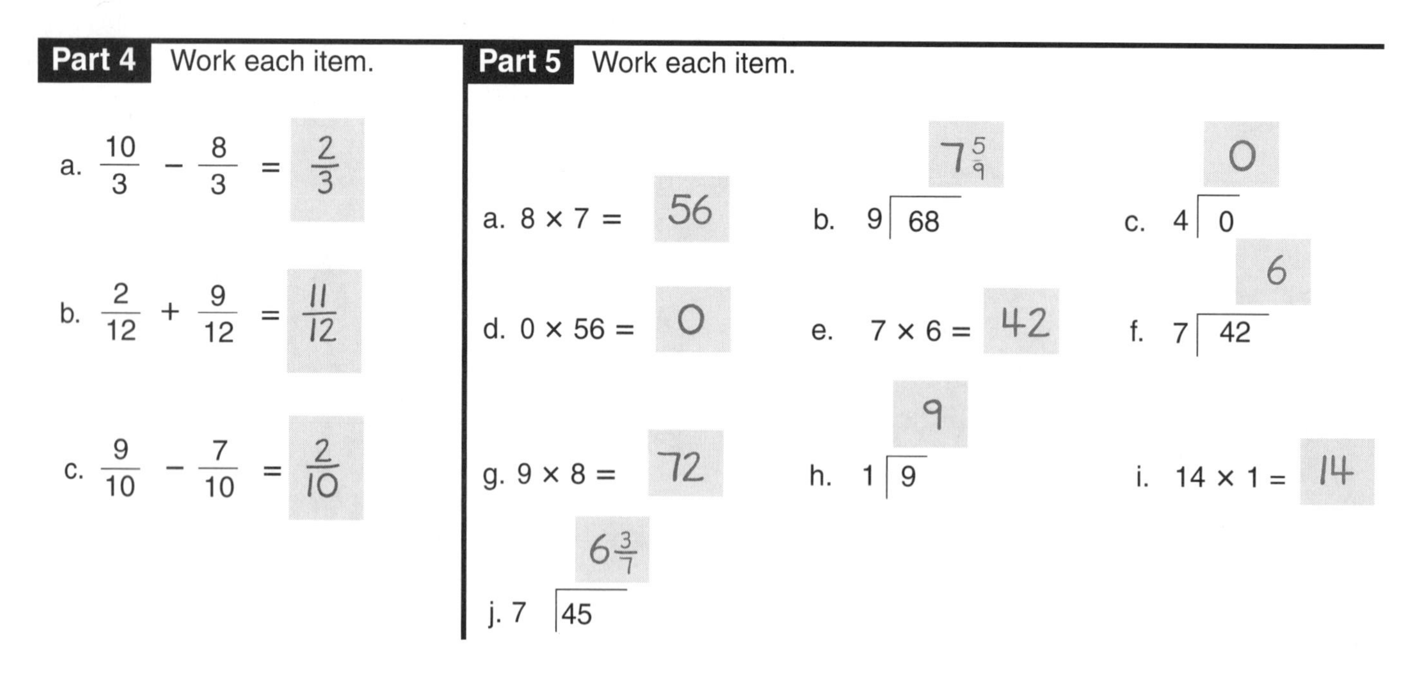

Part 4 Work each item.

a. $\frac{10}{3} - \frac{8}{3} = \frac{2}{3}$

b. $\frac{2}{12} + \frac{9}{12} = \frac{11}{12}$

c. $\frac{9}{10} - \frac{7}{10} = \frac{2}{10}$

Part 5 Work each item.

a. $8 \times 7 = 56$

b. $68 \div 9 = 7\frac{5}{9}$

c. $0 \div 4 = 0$

d. $0 \times 56 = 0$

e. $7 \times 6 = 42$

f. $42 \div 7 = 6$

g. $9 \times 8 = 72$

h. $9 \div 1 = 9$

i. $14 \times 1 = 14$

j. $45 \div 7 = 6\frac{3}{7}$

Placement Test B Answer Key

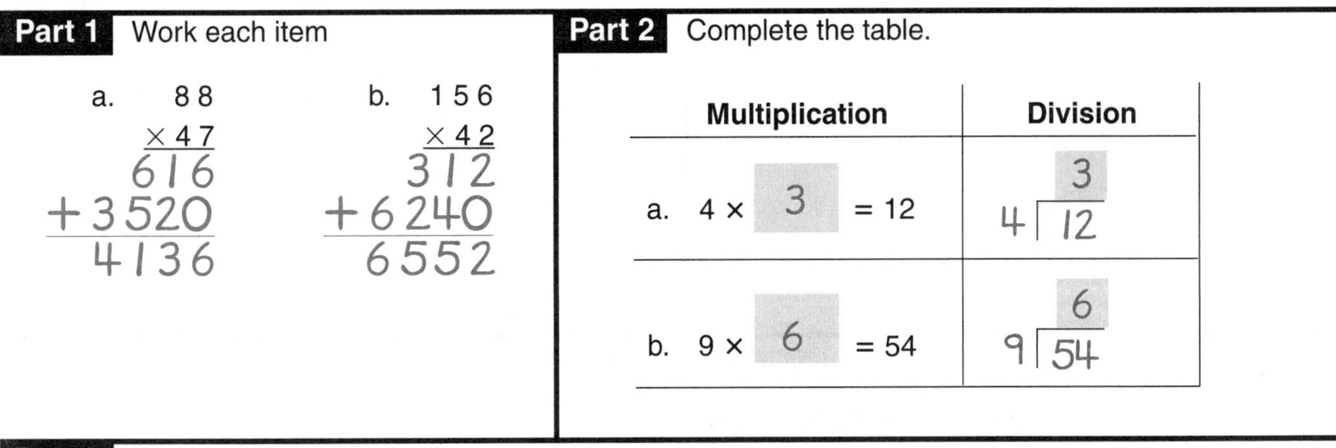

Part 1 Work each item

a.
$$\begin{array}{r} 88 \\ \times 47 \\ \hline 616 \\ +3520 \\ \hline 4136 \end{array}$$

b.
$$\begin{array}{r} 156 \\ \times 42 \\ \hline 312 \\ +6240 \\ \hline 6552 \end{array}$$

Part 2 Complete the table.

	Multiplication	Division
a.	4 × 3 = 12	$4\overline{)12}$ = 3
b.	9 × 6 = 54	$9\overline{)54}$ = 6

Part 3 Answer each question.

This table shows the number of deer and squirrels that live in Hill Park and River Park.

a. How many deer live in River Park? 40 deer

b. What's the total number of squirrels for both parks? 105 squirrels

c. In which park do fewer squirrels live? Hill Park

d. What is the total number for both animals in both parks? 168

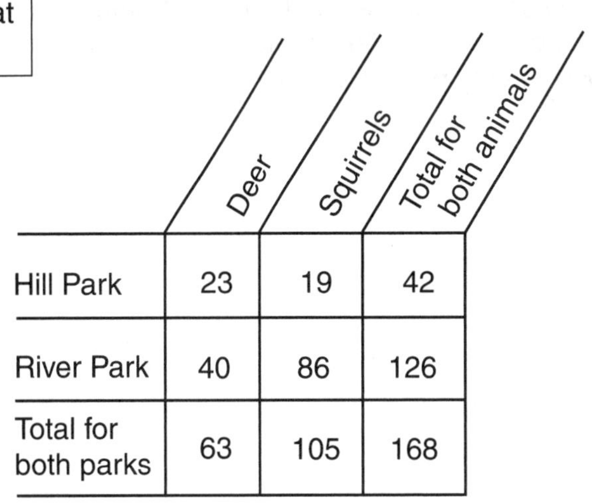

	Deer	Squirrels	Total for both animals
Hill Park	23	19	42
River Park	40	86	126
Total for both parks	63	105	168

Part 4 Write the fraction for each lettered arrow.

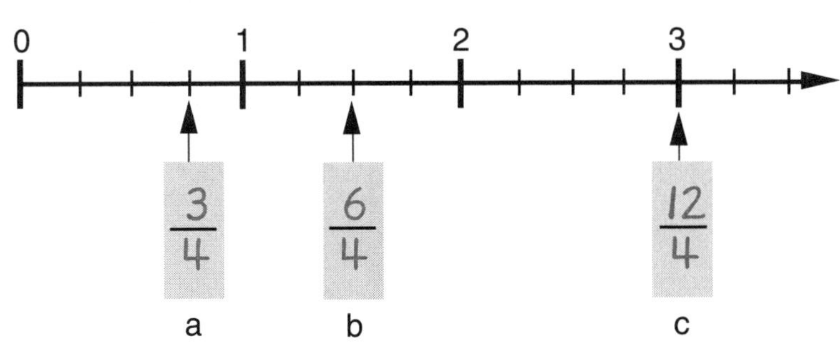

Part 5 Complete the table.

	Fraction Equation	Division
a.	$\frac{24}{3} = 8$	$3\overline{)24}$ = 8
b.	$\frac{28}{7} = 4$	$7\overline{)28}$ = 4

Part 6 Complete the table.

			Total
	51	47	98
	28	72	100
Total	79	119	198

Part 7 Figure out the answer to each question. Show your work.

a. Robert is 25 pounds heavier than Adam. Robert weighs 96 pounds. How many pounds does Adam weigh?

b. The chess club has 31 fewer members than the band. There are 68 people in the chess club. How many people are in the band?

Dif A R
25 → 96

$$96 - 25 = 71$$ pounds

Dif C B
31 68 →

$$31 + 68 = 99$$ people

Copyright © SRA/McGraw-Hill. Permission is granted to reproduce for school use.

Cumulative Tests

CMC Level E has cumulative tests following Lessons 30, 60, 90, and 120. The tests sample the various key skills and discriminations taught in the previous 30-lesson period, as well as important skills taught since the beginning of the level.

The tests appear in Appendix A, Cumulative Tests:

Each test has between 42 and 101 items. The cumulative tests require about 55 minutes to 1 hour and 15 minutes to complete. The teacher presentation for each test appears first, followed by the reproducible blackline masters.

The Percent Summary, Scoring Chart and Test Remedy Chart for each cumulative test is presented immediately after the teacher presentation in Appendix A. The answer key follows the blackline masters for each test. The last pages in Appendix A, after the answer key, are the Remedy Summaries for the Cumulative Tests. The Scoring Chart, answer key, Test Remedy Chart, and Remedy Summaries for the cumulative tests function like the corresponding elements of the 10-Lesson Test. (See 10-Lesson Tests p. 35.)

Scoring

Here is the Percent Summary and Scoring Chart for Cumulative Test 3. (Cumulative Test 3 follows Lesson 90, Test 9.)

CUMULATIVE TEST 3
PERCENT SUMMARY

SCORE	%	SCORE	%	SCORE	%
113	100	101	89	89	79
112	99	100	88	88	78
111	98	98–99	87	87	77
110	97	97	86	86	76
109	96	96	85	85	75
107–108	95	95	84	84	74
106	94	94	83	83	73
105	93	93	82	81–82	72
104	92	92	81	80	71
103	91	90–91	80	79	70
102	90				

CUMULATIVE TEST 3
SCORING CHART

PART	SCORE	POSSIBLE SCORE	PASSING SCORE
1	3 for each question	6	6
2	3 for each item	3	3
3	2 for each item	10	8
4	EACH ITEM Problem for perimeter 1 | Answer and unit name 1 | Problem for area 1 | Answer and unit name 1 | Total 4	12	10
5	3 for each item	6	6
6	2 for each item	4	4
7	2 for each item	6	6
8	3 for each item	6	6
9	1 for each item	7	6
10	1 for each item	3	3
11	3 for each item	6	6
12	Problem 1 | Answer 1 | Total 2	4	4
13	Prime factors for each number 1 | Total 6 | Least common multiple for each item 2 | Total 4	12	10
14	1 for each item	4	3
15	Only circled larger value 1 | Total 4 | Correct Sign 2 | Total 8	12	10
16	2 for each item	6	6
17	1 for each missing cell	6	5
	TOTAL	**113**	

The scoring chart shows how to score each item, the possible score for the part, and passing score for the part. This test has 17 parts and a total possible score of 113.

Remedies

Remedies are to be provided for each part that is not passed. Students do not pass a part if they score less than the number of points indicated in the column, "Passing Score."

A summary table provides information on the exercises in the program that are to be presented to students who do not pass a particular part. Below is the remedies summary that appears with Cumulative Test 3.

CUMULATIVE TEST 3 REMEDIES	
PART	**LESSON and (EXERCISE)**
1	47 (3), 48 (2), 49 (1), 64 (2), 65 (2), 66 (4), 67 (1), 68 (2), 69 (2)
2	27 (4), 28 (6), 29 (3), 30 (2), 31 (5), 32 (2)
3 a, b, c	74 (5), 75 (4)
3 d, e	71 (4), 72 (3), 73 (3), 77 (2), 78 (5), 79 (4)
4	58 (1), 59 (1), 61 (4), 62 (3), 63 (3), 64 (3), 65 (5), 66 (3), 68 (1), 69 (3), 70 (1), 72 (2), 74 (6), 75 (7), 76 (3), 77 (6), 79 (3), 80 (1), 81 (6), 82 (6), 83 (3), 85 (2), 86 (2)
5	74 (4), 75 (3), 76 (4), 77 (5), 79 (1), 80 (2), 81 (3), 84 (1), 85 (3), 86 (4), 87 (2)
6	31 (1), 73 (6), 75 (1), 78 (2)
7	59 (5), 61 (6), 62 (7), 63 (5), 64 (6), 65 (6), 66 (7)
8	43 (2), 44 (6), 45 (2), 46 (4, 6), 47 (6), 48 (6), 66 (2, 5), 67 (2, 5), 68 (3), 69 (5), 71 (5), 72 (4)
9	55 (2), 81 (4), 82 (4), 83 (5), 84 (6), 85 (6), 86 (6), 88 (5), 89 (6)
10	71 (1), 72 (1), 73 (1), 74 (2), 76 (2), 77 (1), 78 (3), 79 (2)
11	34 (2), 35 (2), 36 (4), 37 (1), 38 (5), 39 (2), 41 (3), 42 (2), 43 (1), 44 (3), 45 (3), 46 (3), 47 (5), 48 (3)
12	81 (2), 82 (2)
13	65 (3), 66 (6), 67 (3)
14	1 (5), 2 (1), 5 (4), 6 (7)
15	25 (2), 26 (1), 27 (1), 28 (4), 29 (1)
16	1 (2), 2 (4, 8), 3 (6), 4 (7), 5 (2), 6 (2)
17	22 (4), 23 (7), 24 (7), 25 (5), 28 (2), 29 (5), 30 (3), 31 (2), 32 (6), 33 (5), 34 (5), 37 (6), 38 (6), 39 (6), 41 (7), 42 (5)

For each part of the test that some students do not pass, you would present some or all of the exercises listed. (Present the exercises in the order they are listed. Present them only to the students who did not pass the part. Try to present the remedies at a time other than the regularly scheduled math period.) If students perform perfectly on a remedy, skip to the next new type of remedy exercise for that part. The objective for that exercise will be bold-faced.

The goal of each remedy is to teach students well enough so they can work items of that type in the context presented in the CMC program.

PLACING STUDENTS WHO FAIL 3 OR MORE PARTS OF THE TEST:

As a rule of thumb, if a student fails 3 or more parts of the test, the student is not placed properly in the program, which means that they will continue to have problems with the material. The ideal remedy would be to place students at a lesson in which they would be successful on about 90% of the tasks in each exercise.

PLACING MID-YEAR STUDENTS:

The tests may be used to place students who come in after the school term has started. Here are the steps:

(1) Present the Final Cumulative Test for CMC Level E

(2) Use the scoring chart to determine which of the parts the students passed.

(3) Place students or provide further testing.

If the student passed no more than 4 parts, place the student at the beginning of Level E, or test the student for placement in CMC Level D. If the student passes 19–23 parts, place students so they need remedies for no more than 2 skills. (See example on the next page.)

If the student passed 5 to 18 parts, give the student another cumulative test:

- Cumulative Test 1, if the student passed 5 to 10 parts
- Cumulative Test 2, if the student passed 11 to 14 parts
- Cumulative Test 3, if the student passed 15 to 18 parts.

If the student passed 24 to 27 parts of the Final Cumulative Test, place the student in CMC F.

(4) If you give the student another cumulative test, use the scoring chart for that test to determine which of the parts the student passed and which parts the student failed.

(5) Place students so they need remedies for no more than 2 skills.

Here's an example:

A teacher gives a student the Final Cumulative Test (step 1).

The test is graded and the student passes only 16 parts of it (step 2).

Then, the teacher gives the student the Lesson 90 Cumulative Test 3 (per step 3).

According to the scoring chart for Cumulative Test 3, the student failed Parts 3, 4, 8, 10, 12, and 13. The student missed problems b and c of Part 3.

The remedies table divides the problems for Part 3 into two sections—problems a, b, and c, and problems d and e. The problems the student in our example missed were in the section for a, b, and c.

According to the remedies table for Cumulative Test 3, the remedies for: Part 3 a, b, and c begin on Lesson 74; Part 4 begins on Lesson 58; Part 8 begins on Lesson 43; Part 10 begins on Lesson 71; Part 12 begins on Lesson 81 and Part 13 begins on Lesson 65.

Placing the student on or before the beginning of Lesson 65 would be an acceptable placement because the student would need remedies for no more than two parts of the Cumulative Test (step 5). The student would need remedies for only Part 4 and Part 8. The other "remedies" would be included in the upcoming instruction.

Placing the student beyond Lesson 65 wouldn't be acceptable because the student would need remedies for at least three parts—Part 4, Part 8, and Part 13.

Test Preparation Materials

Level E contains seven Test Preparation lessons that acquaint students with some of the formats and contents of standardized achievement tests. The material appears at the end of *Presentation Book 1.* It is placed there as a reminder that the time for test preparation work may be near.

Reproducible blackline masters for all seven Test Preparation lessons follow the teacher presentation for the test preparation lessons.

For each of the seven Test Preparation lessons, student need (1) a copy of the Multiple-Choice Response Sheet, and (2) specific pages from the test preparation student booklet.

The blackline master for the Multiple-Choice Response Sheet appears immediately following the teacher presentations for the test-taking program.

Connecting Math Concepts, Level E

Multiple-Choice Response Sheet

TEST PREPARATION LESSON ______ NAME ______________________

Sample A: A○ B○ C○ D● E○
Sample B: F○ G○ H○ I○ J○

1.	A○	B○	C○	D○	E○	29.	A○	B○	C○	D○	E○
2.	F○	G○	H○	I○	J○	30.	F○	G○	H○	I○	J○
3.	A○	B○	C○	D○	E○	31.	A○	B○	C○	D○	E○
4.	F○	G○	H○	I○	J○	32.	F○	G○	H○	I○	J○
5.	A○	B○	C○	D○	E○	33.	A○	B○	C○	D○	E○
6.	F○	G○	H○	I○	J○	34.	F○	G○	H○	I○	J○
7.	A○	B○	C○	D○	E○	35.	A○	B○	C○	D○	E○
8.	F○	G○	H○	I○	J○	36.	F○	G○	H○	I○	J○
9.	A○	B○	C○	D○	E○	37.	A○	B○	C○	D○	E○
10.	F○	G○	H○	I○	J○	38.	F○	G○	H○	I○	J○
11.	A○	B○	C○	D○	E○	39.	A○	B○	C○	D○	E○
12.	F○	G○	H○	I○	J○	40.	F○	G○	H○	I○	J○
13.	A○	B○	C○	D○	E○	41.	A○	B○	C○	D○	E○
14.	F○	G○	H○	I○	J○	42.	F○	G○	H○	I○	J○
15.	A○	B○	C○	D○	E○	43.	A○	B○	C○	D○	E○
16.	F○	G○	H○	I○	J○	44.	F○	G○	H○	I○	J○
17.	A○	B○	C○	D○	E○	45.	A○	B○	C○	D○	E○
18.	F○	G○	H○	I○	J○	46.	F○	G○	H○	I○	J○
19.	A○	B○	C○	D○	E○	47.	A○	B○	C○	D○	E○
20.	F○	G○	H○	I○	J○	48.	F○	G○	H○	I○	J○
21.	A○	B○	C○	D○	E○	49.	A○	B○	C○	D○	E○
22.	F○	G○	H○	I○	J○	50.	F○	G○	H○	I○	J○
23.	A○	B○	C○	D○	E○	51.	A○	B○	C○	D○	E○
24.	F○	G○	H○	I○	J○	52.	F○	G○	H○	I○	J○
25.	A○	B○	C○	D○	E○	53.	A○	B○	C○	D○	E○
26.	F○	G○	H○	I○	J○	54.	F○	G○	H○	I○	J○
27.	A○	B○	C○	D○	E○	55.	A○	B○	C○	D○	E○
28.	F○	G○	H○	I○	J○	56.	F○	G○	H○	I○	J○

The blackline masters for the student booklet corresponding to each Test Preparation lesson appear on pages 296–332 of *Presentation Book 1.* This material presents the items to which students respond. They respond by filling in the appropriate bubble on their Multiple-Choice Response Sheet. Students should not write on the pages of the test-taking booklet.

The pages for each student's test-taking material may be assembled into a reusable booklet that contains the Multiple-Choice Response Sheet items for all seven lessons.

Each test preparation lesson has teacher-directed activities. In the last exercise of each lesson, students learn test-taking strategies. These exercises present the test-taking strategies and provide students practice applying them.

Sample Lesson

Here is the teacher and student material for Lesson 4.

Test Preparation Lesson 4

Materials Note:

Each student will need:

- lined paper
- test booklet and Multiple-Choice Response Sheet for Exercises 1 through 6

EXERCISE 1
Distribution

Multiplying Numbers and Unknowns

a. (Direct students to find lesson 4 in their **test booklets** and write their names and indicate lesson 4 on their answer sheets.)

- (Write on the board):

$$5 \times 328 =$$

- Here's a problem. Read the problem. (Signal.) *5 times 3 hundred 28.*
- Say the addition for 3 hundred 28. (Signal.) *3 hundred plus 20 plus 8.*
- (Write to show:)

$$5 \times 328 =$$
$$5 \times (300 + 20 + 8) =$$

- Say the new problem for 5 times 300 plus 20 plus 8. (Point to each value as the students say:) *5 times 300 plus 5 times 20 plus 5 times 8.*

b. (Change to show:)

$$5 \times (A + 20 + C) =$$

- This problem is just like the problem you just worked, except you can't get a number answer when you multiply. I'll say the new multiplication problem. (Point to each value as the students say:) *5 times A plus 5 times 20 plus 5 times C.*
- (Write to show:)

$$5 \times (A + 20 + C) =$$
$$(5 \times A) + (5 \times 20) + (5 \times C) =$$

c. Tell me the answer to each part.

- What's 5 times A? (Signal.) *5A.*
- What's 5 times 20? (Signal.) *100.*
- What's 5 times C? (Signal.) *5C.*
- (Write to show:)

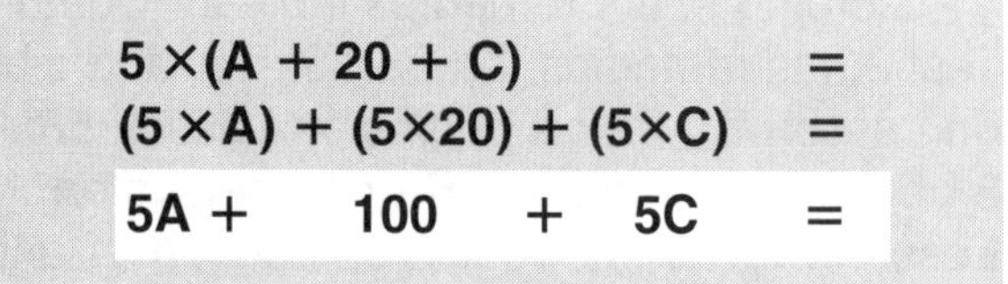

- That's as far as we can work this problem.

d. (Write on the board):

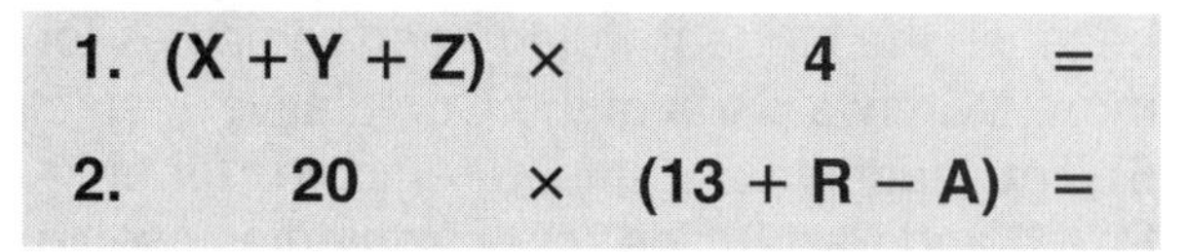

e. Read item 1. Get ready. (Signal.) *X plus Y plus Z times 4.*

- Say the new multiplication for that problem. Get ready. (Signal.) *X times 4 plus Y times 4 plus Z times 4.*

f. Read item 2. Get ready. (Signal.) *20 times 13 plus R minus A.*

- Say the new multiplication for that problem. Get ready. (Signal.) *20 times 13 plus 20 times R minus 20 times A.*

g. (Repeat steps e and f until firm.)

h. Your turn: Copy items 1 and 2. Below each problem, write the new multiplication.

- Raise your hand when you're finished.
- (Observe students and give feedback.)

- (Write to show:)

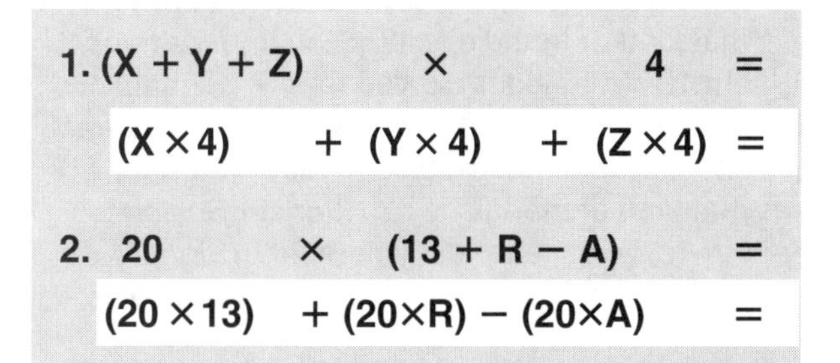

- Here's what you should have so far.

i. Read the first part of the new multiplication for item 1. (Signal.) *X times 4.*

- What does X times 4 equal? (Signal.) *4X.*
- Read the next part. (Signal.) *Y times 4.*
- What does Y times 4 equal? (Signal.) *4Y.*
- Read the last part of the new multiplication for item 1. (Signal.) *Z times 4.*
- What does it equal? (Signal.) *4Z.*
- Below the new multiplication for item 1, you'll write: 4X plus 4Y plus 4Z. Write what each part equals for item 1. Then finish working item 2.
- Raise your hand when you're finished.
- (Observe students and give feedback.)
- (Write to show:)

$$1.\ (X + Y + Z) \times 4 =$$
$$(X \times 4) + (Y \times 4) + (Z \times 4) =$$
$$4X + 4Y + 4Z =$$
$$2.\ 20 \times (13 + R - A) =$$
$$(20 \times 13) + (20 \times R) - (20 \times A) =$$
$$260 + 20R - 20A =$$

- Here's what you should have.

j. Item 2. What does 20 times 13 equal? (Signal.) *260.*

- What does 20 times R equal? (Signal.) *20R.*
- What does 20 times A equal? (Signal.) *20A.*
- So, 20 times 13 plus R **minus** A equals the expression 260 plus 20R **minus** 20A.

k. Look at the answer for item 1 again. What does the expression X plus Y plus Z times 4 equal? Get ready. (Signal.) *4X plus 4Y plus 4Z.*

l. Find item 1 in your **test booklet.** √

- (Teacher reference:)

1 $3 \times (500 + 40 + 7) =$
- **A** 216,290
- **B** 3,780,000
- **C** 1780
- **D** 5400
- **E** None of the above

2 $(6 + R + 8) \times 11 =$
- **F** $17 + 11R + 19$
- **G** $6 + R + 88$
- **H** $66 + 11R + 88$
- **I** $(6 + R) \times 19$
- **J** None of the above

3 $5 \times (2000 + 700 + 2) =$
- **A** 5×2702
- **B** $(5 \times 2000) + (5 \times 700) + (5 \times 2)$
- **C** $10{,}000 + 3500 + 10$
- **D** All of the above
- **E** None of the above

4 $8 \times (3R + 7 + T) =$
- **F** $24R + 15 + 8T$
- **G** $24R + 56 + 8T$
- **H** $(8 + 3R) \times (7 + T)$
- **I** 248RT
- **J** None of the above

5 $(3Q + 5 - 49) \times 2 =$
- **A** $6Q + 7 - 47$
- **B** $6Q + 10 - 47$
- **C** $6Q + 10 - 98$
- **D** $(3Q + 5) \times (2 - 49)$
- **E** $15Q - 98$

- Some of the answers for items 1 through 5 are numbers and some are expressions. Copy the items and work them. Then mark the best answers on your answer sheet.
- Raise your hand when you've marked answers for items 1 through 5.
- (Observe students and give feedback.)

m. Check your work.

- Item 1. 3 times 5 hundred plus 40 plus 7.
- What letter did you mark? (Signal.) *E.*
- Yes, E. The answer is: one thousand 6 hundred 41. It wasn't one of the choices, so you should have marked: None of the above.

n. Item 2. The quantity 6 plus R plus 8 **times** 11.

- What letter did you mark? (Signal.) *H.*
- Yes, H. 66 plus 11R plus 88.

o. Item 3. 5 times the quantity 2000 plus 700 plus 2.

- What letter did you mark? (Signal.) *D.*
- Yes, D. It equals: 5 times 2 thousand 7 hundred 2.
- It also equals 5 times 2000 plus 5 times 7 hundred plus 5 times 2.
- And it equals 10 thousand plus 3 thousand 5 hundred plus 10.
- You should have marked answer D, all of the above.

p. Item 4. 8 times the quantity 3R plus 7 plus T.

- What letter did you mark? (Signal.) *G.*
- Yes, G. It equals: 24R plus 56 plus 8T.

q. Item 5. The quantity 3Q plus 5 minus 49 **times** 2.

- What letter did you mark? (Signal.) *C.*
- Yes, C. It equals: 6Q plus 10 minus 98.

EXERCISE 2
Classification of Triangles

a. Find the triangles above item 7 in your **test booklet.** √

- (Teacher reference:)

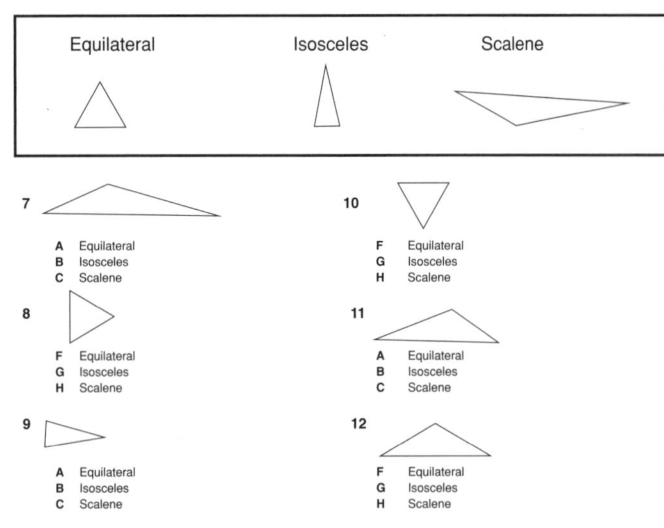

b. Touch the triangle labeled **equilateral.** √
- That triangle is an equilateral triangle. What kind of triangle? (Signal.) *Equilateral.*
- The equilateral triangle has three sides that are the same length.
- How many sides have the same length in an equilateral triangle? (Signal.) *Three.*

c. Touch the triangle labeled **isosceles.** √
- That triangle is an isosceles triangle. What kind of triangle? (Signal.) *Isosceles.*
- The isosceles triangle has two sides that are the same length. Touch the sides that are the same length in that isosceles triangle. √
- How many sides have the same length in an isosceles triangle? (Signal.) *Two.*
- How many sides have the same length in an equilateral triangle? (Signal.) *Three.*

d. (Repeat steps b and c until firm.)

e. Touch the triangle labeled **scalene.** √
- That triangle is a scalene triangle. What kind of triangle? (Signal.) *Scalene.*

f. Each side of a scalene triangle is a different length.

g. Once more: What do we call the triangle with three sides that are the same length? (Signal.) *Equilateral.*
- What do we call the triangle with two sides that are the same length? (Signal.) *Isosceles.*
- What do we call the triangle with each side a different length? (Signal.) *Scalene.*

h. (Repeat step g until firm.)

i. Find item 7. √
- For triangles 7 through 12, mark the letter that best describes it.
- Raise your hand when you've marked a letter for items 7 through 12. Don't mark an answer for item 6.
- (Observe students and give feedback.)

j. Check your work.

k. Item 7. What letter did you mark? (Signal.) *C.*
- What kind of triangle is it? (Signal.) *Scalene.*

l. Item 8. What letter did you mark? (Signal.) *F.*
- What kind of triangle is it? (Signal.) *Equilateral.*

m. Item 9. What letter did you mark? (Signal.) *B.*
- What kind of triangle is it? (Signal.) *Isosceles.*

n. Item 10. What letter did you mark? (Signal.) *F.*
- What kind of triangle is it? (Signal.) *Equilateral.*

o. Item 11. What letter did you mark? (Signal.) *C.*
- What kind of triangle is it? (Signal.) *Scalene.*

p. Item 12. What letter did you mark? (Signal.) *G.*
- What kind of triangle is it? (Signal.) *Isosceles.*

EXERCISE 3
Exponents

a. Find item 13 in your **test booklet.** √
- (Teacher reference:)

13 $5 \times 5 \times 5 =$ [?]
- A 3×5
- B $5 + 3$
- C 5^3
- D 3^5
- E None of the above

14 [?] $= 9^4$
- F $9 + 4$
- G $9 + 9 + 9 + 9$
- H $9 \times 9 \times 9 \times 9$
- I 9×4
- J None of the above

15 [?] $= 2^6$
- A $2 \times 2 \times 2 \times 2 \times 2 \times 2$
- B 2×6
- C $2 + 6$
- D $2 \times 2 \times 2 \times 2 \times 2$
- E 6×6

16 $8 \times 8 \times 8 =$ [?]
- F 3^8
- G 3×8
- H $8 + 3$
- I 8^3
- J None of the above

17 [?] $= R^2$
- A $2 \times R$
- B $R \times R$
- C $R + 2$
- D $R \times R \times R$
- E None of the above

18 $43 \times 43 \times 43 \times 43 \times 43 =$ [?]
- F 5^{43}
- G $43 + 5$
- H 5×43
- I 43^5
- J None of the above

- For items 13 through 18, you're going to figure out the complete equation with the multiplication and the base number and the exponent it equals.

b. Item 13 shows: 5 times 5 times 5.
- What's the base number? (Signal.) *5.*
- Yes, 5 times 5 times 5 equals 5 to what exponent? (Signal.) *3.*
- Yes, 5 times 5 times 5 equals 5 to the third.
- Say the complete equation for item 13. (Signal.) *5 times 5 times 5 equals 5 to the third.*

c. Item 14 shows: 9 to the fourth.
- Say the complete equation for item 14. (Signal.) *9 times 9 times 9 times 9 equals 9 to the fourth.*

d. Item 15 shows: 2 to the sixth.
- Say the complete equation for item 15. (Signal.) *2 times 2 times 2 times 2 times 2 times 2 equals 2 to the sixth.*

e. Item 16 shows: 8 times 8 times 8.
- Say the complete equation for item 15. (Signal.) *8 times 8 times 8 equals 8 to the third.*

f. Your turn: Work items 13 through 18.
- Raise your hand when you've marked the answers for items 13 through 18.
- (Observe students and give feedback.)

g. Check your work.
- Item 13 shows: 5 times 5 times 5.
- What letter did you mark? (Signal.) *C.* Yes, it equals 5 to the third.

h. Item 14 shows: 9 to the fourth.
- What letter did you mark? (Signal.) *H.*

Yes, it equals 9 times 9 times 9 times 9.

i. Item 15 shows: 2 to the sixth.
   What letter did you mark? (Signal.) *A.*
   Yes, it equals 2 times 2 times 2 times 2 times 2 times 2.

j. Item 16 shows: 8 times 8 times 8.
- What letter did you mark? (Signal.) *I.*
  Yes, it equals 8 to the third.

k. Item 17 shows: R to the second.
- What letter did you mark? (Signal.) *B.*
  Yes, R times R equals R to the second.

l. Item 18 shows: 43 times 43 times 43 times 43 times 43.
- What letter did you mark? (Signal.) *I.*
  Yes, it equals 43 to the fifth.

EXERCISE 4 Geometry Shapes

a. Find the figures in the box above item 19 in your **test booklet.** √
- (Teacher reference:)

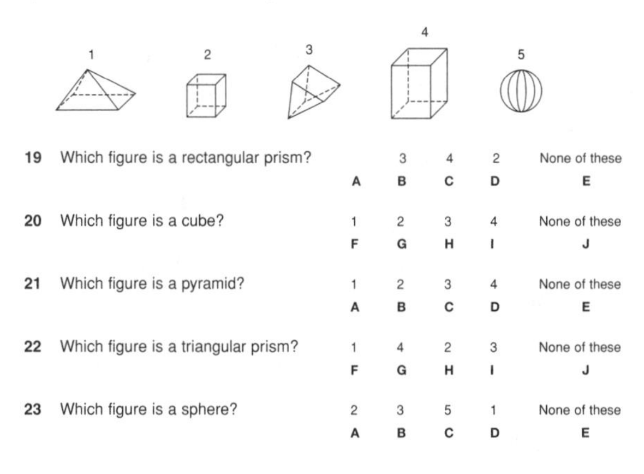

19	Which figure is a rectangular prism?		3	4	2	None of these
		A	B	C	D	E
20	Which figure is a cube?	1	2	3	4	None of these
		F	G	H	I	J
21	Which figure is a pyramid?	1	2	3	4	None of these
		A	B	C	D	E
22	Which figure is a triangular prism?	1	4	2	3	None of these
		F	G	H	I	J
23	Which figure is a sphere?	2	3	5	1	None of these
		A	B	C	D	E

- The first figure is a pyramid. Remember, a pyramid comes to a point.
  What's the first figure? (Signal.) *A pyramid.*
- The next figure is called a rectangular prism.
  What's the figure? (Signal.) *A rectangular prism.*
- The last figure is a triangular prism.
  What's the last figure? (Signal.) *A triangular prism.*

b. Touch figure 1 below the box. √
- What is the figure called? (Signal.) *A pyramid.*
- Touch figure 2. √
- What is it called? (Signal.) *A cube.*
- Touch figure 3. √
- What is it called? (Signal.) *A triangular prism.*
- Touch figure 4. √
- What is it called? (Signal.) *A rectangular prism.*
- Touch figure 5. √
- What is it called? (Signal.) *A sphere.*

c. (Repeat step b until firm.)

d. Work items 19 through 23.
- Raise your hand when you're finished.
- (Observe students and give feedback.)

e. Check your work.
- Item 19 asks which figure is a rectangular prism.
- Everybody, which figure? (Signal.) *4.*
- Which letter did you mark? (Signal.) *C.*

f. Item 20 asks which figure is a cube.
- Everybody, which figure? (Signal.) *2.*
- Which letter did you mark? (Signal.) *G.*

g. Item 21 asks which figure is a pyramid.
- Everybody, which figure? (Signal.) *1.*
- Which letter did you mark? (Signal.) *A.*

h. Item 22 asks which figure is a triangular prism.
- Everybody, which figure? (Signal.) *3.*
- Which letter did you mark? (Signal.) *I.*

i. Item 23 asks which figure is a sphere.
- Everybody, which figure? (Signal.) *5.*
- Which letter did you mark? (Signal.) *C.*

EXERCISE 5 Mixed Numbers to Improper Fractions

a. Find item 25 in your **test booklet.** √
- These are mixed numbers. You'll change them into improper fractions.

b. Work items 25 through 29. Don't mark an answer for item 24.
- Pencils down when you've marked answers through item 29.
- (Observe students and give feedback.)

c. Check your work.
- Item 25. Tell me the fraction for 3 and 2-fifths. Get ready. (Signal.) *17-fifths.*
- What letter did you mark? (Signal.) *D.*

d. Item 26. Tell me the fraction for 7 and 1-ninth. Get ready. (Signal.) *64-ninths.*
- What letter did you mark? (Signal.) *F.*

e. Item 27. Tell me the fraction for 2 and 4-fifths. Get ready. (Signal.) *14-fifths.*
- What letter did you mark? (Signal.) *B.*

g. Item 28. Tell me the fraction for 6 and 1-half. Get ready. (Signal.) *13-halves.*
- What letter did you mark? (Signal.) *G.*

h. Item 29. Tell me the fraction for 1 and 9-tenths. Get ready. (Signal.) *19-tenths.*
- What letter did you mark? (Signal.) *C.*

EXERCISE 6 Symmetry

a. Find the figures above item 31 in your **test booklet.** √
- (Teacher reference:)

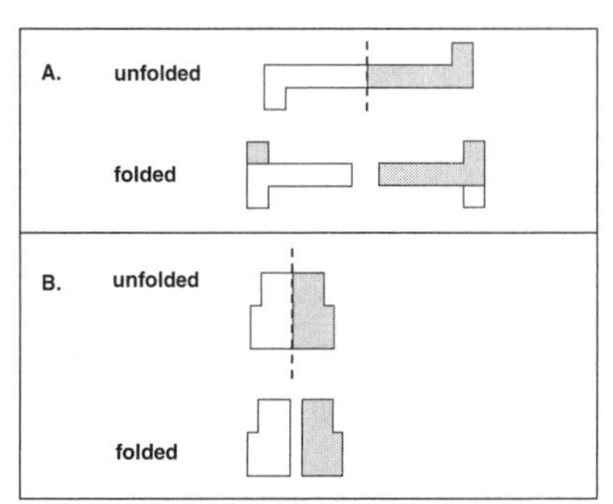

- Picture A shows a figure that cannot be folded so that both halves look like halves of the original figure.
- Below the unfolded figure in picture A, you can see both sides of the folded figure. On the left, you can see the folded figure with the white side showing. You can see parts of the shaded side sticking out.
- To the right, you can see the folded figure with the shaded side showing. Part of the white side is sticking out.

b. Touch the unfolded figure in picture B. √
- If you folded it along the dotted line, the folded figure would look like both halves of the original figure.
- You can see both sides of the folded figure below. When it's turned so that the white side is showing, it looks just like the white side of the original figure.
- When the folded figure is turned so that the shaded side is showing, it looks just like the shaded side of the original.
- So, one of the features of figure B is that it's symmetrical.
- What is a feature of figure B? **(Signal.)** *It's symmetrical.*

c. Find item 31. √
- One of the figures is symmetrical. It can be folded along the dotted line so that the two halves are the same. Work item 31. √
- Item 31. What letter did you mark? **(Signal.)** *A.* Yes, A is the only figure that will have identical sides when they are folded. The dotted line for figure A shows a line of symmetry.

d. Work item 32.
- Raise your hand when you've marked your answer. √
- Item 32. What letter did you mark? **(Signal.)** *I.* Yes, I. The dotted line for I shows a line of symmetry.

e. Item 33 is different. Item 33 asks: Which figure **does not** have a line of symmetry?
- Work item 33.
- Raise your hand when you've marked your answer. √
- Item 33. What letter did you mark? **(Signal.)** *C.* Yes, C. Figure C does not have a line of symmetry.

f. Work items 34 and 35.
- Raise your hand when you've done that much. √

g. Check your work.
- Item 34. What letter did you mark? **(Signal.)** *J.* Yes, figure J is the only figure that doesn't have a line of symmetry.

h. Item 35. What letter did you mark? **(Signal.)** *B.* Yes, figure B is the only figure that has a line of symmetry.

i. The figures in item 36 don't have lines shown. One of them does have a line of symmetry.
- Mark the letter of the figure that has a line of symmetry.
- Raise your hand when you've done that much. √
- Item 36. What letter did you mark? **(Signal.)** *G.* Yes, because you could fold figure G so that both sides match, it has a line of symmetry. None of the other figures has a line of symmetry.

j. Item 37. One of the figures does **not** have a line of symmetry. All the others do. Mark the letter of the figure that doesn't have a line of symmetry.
- Raise your hand when you've done that much. √
- Item 37. What letter did you mark? **(Signal.)** *D.* Yes, each of the other figures has a line of symmetry. None of the other figures has a line of symmetry.

k. Work items 38 and 39.
- Raise your hand when you've done that much. √

l. Check your work.
- Item 38. What letter did you mark? **(Signal.)** *H.* Yes, that figure has a line of symmetry because you could fold it so that both halves match.

m. Item 39. What letter did you mark? **(Signal.)** *A.* Yes, A is the only figure that doesn't have a line of symmetry.

EXERCISE 7
Averages

a. For some problems, you have to find the average. If you wanted to find the average temperature for 16 days, what would you do? **(Call on a student. Idea:** *Add the temperatures for the 16 days, then divide by 16.***)**
- Yes, add the temperatures for the 16 days, and then divide by 16.
- If you wanted to find the average temperature for 9 days, what would you do? **(Signal.)** *Add the temperatures for the 9 days, then divide by 9.*

b. Find item 41 in your **test booklet.** √
- To find the average score that 6 students got on a test, you add up the 6 scores. Then what do you do? **(Signal.)** *Divide by 6.*
- Mark the choice that shows what you'd do. Don't mark an answer for item 40.
- Raise your hand when you've marked an answer for item 41. √
- Everybody, first you add up all the scores. Then what do you do? **(Signal.)** *Divide by 6.*
- What letter did you mark? **(Signal)** *C.* You divide by 6 to find the average score that 6 students got on a test.

c. Work items 42 and 43.
- Raise your hand when you've finished. √

d. Check your work.
- Item 42 says: To find the average height of 9 students, you add up all the heights. Then what do you do? **(Signal.)** *Divide by 9.*
- What letter did you mark? **(Signal.)** *G.*

e. Item 43 says: To find the average price of 11 watches, what do you do? **(Call on a student. Idea:** *Add all the prices and divide by 11.***)**
- What letter did you mark? **(Signal.)** *D.*

EXERCISE 8
Test-Taking Rules
What to Do When You're Running Out of Time

a. There are three rules that help you do well when you're taking a test.
b. Who can tell me rule 1? (Call on a student. Praise close responses to the rule: *Work the problems that you can work.*)
- Yes, rule 1 is: Work the problems that you can work.
- Everybody, what's rule 1? (Signal.) *Work the problems that you can work.*

c. What does that rule mean if you're working a hard problem? (Call on a student. Idea: *Write the problem on your paper and work it.*)
- Yes, don't try to do hard problems in your head. Work them on paper.

d. Who can tell me rule 2? (Call on a student. Praise close responses to the rule: *If you can't work a problem, skip it and come back to it.*)
- Yes, rule 2 is: If you can't work a problem, skip it and come back to it.
- Everybody, what's rule 2? (Signal.) *If you can't work a problem, skip it and come back to it.*

e. Who can tell me rule 3? (Call on a student. Praise close responses to the rule: *Make sure that each problem has one and only one answer.*)
- Yes, rule 3 is: Make sure that each problem has one and only one answer.
- Everybody, what's rule 3? (Signal.) *Make sure that each problem has one and only one answer.*

f. Look at your answer sheet and find the first item you'd mark if there was only one minute left.
- Everybody, what's the number of the first item you'd mark? (Signal.) *6.*
- Find the next item you'd mark. What's the number of the next item? (Signal.) *24.*
- What's the number of the next item you'd mark? (Signal.) *30.*
- What's the number of the next item you'd mark? (Signal.) *40.*
- What's the number of the next item you'd mark? (Signal.) *44.*
- What's the number of the **last** item you'd mark? (Signal.) *56.*

g. (Repeat step f until firm.)
h. We're going to pretend you're taking a test, and there's not much time left. You haven't answered items 6, 24, 30, 40, and 44 through 56. So, when I tell you there's only one minute left, you'll mark one and only one answer for each of those items.
i. Get ready to mark the answers. After you're finished, we'll find out how many more points you scored by following the rules for doing well on tests.
j. Here we go. There is only one minute left. Finish up your paper.
k. (Reinforce students who quickly fill in one and only one answer for all of the problems on the answer sheet.)
- (Prompt students who don't fill answers in quickly to start marking answers more quickly.)
- (Alert students who have more than one answer filled in on any items to make sure that there's only one answer per item.)

l. (After one minute, direct students to correct their answer sheet.)
m. Check your work.
- For the items you just marked, I'll tell you the make-believe answer. Mark it with a **C** if you marked the correct answer and an **X** if you didn't mark it. Raise your hand after I say each answer if you guessed the right one.
- Item 6. The answer is **I.** (Acknowledge students who raise their hands.)
- Item 24. The answer is **H.** (Acknowledge students who raise their hands.)
- (Repeat for items: 30, G; 40, I; 44, J; 45, E; 46, G; 47, D; 48, F; 49, C; 50, G; 51, D; 52, H; 53, A; 54, J; 55, B; 56, F.)

n. Count the Cs you wrote next to the numbers.
- Raise your hand if you got six or more of them correct. (Students respond.)
- Raise your hand if you got five of the items correct. (Students respond.)

o. (Repeat for four, three, two, one, and zero of them correct.)
- Most of you got two to four of the items correct. You wouldn't have gotten any of these problems correct if you hadn't filled in answers for those items.

Test-Taking Strategies

The Test Preparation material teaches three critical test-taking strategies, in addition to acquainting students with some of the formats and content of standardized achievement tests. In Lesson 1, Exercise 7, the three strategies are introduced:

(1) Work the problems that you can work.
(2) If you don't know how to work a problem, skip it and come back to it.
(3) Make sure that each problem has one and only one answer.

Students are taught what each rule means, and they are taught to apply the rules. The first rule, "Work the problems that you can work," means that students should write down the problems that they can't work in their head and work them to figure out the answer. Exercises 1 and 3 of Test Preparation Lesson 4 show examples of problem types students are trained to work on paper. In Exercise 1, students are directed to copy each item and distribute the product before marking the answer. In Exercise 3, students are directed to copy and complete each equation with exponents before marking the answer.

Students who are not taught this strategy often perform poorly on standardized tests because they incorrectly answer problems that they know how to work. These students don't write down and work those problems because the test directions don't tell them to, and consequently, they get the answer wrong.

Throughout the remaining lessons, students are trained to apply this strategy and work various types of problems.

Students are taught that the second rule, "If you don't know how to work a problem, skip it and come back to it," means that they should not spend a lot of time on problems that they don't know how to work. Students should skip problems that they can't work and come back to them if they have time. Sometimes students who take standardized tests spend too much time on one problem and don't have time to answer many problems that they are capable of answering correctly. The practice students receive in the CMC Test Preparation program teaches them how to avoid spending too much time on problems they can't work quickly.

The last rule, "Make sure that each item has one and only one answer," means that when there is only one minute remaining in the test, students should guess on the items that aren't filled in and mark one answer for each of them. Exercise 7 of Lesson 1 teaches students to look over their answer sheet and identify the items that are not filled in. Earlier in Test Preparation Lesson 1, students were directed to skip items 8 and 16. These items were omitted to provide students practice in identifying items that are not filled in.

During Lessons 2–7, students are directed to skip a few items on their Multiple-Choice Response Sheet. On the last exercise of these lessons, the teacher tells students to pretend that there is only one minute left and they are to mark answers for all items that don't have answers. Students mark an answer for each item. At the end of the exercise, the teacher indicates the correct answers for items that students did not mark. Students mark the correct answers and tally the number of correct guesses for those items to see how much their score improved by guessing.

Teaching the Program

Level E is designed to be presented to the entire class. You should generally be able to teach one lesson during a 50–55 minute period. Students' independent work requires another 15–25 minutes. The independent work is usually scheduled as homework.

Organization

- Arrange seating so you can receive very quick information on high performers and lower performers. A good plan is to organize the students something like this:

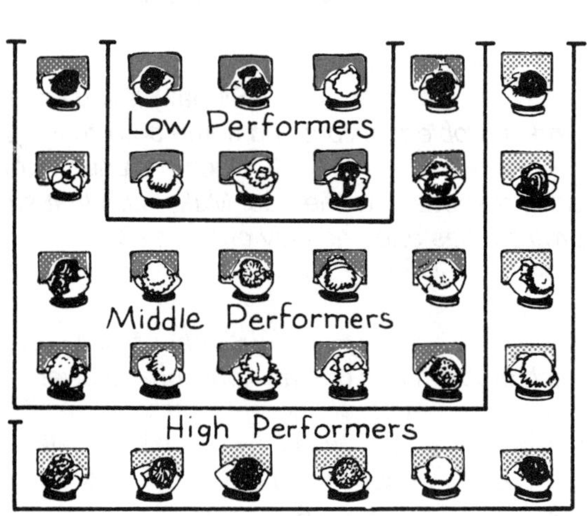

The lowest performers are closest to the front of the classroom. Middle performers are arranged around the lowest performers. Highest performers are arranged around the periphery. With this arrangement, you can position yourself so that, by taking a few steps during the time that students are working problems, you can sample low, average, and high performers.

While different variations of this arrangement are possible, be careful not to seat low performers far from the front-center of the room. The highest performers, understandably, can be farthest from the center because they attend better, learn faster, and need less observation and feedback.

Teaching

When you teach the program, a basic rule is that **you should not present from the front of the room unless you are showing something on the board.**

For most of the activities, you direct students to work specified problems. For these activities, you should present from somewhere in the middle of the room (in no set place) and, as students work each problem, observe an adequate sample of students. Although you won't be able to observe every child working every problem, you can observe at least half a dozen students in approximately 30 seconds.

Rehearse the lesson before presenting it to the class. Each lesson has a script that you will follow. Don't simply read the script, but act it out. Attend to the shaded boxes that show board displays and how you'll change the displays. If you keep the changes in mind, you'll be much more fluent in presenting the activity.

Watch your wording. Non-board activities are much easier than board activities. The board formats are usually designed so they are manageable if you have an idea of the steps you'll take. If you rehearse each of the early lessons before presenting them, you'll soon learn how to present efficiently from the script. In later lessons, you should scan the list of skills at the beginning of each lesson. New skills are in boldface type. If a new skill is introduced in that lesson, rehearse it. Most of what occurs in the lesson will not be new, but a variation of what you've presented earlier, so you may not need to rehearse these activities.

Remind students about the two important rules for doing well in this program: **Always work problems the way they are shown** and: **No shortcuts are permitted.**

Remember that everything introduced will be used later. Reinforce students who apply what they learn. Always require students to rework incorrect problems.

Using the Teacher Presentation Scripts

The script for each lesson indicates precisely how to present each structured activity. The script shows what you can say, what you can do, and what the students' responses should be.

What you say appears in **blue** type:

You say this.

What you do appears in parentheses:

(You do this.)

The responses of the students are in italics.

Students say this.

Follow the specified wording in the script. While wording variations from the specified script are not always dangerous, you will be assured of communicating clearly with the students if you follow the script exactly. The wording is controlled, and the tasks are arranged so they focus clearly on important aspects of what the students are to do. Although you may feel uncomfortable "reading" a script (and you may feel that the students will not pay attention), try to present the exercises as if you're saying something important to the students. If you do, you'll find that working from a script is not difficult and that students respond well to what you say.

A sample script appears on page 29. The arrows show five different things you'll do in addition to delivering the wording in the script.

- You'll **signal** to make sure that group responses involve all the students. (arrow 1)
- You'll **firm** critical parts of the exercises. (arrow 2)
- You'll **pace** your presentation based on what the students are doing. You'll judge whether to proceed quickly or to wait a few more seconds before moving on with the presentation. (arrow 3)
- For some exercises, you'll **write** things on the board, and you'll often **change** the board display. (arrow 4)
- You'll **check** students' written work to ensure mastery of the content. (arrow 5)

ARROW 1: GROUP RESPONSES (SIGNAL.)

Some of the tasks call for group responses. If students respond together with brisk unison responses, you receive good information about whether most of the students are performing correctly. The simplest way to **signal** students to respond together is to adopt a timing practice—just like the timing in a musical piece.

A signal follows a question, a direction (as shown by arrow 1) or the words, "Get ready."

You can signal by nodding, clapping one time, snapping your fingers, or tapping your foot. After initially establishing the timing for signals, you can signal through voice inflection only.

Students will not be able to initiate responses together at the appropriate rate unless you follow these rules:

a) Talk first. Pause a standard length of time (possibly 1 second), then signal. Never signal when you talk. Don't change the timing for your signal. Students are to respond on your signal—not after it or before it.

b) Model responses that are paced reasonably. Don't permit students to produce slow, droning responses. These are dangerous because they rob you of the information that can be derived from appropriate group responses. When students make droning responses, many of them are copying responses of others. If students are required to respond at a reasonable speaking rate, all students must initiate responses; therefore, it's relatively easy to determine which students are not responding and which are saying the wrong response. Also, don't permit students to respond at a very fast rate or to "jump" your signal. Listen very carefully to the **first** part of the response.

To correct oral responses that are too fast or too slow, show students exactly what you want them to do. For example:

- My turn to read the equation: 14 plus some number equals 96.
- Your turn: Read the equation. *14 plus some number equals 96.*
- Good reading it the right way.

c) Do not respond with the students unless you are trying to work with them on a difficult response. You present only what's in blue. You do not say the answers with the students, and you should not move your lips or give other spurious clues about the answer.

Think of signals this way: If you use them correctly, they provide you with much diagnostic information. A weak response suggests that you should repeat a task and provides information about which students may need more help. Signals are, therefore, important early in the program. After students have learned the routine, the students will be able to respond on cue with no signal. That will happen, however, only if you always give your signals at the end of a constant time interval after you complete what you say.

ARROW 2: FIRMING (REPEAT UNTIL FIRM.)

When students make mistakes, you correct them. A correction may occur during any part of the teacher presentation that calls for the students to respond. It may also occur in connection with what the students are writing. Here are the rules for corrections:

- You correct a mistake on an oral task as soon as you hear it.

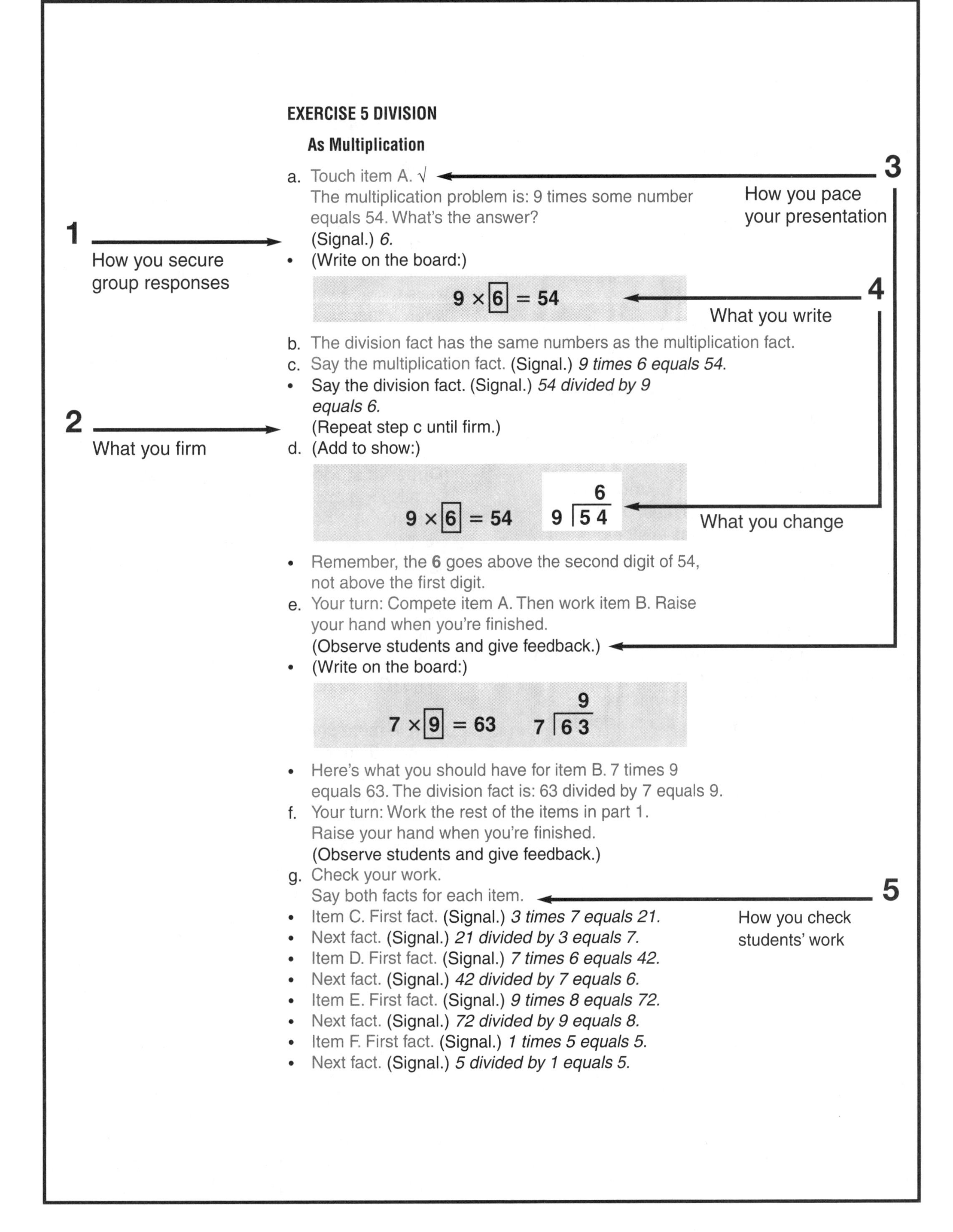

EXERCISE 5 DIVISION

As Multiplication

a. Touch item A. √
The multiplication problem is: 9 times some number equals 54. What's the answer?
(Signal.) *6.*
- (Write on the board:)

$$9 \times \boxed{6} = 54$$

b. The division fact has the same numbers as the multiplication fact.
c. Say the multiplication fact. (Signal.) *9 times 6 equals 54.*
- Say the division fact. (Signal.) *54 divided by 9 equals 6.*
(Repeat step c until firm.)

d. (Add to show:)

$$9 \times \boxed{6} = 54 \qquad 9\overline{)54}^{\;6}$$

- Remember, the **6** goes above the second digit of 54, not above the first digit.

e. Your turn: Compete item A. Then work item B. Raise your hand when you're finished.
(Observe students and give feedback.)
- (Write on the board:)

$$7 \times \boxed{9} = 63 \qquad 7\overline{)63}^{\;9}$$

- Here's what you should have for item B. 7 times 9 equals 63. The division fact is: 63 divided by 7 equals 9.

f. Your turn: Work the rest of the items in part 1.
Raise your hand when you're finished.
(Observe students and give feedback.)

g. Check your work.
Say both facts for each item.
- Item C. First fact. (Signal.) *3 times 7 equals 21.*
- Next fact. (Signal.) *21 divided by 3 equals 7.*
- Item D. First fact. (Signal.) *7 times 6 equals 42.*
- Next fact. (Signal.) *42 divided by 7 equals 6.*
- Item E. First fact. (Signal.) *9 times 8 equals 72.*
- Next fact. (Signal.) *72 divided by 9 equals 8.*
- Item F. First fact. (Signal.) *1 times 5 equals 5.*
- Next fact. (Signal.) *5 divided by 1 equals 5.*

A mistake is either saying the wrong thing or not responding.

To correct: Say the correct answer. Repeat the task the students missed.

For example: The multiplication problem is: 9 times some number equals 54. What is the answer? (Signal.)

If some students do not respond, respond late, or say anything but 6, there's a mistake. As soon as you hear the mistake, correct it.

Say the correct answer: It's 6.

(Repeat the task.)

Listen again: 9 times some number equals 54. What's the answer? (Signal.) *Six.*

Remember, wherever there's a signal, there's a place where students may make mistakes. You correct mistakes as soon as you hear them.

A special correction is needed when correcting mistakes on tasks that teach a relationship. This type of correction is marked with the note: **(Repeat step ______ until firm.)**

The note **(Repeat step ______ until firm)** usually occurs when students must produce a series of related responses (as in step c).

When you repeat-until-firm, you follow these steps:

1) **Correct the mistake.** (Tell the answer and repeat the task that was missed.)

2) **Return to the beginning of the specified step and present the entire step.**

For example, students make a mistake in step c; when the teacher says, Say the division fact, some students don't respond.

1) Correct the mistake:

- The division fact is 54 divided by 9 equals 6. Say the division fact. (Signal.)
  54 divided by 9 equals 6.

2) Repeat step c.

- Listen: Say the multiplication fact. (Signal.) *9 times 6 equals 54.*
- Say the division fact. (Signal.)
- *54 divided by 9 equals 6.*

When you repeat-until-firm, you present the context in which the mistake occurred, and the students show you through their responses whether or not the correction worked, whether or not they are firm.

The repeat-until-firm direction appears only in the most critical parts of new-teaching exercises. It usually focuses on knowledge that is very important for later work. As a general procedure, follow the repeat-until-firm directions. However, if you're quite sure that the mistake was a "glitch" and does not mean that the students lack understanding, you need not follow the repeat-until-firm direction.

ARROW 3: PACING YOUR PRESENTATION AND INTERACTING WITH STUDENTS AS THEY WORK (OBSERVE STUDENTS AND GIVE FEEDBACK AND √.)

You should pace your verbal presentation at a normal speaking rate—as if you were telling somebody something important.

The arrows for number 3 on page 29 show two ways to pace your presentation for activities where students write, or touch or find parts of their workbook or textbook page. The first is a √. The second is a note to **(Observe students and give feedback).** Both indicate that you will interact with students. Some interactions will serve to correct mistakes. Others reinforce desired behaviors. In other words, √ and **(Observe students and give feedback)** are signals for managing students and giving feedback that helps the students perform better.

A √ is a note to check what the students are doing. It requires only a second or two. If you are positioned close to several average-performing students, check whether they are responding appropriately. If they are, proceed with the presentation.

The **(Observe students and give feedback)** direction implies a more elaborate response. You sample more students and you give feedback, not only to individual students, but to the group. Here are the basic rules for what to do and what not to do when you observe and give feedback.

a) Move from the front of the room to a place where you can quickly sample the performance of low, middle, and high performers.

b) As soon as students start to work, start observing. As you observe, make comments to the whole class. Focus these comments on students who are following directions, working quickly, and working accurately. "Wow, a couple of students are almost finished. I haven't seen one mistake so far."

c) Students raise their hands to indicate that they are finished. (Alternatively, you may have them put their pencils down when they are finished. They are not to work ahead.) Acknowledge students who are finished.

d) If you observe mistakes, do **not** provide a great deal of individual help. Point out any mistakes, but do not work the problems for the students. For instance, if a student gets one of the problems wrong, point to it and say, "You made a mistake." If students don't line their numerals up correctly, say, "You'd better erase that and try again. Your numerals are not lined up." If students are not following instructions that you give, tell them, "You didn't follow my directions. You have to listen very carefully."

e) Do not wait for the slowest students to complete the problems before presenting the workcheck during which students correct their work and fix any mistakes. Allow students a **reasonable** amount of time. You can usually use the middle performers as a gauge for what is reasonable. As you observe that they are completing their work, announce, "Okay, you have about 10 seconds more to finish up." At the end of that time, continue with the exercise.

f) During the workcheck, continue to circulate among the students and make sure that they are checking their work. They should fix any mistakes. Praise students who are following the procedure. Allow a reasonable amount of time for them to check each problem. Do not wait for the slowest students to finish their check. Try to keep the workcheck moving as quickly as possible.

g) If you observe a serious problem that is not unique to the lowest performers, tell the class, "Stop. We seem to have a serious problem." Repeat the part of the exercise that gives them information about what they are to do. ***Note:*** Do not provide new teaching or new problems. Simply repeat the part of the exercise that gives students the information they need and reassign the work. "Let's see who can get it this time."

h) When higher-performing students do their independent work, you may want to go over any parts of the lesson with the students who had trouble with the structured work (made mistakes or didn't finish). Make sure that you check all the problems worked by the lower performers and give them feedback. Show them what they did wrong. Keep your explanations simple. The lengthier your explanations, the more they'll probably get confused. If there are serious problems, repeat the exercise that presented difficulties for the lower performers.

If you follow the procedures for observing students and giving feedback, your students will work faster and more accurately. They will also become facile at following your directions.

If you don't follow these guidelines, you may think that you are helping students, but you will actually be reinforcing them for undesirable behaviors.

- If you wait far beyond a reasonable time period before presenting the workcheck, you punish those who worked quickly and accurately. Soon, they will learn that there is no payoff for doing well—no praise, no recognition—but instead a long wait while you give attention to those who are slow.
- If you don't make announcements about students who are doing well and working quickly, the class will not understand what's expected. Students will probably not improve much.
- If you provide extensive individual help on independent work, you will actually reinforce students for not listening to your directions, for being dependent on your help. Furthermore, this dependency becomes contagious. If you provide extensive individual guidance, it doesn't take other students in the class long to discover that they don't have to listen to your directions, that they can raise their hand and receive help, and that students who have the most serious problems receive the most teacher attention. These expectations are the opposite of the ones you want to induce. You want students to be self-reliant and to have **reasons** for learning and remembering what you say when you instruct them. The simplest reasons are that they will use what they have just been shown and that they will receive reinforcement for performing well.
- If you provide lengthy explanations and extensive reteaching to correct any problems you observe, you run a serious risk of further confusing the students. Their problem is that they didn't attend to or couldn't perform on some detail that you covered in your initial presentation. So tell them what they didn't attend to and repeat the activity (or the step) that gives them the information they need. This approach shows them how to process the information you already presented. A different demonstration or explanation, however, may not show them how to link what you said originally with the new demonstration.

Because Level E is carefully designed, it is possible to teach all the students the desired behaviors of self-reliance, following instructions, and working fast and accurately. If you follow the management rules outlined above, by the time the students have reached Lesson 15, all students should be able to complete assigned work within a reasonable period of time and have reasons to feel good about their ability to do math. That's what you want to happen. Follow the rules, and it will happen. As they improve, you should tell them about it. "What's this? Everybody's finished with that problem already? That's impressive."

ARROW 4: BOARD WORK

What you **write** on the board and what you **change** is indicated with display boxes. In the sample exercise, you first write the problem in step a:

$$9 \times \boxed{6} = 54$$

Then you write a second problem in step b:

$$9\overline{)54}^{\;6}$$

What you present initially is shown in a gray box:

$$9 \times \boxed{6} = 54 \qquad 9\overline{)54}^{\;6}$$

Any changes in that display (additions or alterations) are shown in white. Scanning the boxes shows both what you'll write and how you'll change the display.

ARROW 5: WORKCHECKS (CHECK YOUR WORK.)

It is important to observe students to make sure that they are both attending to workchecks and are correcting their mistakes.

The simplest procedure is to use a colored pen for checking. Students should write their work in pencil so they can erase and make any corrections that are necessary as they work. When you indicate that it is time to "Check your work," they put down their pencils and pick up their marking pens. If their work or answer is correct, they mark a **C** for the problem. If their work is wrong, they mark an **X.** Students correct all mistakes before handing in their work.

If you establish the organizational procedures at the beginning of the program, students will learn more and learn faster because they will be far more likely to learn from their mistakes. They will not be as tempted to cheat. Instead they will be more likely to read what they have written on their paper, and they will more easily learn that they will use everything that is introduced in the program.

Independent Work

The goal of the independent work is to provide review of previously taught work, requiring about 20–30 minutes per lesson. Starting with Lesson 31, students are to refer to an answer key when doing their independent work. The key shows the answer to every other item. The key does not show the work. Students are to refer to the answer key and see if each answer corresponds. If not, students are to rework the problem and try to obtain the correct answer.

The amount of independent work increases around Lesson 71. Before Lesson 71, students work an average of about 5 sets of problems. The number of sets increases to about 8 by the last 15 lessons of the program.

Do not feel obliged to present all the independent work to your students. If the independent work becomes too demanding and requires too much time, assign only parts of it. Try to include the most recently taught material and the tasks that require more practice.

Starting with Lesson 105 and continuing to the end of the program, present all the independent work. It is final preparation for the end-of-program test, which covers all the skills and problem types taught in Level E. One possible plan is to present only three lessons a week during this period and permit students to complete their independent work as part of the math period. This would give you the opportunity to provide feedback on any parts that present difficulties. It would also provide the students with a comprehensive review.

The guiding rule for the independent work is that it should not be punishing for the students. If it is excessive, reduce it. Many groups, however, will be facile enough with the problem-solving strategies they have learned to complete the longer independent-work assignments in less than 30 minutes.

Grading Papers—Feedback

The teacher material includes a separate *Answer Key.* The key shows the work for all problems presented during the lesson and as independent work. When students are taught a particular method for working problems, they should follow the steps specified in the key. You should indicate that the work for a problem is wrong if the procedure is not followed.

After completing each lesson and before presenting the next lesson, follow these steps:

1) Make sure that **all** errors marked by the students during workchecks have been corrected.

Here's how a corrected mistake should look:

$$\begin{array}{r} 6\,0\,{}^{1}0 \\ -1\,2\,7 \\ \hline 5\,2\,3 \end{array} \qquad \begin{array}{r} {}^{5}\,{}^{9}\, \\ \not{6}\,\not{0}\,{}^{1}0 \\ -1\,2\,7 \\ \hline 4\,7\,3 \end{array}$$

The **X** indicates that it was originally wrong. The correct work is shown next to the original problem. This procedure is better than requiring students to erase mistakes. (After they have been erased, you don't know what type of error students made and therefore, what types of adjustments would be implied for the next lesson.)

2) Conduct a workcheck for the independent work. One procedure is to provide a structured workcheck of independent work at the beginning of the period. Do not attempt to provide students with complete information about each problem. Read the answers. Students are to mark any mistakes. The workcheck should not take more than four minutes. Students are to correct errors at a later time. You should have some method for checking off each student's name for every lesson. The check shows that the student made corrections and turned in a corrected paper.

3) Spot check each student's corrected paper. Attend to three aspects of the student's work:

a) Were all the mistakes corrected?

b) Is the appropriate work shown for each correction (not just the right answer)?

c) Did the student perform acceptably on tasks that tended to be missed by other students? The answer to question c provides you with information on the students' performance on difficult tasks.

Note: Starting with Lesson 31, the student textbook provides answers to every other item on the independent work. Students check their work before turning in problems. However, you should spot check the work for these problems because some students may attempt to show the correct answer (which they read in the answer key) without showing the correct steps for the solution.

4) Award points for independent work performance. A good plan is to award one point for completing the independent work, one point for completing all mistakes, and three points for making no more than four errors on the independent work. Students who do well can earn five points for each lesson. These points can be used as part of the basis for assigning grades. The independent work would be worth approximately one-third of the grade. The rest of the grade would be based on the 10-lesson tests. (The independent work would provide students with up to 45 points for a ten-lesson period; each ten-lesson test provides another possible 100 points—100% for a perfect test score.)

Unacceptable Error Rates

During structured activities, firm the students to make sure they can perform on each activity quickly and accurately (if not on the first attempt, after the firming has been provided).

Students' independent work should also be monitored. Specifically, no more than 30 percent of the students should make mistakes on any independent activity. On the first lesson that a recently taught skill is perfectly "independent," error rates may exceed the ideal (more than 30 percent of the students making mistakes). However, if an excessive error rate continues, there is a problem that should be corrected.

Consider whether the preceding steps you've taken are adequate. High error rates on independent practice may be the result of the following:

a) The students may not be placed appropriately in the program.

b) The initial presentation may not have provided adequate firming. (The students made mistakes that were not corrected. The parts of the teacher presentation in which errors occurred were not repeated until firm.)

c) Students may have received inappropriate help. (When they worked structured problems earlier, they received too much help and became dependent on the help.)

d) Students may not have been required to follow directions carefully. (If students do not learn early in the program that they are to follow directions precisely, serious problems may result later.)

Consider these possibilities if students tend to have many problems with independent work. If you look at their work as feedback about the way you are presenting material, the mistakes can be a source of information that is useful to you in showing you how to teach more effectively. Also make sure that you do not permit high error rates to continue. The simplest procedure is to show the students the types of mistakes they are making and given them information about what they should be doing. Then award bonus points (or some other form of reward) for doing well on independent work.

Inducing Appropriate Learning Behaviors

Students who have not been through earlier levels of *Connecting Math Concepts* may have notions about learning math that are highly inappropriate. For example, they may not follow directions. They may tend to copy what neighbors are doing, work ahead, and not use the specific solution strategies that have been taught. Their work may be characterized by being careless—missing signs in equations, inappropriate shortcuts, answers shown without the work being shown, and answers to word problems that lack the unit name. What preempts these students most from learning is their failure to attend to what the teacher says when presenting exercises. The paradox is that the more the teacher tries to explain and to stress important points, the slower the exercise moves; the less students attend; and the less information they remember.

Exercises that are the most difficult for these students to attend to (and the most difficult for the teacher to present effectively) are those that have long explanations. The great temptation is to make these explanations seem more enticing, to dramatize and stress important parts. A far more effective procedure is to move fast enough to keep the students attentive.

The general rule is to **go fast** on parts that do not require responses from the students; **go more slowly** and be more emphatic when presenting directions for what the students are to do.

Here's an example, from Lesson 22:

a. Find part 6 in your workbook. √

- You're going to complete each equation and show the fraction you multiplied by. If you multiply by 1, you know that the two fractions shown are equal. So you write a simple equation that shows the two equivalent fractions. If you do not multiply by 1, the fractions are not equal and you do not write an equation below.

b. Work problem A. Raise your hand when you're finished. (Observe students and give feedback.) (Write on the board:)

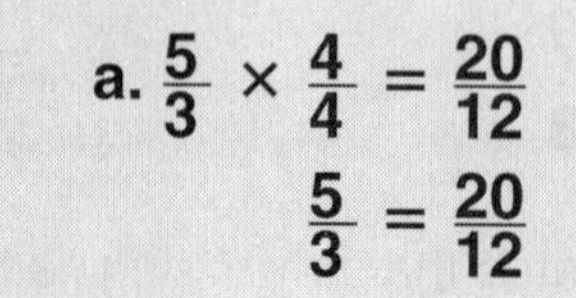

$$\text{a. } \frac{5}{3} \times \frac{4}{4} = \frac{20}{12}$$
$$\frac{5}{3} = \frac{20}{12}$$

- Check your work. You should have: 5-thirds times 4-fourths equals 20-twelfths. Did you multiply 5-thirds by 1? *Yes.*
- So you should have written the equation: 5-thirds equals 20-twelfths. Raise your hand if you got it right.

Step a consists of teacher talk with no student responses. Present this part of the script very quickly. Don't try to stress the points. Treat the entire step as something the students know, and therefore, something that you're summarizing in a perfunctory manner.

When you provide the instructions in step b, use a different tone of voice—one that is louder and that makes the directions very clear.

If you follow the general guideline of going fast on parts that require no student responses and of providing greater emphasis on parts that tell students what they are to do, students will attend better to what you say. They'll learn to listen because they'll learn the link between your explanations and what they'll do.

Here are other guidelines for reinforcing appropriate learning behaviors for students who do not perform well in the first ten lessons of the program:

1) During the first ten lessons, hold students to a high criterion of performance. Remind them that they are to follow the procedures that you show them.

2) After the first in-program test (Test 1), provide the specified remedies (see section on **Marking In-program Tests**); then repeat Lessons 6 through 10. Tell students, "We're going to do these lessons again. This time, we'll do them perfectly." Be positive. Reinforce students for following directions and not making the kinds of mistakes they had been making.

Once students have completed several lessons perfectly, they understand your criteria for what they should do to perform acceptably. For some students the relearning required to perform well is substantial, so be patient, but persistent.

10-Lesson Tests

Level E has a series of 12 criterion-referenced mastery tests that permit you to monitor the performance of students on the program material that is presented. Following every tenth lesson, a test assesses the most important skills taught in the previous ten lessons. Each 10-lesson test, therefore, provides you with information about how well-prepared students are to proceed in the program. The 10-lesson tests are presented in the student textbook.

The 10-Lesson tests can also be used to help place students who are new to *Connecting Math Concepts, Level E.* (See **Cumulative Tests,** Placing mid-year students, page 18.) Several of the 10-lesson tests include content unique to CMC. Holding students accountable who haven't received instruction on content unique to CMC isn't appropriate. To alert teachers and students to material that is unique, parts of the test are gray-screened. Teacher presentation that is gray-screened should not be presented to students who have not received the preceding 10 lessons of instruction in the program. Students new to the program should ignore material in their textbooks or workbooks that is gray-screened on the 10-lesson tests.

Part 2 of Test 1 tests number families, which are unique to CMC. The teacher presentation referring to Part 2 is gray-screened, and Part 2 of the student material is also gray-screened. The gray screen indicates that Part 2 should not be presented to or completed by students who have not received the first 10 lessons of instruction in CMC E. On 10-lesson Test 10 (below), Parts 1, 4, and 10 of the student material contain segments of the directions that are gray-screened. Part 1 refers to fraction number families and ratio tables. Parts 4 and 10 refer to number families. Number families and ratio tables are unique to CMC. The gray screen indicates to students who have not received instruction in CMC E from Lessons 91 to 100 to ignore that segment of the directions. Students are expected to complete the word problems for those parts, however.

Sometimes, students copy from their neighbors. A good method for discovering who is copying is to spread students out during the test if it's physically possible to do so. Discrepancies in the test performance and daily performance of some students pinpoint which students may be copying.

If copying is occurring, reassign seating so that the students who tend to copy are either separated from those who know the answers or seated near the front-center of the room where it is easier for you to monitor them.

Here's Test 10, which is presented after Lesson 100:

Test 10

Part 1 **Make a fraction number family and ratio table. Answer the questions.**

The amount of paper Andy recycled this year is $\frac{6}{5}$ of the amount he recycled last year. This year, he recycled 155 tons.

1. How much paper did he recycle last year?
2. How much more paper did he recycle this year, compared to last year?

Part 2 **Find the area and the perimeter of the triangle.**

25.5 cm
19.2 cm
10 cm
28 cm

Part 3 **Copy each fraction. Cross out zeros and complete the equation with the simpliified fraction.**

a. $\frac{4,030}{2,010} = \blacksquare$ b. $\frac{70}{300} = \blacksquare$ c. $\frac{11,000}{1,600} = \blacksquare$

Part 4 **For each item, make a number family. Answer the question.**

a. A truck started out with 624 boxes. The truck made lots of deliveries. At the end of the day, there were 195 boxes on the truck. How many boxes were delivered?
b. Sarah had 590 buttons. She found some more buttons in a drawer. She now has a total of 626 buttons. How many buttons did she find?
c. In the morning, Mark went to the orchard and picked apples. Later, he picked 128 apples. In all he picked 300 apples. How many apples did Mark pick in the morning?

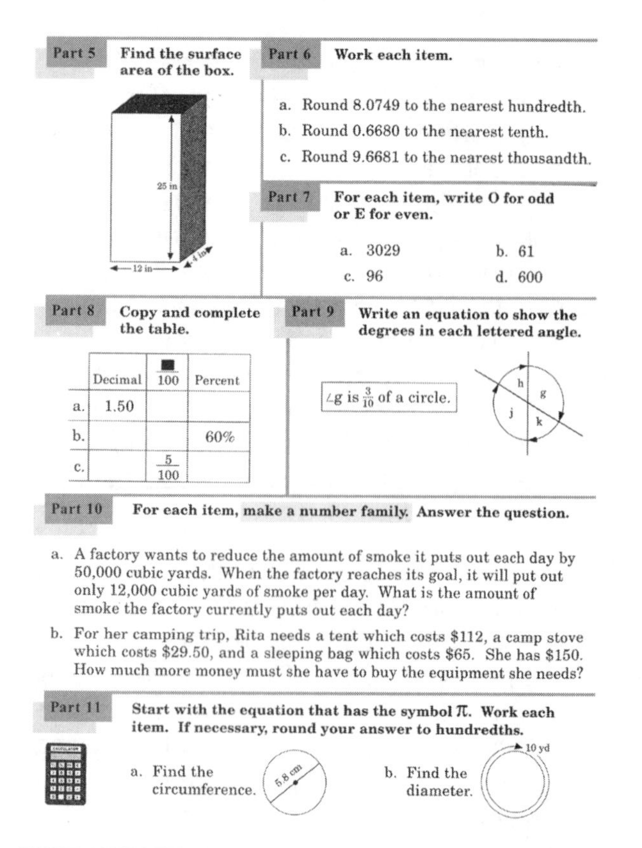

Part 5 Find the surface area of the box.

25 in, 12 in, 4 in

Part 6 Work each item.

a. Round 8.0749 to the nearest hundredth.
b. Round 0.6680 to the nearest tenth.
c. Round 9.6681 to the nearest thousandth.

Part 7 For each item, write O for odd or E for even.

a. 3029 b. 61
c. 96 d. 600

Part 8 Copy and complete the table.

	Decimal	$\frac{■}{100}$	Percent
a.	1.50		
b.			60%
c.		$\frac{5}{100}$	

Part 9 Write an equation to show the degrees in each lettered angle.

$\angle g$ is $\frac{3}{10}$ of a circle.

h, g, j, k

Part 10 For each item, make a number family. Answer the question.

a. A factory wants to reduce the amount of smoke it puts out each day by 50,000 cubic yards. When the factory reaches its goal, it will put out only 12,000 cubic yards of smoke per day. What is the amount of smoke the factory currently puts out each day?

b. For her camping trip, Rita needs a tent which costs $112, a camp stove which costs $29.50, and a sleeping bag which costs $65. She has $150. How much more money must she have to buy the equipment she needs?

Part 11 Start with the equation that has the symbol π. Work each item. If necessary, round your answer to hundredths.

a. Find the circumference. (6.8 cm)
b. Find the diameter. (10 yd)

TEST ANSWER KEY

The teacher's *Answer Key* provides the correct answers for each lesson and 10-lesson test. The answer key for each test shows the correct work for each item, and a table for assigning percent grades based on the number of points earned.

Here's the answer key for Test 10:

TEST 10 PERCENT SUMMARY					
SCORE	**%**	**SCORE**	**%**	**SCORE**	**%**
59	100	53	90	47	80
58	98	52	88	46	78
57	97	51	86	45	76
56	95	50	85	44	75
55	93	49	83	43	73
54	92	48	81	42	71

TEST 10 SCORING CHART			
PART	**SCORE**	**POSSIBLE SCORE**	**PASSING SCORE**
1	3 for each question	6	6
2	Area 1; Unit Name 1; Perimeter 1; Unit Name 1	4	3
3	1 for each item	3	3
4	2 for each item	6	6
5	Area 3; Unit Name 1	4	4
6	2 for each item	6	4
7	1 for each item	4	4
8	EACH ITEM: Each missing cell 1; Total 2	6	5
9	2 for each equation	8	6
10	3 for each item	6	Parts 10, 11 combined 9
11	3 for each item	6	
	TOTAL	**59**	

The percent-conversion table shows the percentage grade you'd award for students who have a perfect score of 59, a score of 58, and so forth.

The answers for each part of the test indicate the possible points for each item, the possible points for the part and the passing criterion.

Students fail a part of the test if they score fewer than the specified number of passing points.

The Test 10 Scoring Chart indicates that the passing score for Parts 10 and 11 combined is 9 points. (Students can miss 1 problem in either part.) If a student doesn't earn 9 points for those parts, the student fails the parts in which the student made errors. If the student missed one problem in each of the parts, the student fails both parts. If a student missed 2 problems in Part 10, and didn't make any errors in Part 11, the student fails only Part 10.

Note that points are sometimes awarded for working different parts of the problem. For example, for Part 2, students earn 1 point for the area, 1 point for the perimeter, and 1 point for each of the units. For Part 5, students earn 3 points for the area and 1 point for the units.

MARKING 10-LESSON TESTS

Use the criteria in the *Answer Key* for marking each student's test. Record the results on the **Group Summary of Test Performance** (provided on page 189 of the *Teacher's Guide*).

Here's how the results could be summarized following Test 10:

Remedy Summary—Group Summary of Test Performance

Note: Test remedies are specified in the *Answer Key*. Percent Summary is also specified in the *Answer Key*.

Name	Test 10 — Check parts not passed											Total %
	1	2	3	4	5	6	7	8	9	10	11	
1. Amanda Adams			✓		✓							84%
2. William Alberts			✓									92%
3. Henry Bowman	✓		✓					✓	✓	✓	✓	70%
4. Phillip Caswell												89%
5. Zoë Collier	✓											87%
6. Chan Won Lee			✓								✓	83%
Number of Students Not Passed = NP	2	0	4	0	1	0	0	1	1	1	2	
Total number of students = T	6	6	6	6	6	6	6	6	6	6	6	
Remedy needed if NP/T = 25% or more	Y	N	Y	N	N	N	N	N	N	N	Y	

The summary sheet provides you with a cumulative record of each student's performance on the 10-lesson tests.

Summarize each student's performance.

- Make a check in the appropriate columns to indicate any part of the test that was failed.
- At the bottom of each column, write the total number of failures for that part, and the total number of students in the class. Then divide the number of failures by the number of students to determine the failure rate for each part.
- Provide a group remedy for each part that has a failure rate of 25 percent (.25) or more.

TEST REMEDIES

The *Presentation Book* specifies remedies for each test. Any necessary remedies should be presented before the next lesson (Lesson 101).

Here are the remedies for Test 10:

TEST 10 REMEDIES				
PART	**LESSON**	**EXERCISE**	**TEXTBOOK PART**	**WORKBOOK PART**
1	91	4	5	–
	94	–	15	–
2	97	3	3	–
	98	2	3	–
3	96	1 steps b–f	2	–
	98	4	5	–
4	96	2	3	–
	97	4	4	–
5	95	3	4	–
	97	1	1	–
6	91	7	9	–
	92	3	4	–
7	92	4	5	–
	93	3	4, 5	–
8	93	6	–	1
	96	–	9	–
9	91	2	3	–
	96	–	11	–
10	97	2	2	–
	98	3	4	–
11	94	3	4	–
	95	6	7	

If the same students predictably fail parts of the test, it may be possible to provide remedies for those students as the others do a manageable extension activity. The program is designed so students use everything that has been taught. If individual students are weak on a particular skill, they will have trouble later in the program when that particular skill becomes a component in a larger operation or more complex application.

If students consistently fail tests, they are probably not placed appropriately in CMC E.

On the completed Group Test Summary for Mastery Test 10, more than .25 of the students failed Parts 1, 3, and 11. After the teacher provides group remedies, Amanda Adams and Henry Bowman need individual remedies. Henry Bowman failed several parts. If Henry receives individual remedies for Parts 8, 9, 10, and 11, passes the retest for Test 10, but then later fails Mastery Test 11, he should probably be placed in a less challenging group.

Lesson Objectives

Each lesson in the *Presentation Books* begins with objectives that show the various skills that are being taught and the order of activities in the lesson.

Here are the objectives for Lesson 9:

Objectives

- Write division problems and answers for fractions that equal whole numbers. (Exercise 1)
- Use a calculator to figure out missing numbers in number families. (Exercise 2)
- Multiply two fractions. (Exercise 3)
  Note: The strategy is to multiply on top and write the answer on top; multiply on the bottom and write the answer on the bottom.
- **Work the same 3-by-3 table twice, first using the columns as number families, then using the rows as number families.** (Exercise 4)
- Write fractions for whole numbers from descriptions. (Exercise 5)
- Work column multiplication problems that involve carrying for both the ones digit and tens digit of the multiplier. (Exercise 6)
- Work division problems that have a single-digit answer and a remainder. (Exercise 7)

Some of the objectives are in regular type:

- Use a calculator to figure out missing numbers in number families. (Exercise 2)

These are objectives for exercises that are versions of exercises from the preceding lesson.

Some of the objectives are in bold type:

- **Multiply two fractions.** (Exercise 3)

These objectives signal a new activity or a variation that is more difficult than earlier examples. It's a good idea to rehearse exercises signaled by bold type before presenting them to the students.

Tracks

The various **tracks** in Level E move toward problem-solving applications. To master any type of advanced problem, the students must have knowledge about how to translate the problem into an equation or into a form that permits calculation. Once the problem has been appropriately translated, the students must have the skills needed to perform the calculations. The calculation skills are tool skills that are needed for more advanced problem solving. Level E teaches the tool skills first, then presents problem-solving applications that use the tool skills. The tracks are divided accordingly into **tool skills** and **applications.**

TOOL SKILLS

The tool skills are presented first in this guide. They include all the calculation skills, basic relationships (e.g., between multiplication and division and between division and fractions), and the component representations (such as number families) that will be used later in the more elaborate applications. Tool skills taught in Level E include whole number operations, calculator skills, number relationships, operational relationships, place value and rounding, fractions, whole number properties, mental arithmetic, mixed number operations, number families, decimal operations, and the coordinate system.

Whole Number Operations

REVIEW

Level E does not teach or review facts. Review is provided for column multiplication and short division (one-digit divisors). The review occurs in Lessons 2 through 32. Work with column multiplication begins in Lesson 2, with problems that have zero in the multiplicand.

For example:

$$\begin{array}{r} 493 \\ \times\ 50 \\ \hline \end{array}$$

Students use the procedure of copying the zero in the ones column, then multiplying by the tens digit:

$$\begin{array}{r} {}^{4\,1}493 \\ \times\ 50 \\ \hline 24{,}650 \end{array}$$

In Lesson 8, students work problems that multiply a three-digit value times a two-digit value.

For example:

$$\begin{array}{r} 393 \\ \times\ 76 \\ \hline \end{array}$$

Various subtypes of short-division problems are reviewed in Lessons 4 through 32. The first exercises use the same procedures used in Level D. If the answer has a remainder, students write the fact number below, then subtract and show the remainder in the answer.

Here's the first part of the exercise from Lesson 4:

a. In each of these problems, the number under the division sign is not a fact number.

b. Problem A: 38 divided by 5.
5 times 7 does not equal 38. The answer is 7 and a remainder. You're going to show the correct number for 5 times 7 below. Then you're going to subtract and show the remainder.

- The fact is: 5 times 7 equals **35.** So write **35** below 38. √
- (Write on the board:)

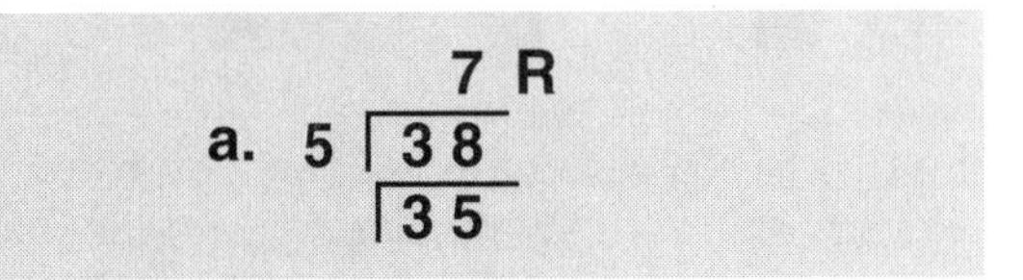

- Now you show the remainder. In your head, you subtract 38 minus 35. What's the answer? (Signal.) *3.*
- You write **3** as the remainder.
- (Write to show:)

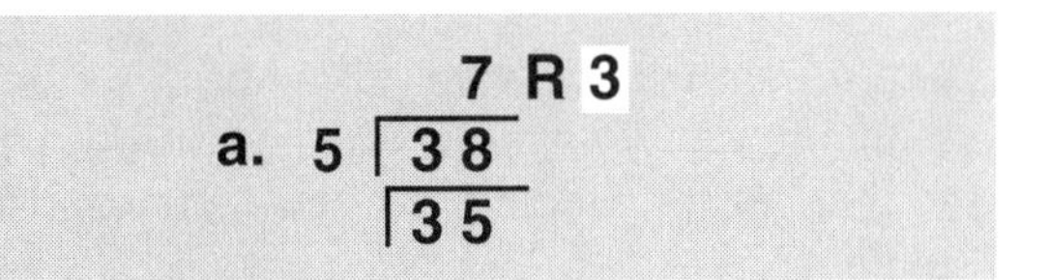

- Write the remainder after the **R** in a problem A. √

c. Problem B. 4 times 5 does not equal 21. Start with 4 and say the multiplication fact. (Signal.) *4 times 5 equals 20.*

- Write **20** below. Then subtract in your head and write the remainder. Raise your hand when you're finished.
- (Write on the board:)

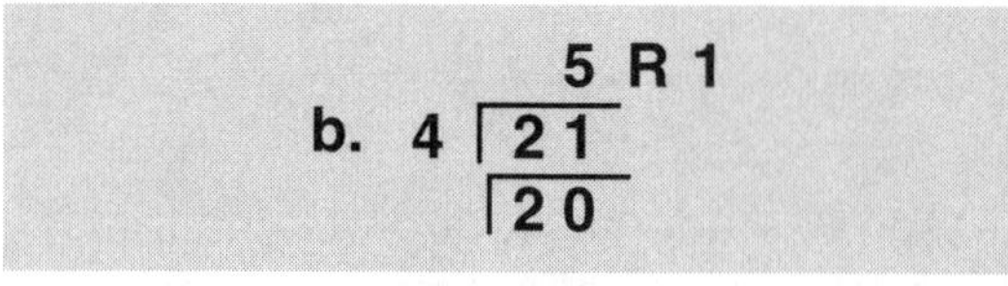

- Here's what you should have. 4 times 5 is 20. 21 minus 20 is 1. That's the remainder.

> ***Teaching note:*** Follow the specified teacher wording. Students are to subtract in their heads and write the answer as the remainder. They do not write the answer below.

Through Lesson 15, students work problems of the type introduced in Lesson 4. All problems have a single-digit answer and a remainder. Some of the problems have an answer of zero with a remainder.

For example: **9⟌7**

These problems are particularly important because they prepare students for problems that have zero as part of a multi-digit answer.

Beginning in Lesson 16, students work problems without writing the correct fact number below.

Here's the first part of the introduction:

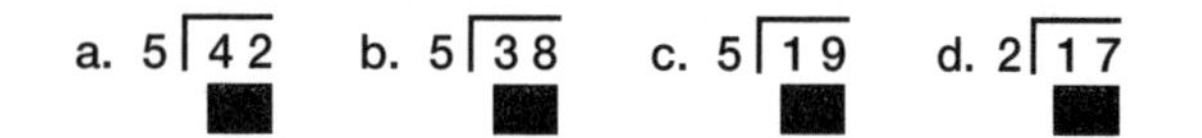

a. For these problems, the division sign below is blocked out. You're not going to write the fact number below. But you'll have to figure it out so that you can write the answer.

b. (Write on the board:)

5⟌47

- Here's a sample problem. 47 is not a number for counting by 5. Raise your hand when you know the number for counting by 5 that comes just before 47.
- Everybody, what number? (Signal.) *45.*
- I'm not going to write that number. But you'll have to remember it so you can ask, How many times does 5 go into 45? (Signal.) *9.*
- (Write to show:)

- And what's the remainder? (Signal.) *2.*
- (Write to show:)

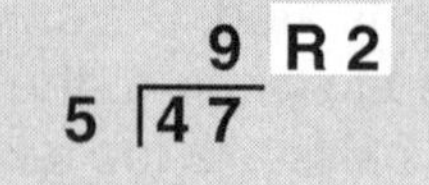

- Yes, 47 minus 45 equals 2. That's the remainder.

c. Problem A: 42 divided by 5. Write the number of times 5 goes into 42. Then write the remainder. Raise your hand when you're finished. √

- Everybody, how many times does 5 go into 42? (Signal.) *8.*
- Yes, 5 times 8 is 40. That's as close to 42 as you can get. So 8 goes in the answer. Everybody, what's the remainder? (Signal.) *2.*
- Yes, 42 minus 40 is 2.

The problems have a blocked out section below the dividend. This discourages students from writing the fact number below. Students will follow the steps of identifying the fact number, writing the missing factor for that number, subtracting that number from the dividend and writing the remainder.

Students continue to work problems that have a single-digit answer through Lesson 19. Answers with more than one digit are introduced in Lesson 21. These problems have one digit in the answer for every digit in the dividend.

Here's the exercise from Lesson 22:

b. Problem A. Say the problem for the first digit under the division sign. (Signal.) *7 divided by 3.*

- The answer is 2 with a remainder of 1. Write the **2** above the 7 and write the remainder in front of the **5.** √
- (Write on the board:)

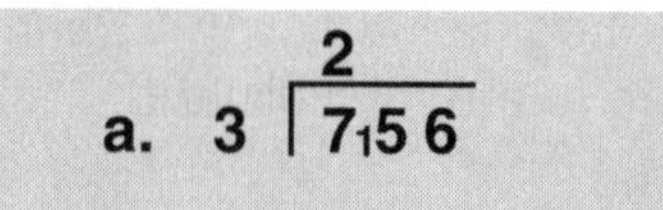

- Here's what you should have so far.
- The next problem is 15 divided by 3. Write the answer above the 5. Then work the problem for the last digit. Raise your hand when you're finished. (Observe students and give feedback.)

• (Write to show:)

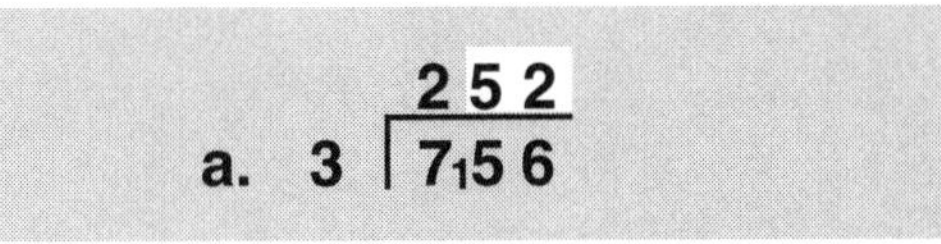

• Here's what you should have. 15 divided by 3 is 5. 6 divided by 3 is 2. So the answer is 252.

c. Problem B. Say the problem for the first digit. (Signal.) *7 divided by 4.*

• The answer has a remainder. Write the answer. Then write the remainder in front of the **2.** Raise your hand when you've done that much.

• (Write on the board:)

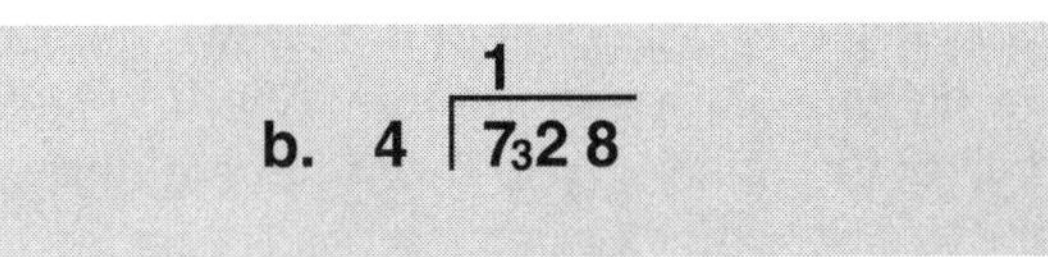

• Here's what you should have. 7 divided by 4 is 1 with a remainder of 3. Say the next problem you'll work. (Signal.) *32 divided by 4.*

• Work that problem. Write the answer. Then write the answer for the last digit of 728. Raise your hand when you're finished.
(Observe students and give feedback.)

• (Write to show:)

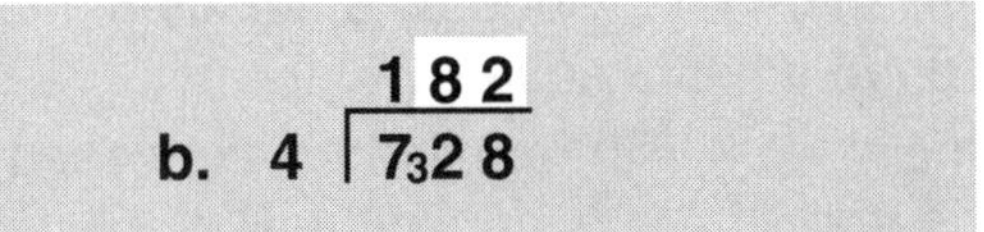

• Here's what you should have. 32 divided by 4 is 8. 8 divided by 4 is 2. So that answer is 182.

Teaching note: For problem a, you do the work for the first digit. For problem b, you do less work. You don't show students how to write the answer and the remainder. You direct them to write it. The exercise is designed to move the students progressively toward working independently. Follow the teacher wording carefully so that students learn that you will first show them what to do, then you'll require them to do it.

Expect students to resist the new way of working these problems. Students who did not go through Level D will insist on working problems the long way—showing the fact number, the subtraction, etc. Remind students: "We don't always do things the same way in this program. Part of being a smart math student involves working problems different ways." Praise students who work the problems the new way. "See how much faster it is to do it the new way?"

In Lesson 25, students work problems that do not have a digit in the answer for every digit in the dividend. Students underline the problem they'll work, then write the answer above the last underlined digit.

Here's the first part of the exercise from Lesson 26:

a. 5⟌470 b. 3⟌525 c. 4⟌356 d. 6⟌144

b. Problem A. Say the problem for the fist digit. (Signal.) *4 divided by 5.*

• Is 4 big enough? (Signal.) *No.*

• Underline the fist two digits. √

• Say the problem for the underlined part. (Signal.) *47 divided by 5.*

• The answer has a remainder. Write the answer and the remainder. Raise your hand when you've done that much.
(Observe students and give feedback.)

• (Write on the board:)

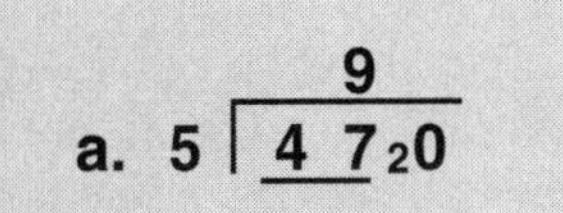

• Here's what you should have. 47 divided by 5 is 9 with a remainder of 2.

• Say the next problem you'll work. (Signal.) *20 divided by 5.*

• Work that problem and write the answer. Raise your hand when you're finished.

• (Write to show:)

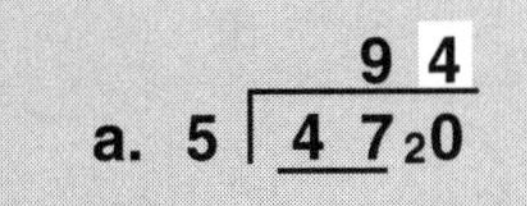

• Here's what you should have.

c. Problem B. Say the problem for the first digit. (Signal.) *5 divided by 3.*

• Is 5 big enough? (Signal.) *Yes.*

• Work problem B. Raise your hand when you're finished.
(Observe students and give feedback.)

• (Write on the board:)

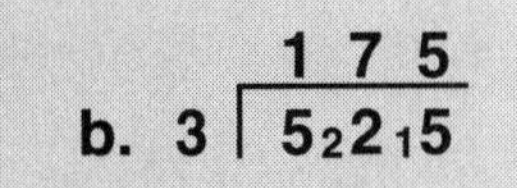

- Here's what you should have.

Teaching note: Here's the test for the first digits: If the first digit under the division sign is smaller than the number you divide by, you underline **two digits** and work a two-digit problem. If students have trouble, talk them through the analysis: "What's the first digit under the division sign? . . . Is that smaller than the number you're dividing by?" If the answer is **yes,** say, "You have to work a two-digit problem. Underline the first two digits."

Answers with zero are introduced in Lesson 29. Here's the first part of the exercise from Lesson 29:

a. (Write on the board:)

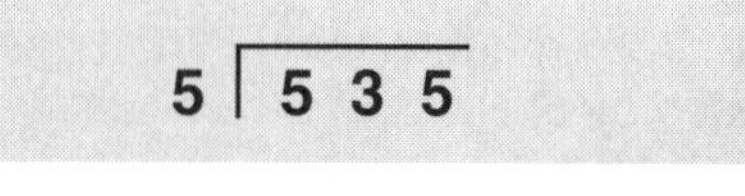

- You've worked problems that start out with digits that are too small. Sometimes a digit in the **middle** of the problem is too small. When that happens, you must write a zero above that digit. After the first digit of the answer, **you must have a digit above every digit under the division sign.**
- Once more: After the first digit of the answer, you must have a digit above every digit under the division sign.
- Look at the problem on the board. Everybody, say the problem for the first digit. (Signal.) *5 divided by 5.*
- Is 5 big enough? (Signal.) *Yes.*
- What's the answer? (Signal.) *1.*
- (Write to show:)

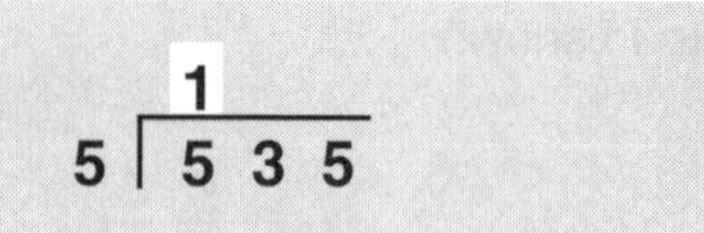

b. Say the next problem. (Signal.) *3 divided by 5.*
- Is 3 big enough? (Signal.) *No.*
- So the answer is zero.
- (Write to show:)

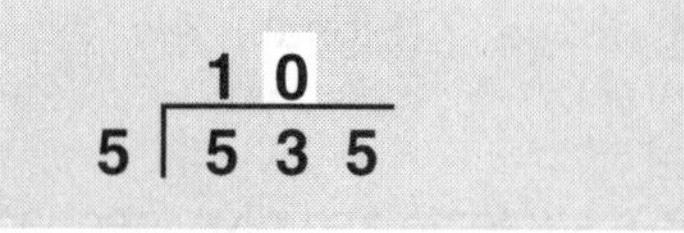

c. Now I work a **2-digit problem.**
- (Underline **35.**)
- Say the 2-digit problem for 35. (Signal.) *35 divided by 5.*
- What's the answer? (Signal.) *7.*
- (Write to show:)

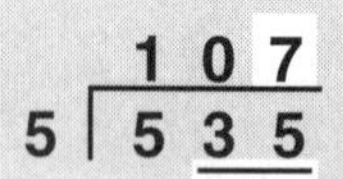

- The answer is 107. If you don't write a zero, you get a silly answer—17 instead of 107.

Teaching note: Students tend to have trouble with zeros in the answer. Part of their problem results from the strange conventions used for expressing answers. If the first digit of the answer is zero, we don't write it. If a middle digit of the answer is zero, we do write it. Stress the rule: After the first digit of the answer, you **must** have a digit above every digit under the division sign.

Beginning in Lesson 32, students express the remainder as a fraction. The reason for showing the answer as a whole number and fraction is that this notation preserves the integrity of the relationship between multiplication and division. Division is simply the inverse of multiplication. If 3 times 5 equals 15, 15 divided by 5 is 3. Similarly, if 34 divided by 5 equals 6 and 4/5, 6 and 4/5 times 5 equals 34.

Initial work with remainders expressed with an **R** is reasonable because the **R** is a simple extension of the steps that students follow when working the problem. If there's a remainder, they write the remainder in front of the next digit:

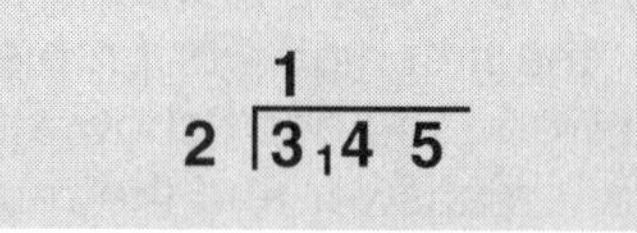

After the last digit, they simply separate the remainder from the rest of the answer with the letter **R:**

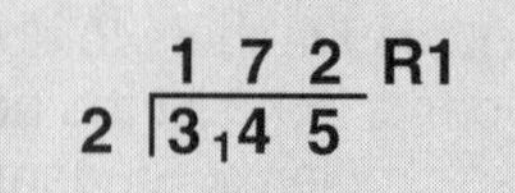

The rationale provided the students for converting the remainder into a fraction is that **if the problem divides by 5, you can divide the remainder by 5.** If the problem divides by 3, you can divide the remainder by 3.

Before working complete problems, students apply this procedure to a series of problems that show the answer with the remainder. Students determine the number the problem divides by and simply divide the remainder by that number. ***Note:*** Before this exercise is introduced, students practice saying fractions as division problems and have written division problems from fractions and vice versa.

In Lesson 37, students apply everything they have learned about division to work a set of problems that have one-digit or two-digit answers, that have zero in the answer, and that have remainders.

Here's the exercise:

a. These are division problems that have a remainder. You're going to write the answer to each problem as a mixed number. First you'll write the whole number part of the answer. Then you'll figure out the fraction for the remainder.

b. Copy and work problem A. Raise your hand when you're finished.
(Observe students and give feedback.)

- (Write on the board:)

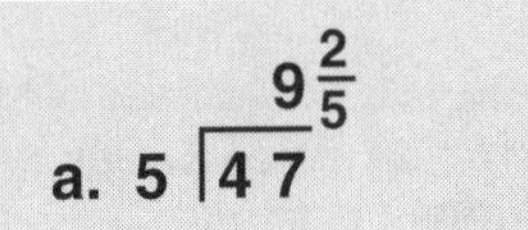

- Here's what you should have. 47 divided by 5. The answer is 9 and 2-fifths.

c. Your turn: Work the rest of the problems in part 4. Raise your hand when you're finished.
(Observe students and give feedback.)

d. (Write on the board:)

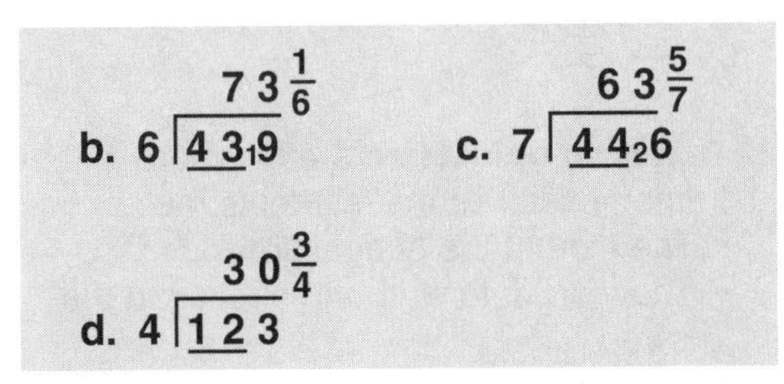

- Check your work. Here's what you should have for problems B through D. Raise your hand if you got everything right.

Teaching note: When you observe and give feedback for an exercise like the one above, you should not have to provide teaching of any type. You should not have to tell students what to do. Instead, you should be able to **ask them questions about what they have done.** If students have trouble with the fraction, ask "What's the remainder? . . . What are you dividing by in this problem? . . . Say the fraction."

If students make the mistake of writing the first digit of the answer in the wrong place in problem b, say:

"Say the problem for the first digit under the division sign." *4 divided by 6.*

"Is 4 big enough?" *No.*

"Say the problem for the first two digits." *43 divided by 6.*

"Did you underline the first two digits?" *Yes.*

"Did you write your answer above the **last** underlined digit?" *No.*

"Do it."

If students omit the zero in problem D, say:

"Say the problem for the last digit under the division sign." *3 divided by 4.*

"What's the answer?" *Zero.*

"Write it where it belongs."

Remember, the goal of the earlier teaching is to provide students with the precise ways of working problems. This teaching also provides you with specific questions that target critical steps where mistakes are likely.

LONG DIVISION

Level E presents short-division problems and long-division problems. Long division is different from short division in two ways:

1) The divisor has two digits.
2) The work for long division shows work below the dividend.

This is long division:

$$52 \overline{)161} = 3\tfrac{5}{52} \qquad \begin{array}{r} 161 \\ -156 \\ \hline 5 \end{array}$$

This is short division:

$$5 \overline{)16_11} = 32\tfrac{1}{5}$$

The convention used in Level E is that all problems with single-digit divisors are worked as short division. The reason is that there is no need to write out the steps (which can be worked mentally).

All problems that have a 2-digit divisor are worked as long division. The reasons are that the calculations cannot be done mentally, and also that the estimated answer might not be correct. This is not revealed in some cases until students multiply and subtract:

```
       4
 56 |290
    -224
      66
```

The transition to long division begins in Lessons 43. The students operate on problems that are partly worked:

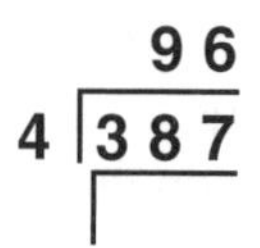

The whole number in the answer is shown, but not the remainder. Students use a new procedure to figure out the remainder. The procedure is the one they will use later when working problems that divide by a two-digit value: multiply the quotient (96) by the divisor (4). They write the product (384) under the second division sign. They subtract and write the difference below. They then write the fraction 3/4 in the answer above:

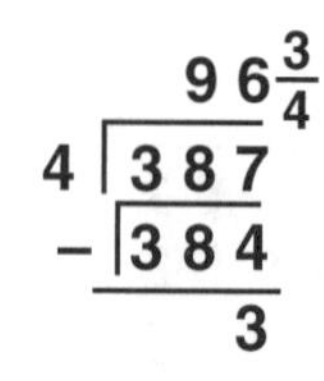

Here's part of the exercise from Lesson 43 following a board demonstration:

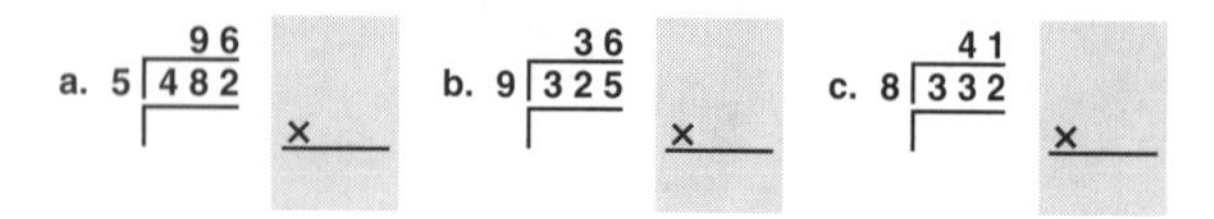

c. Problem A. The remainder is not shown. We'll figure it out by multiplying and subtracting. Say the multiplication problem. (Signal.) *96 times 5.*

- Work that problem. Write the answer under the second division sign. Raise your hand when you are finished.
  (Observe students and give feedback.)
- Everybody, what does 96 times 5 equal? (Signal.) *480.*
- That's less than 482.
- (Write on the board:)

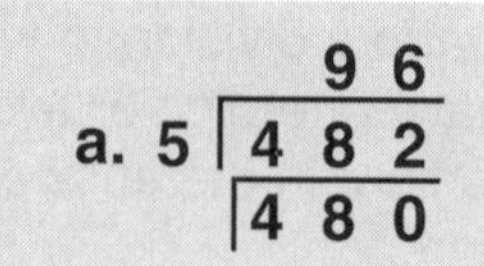

- Make the minus sign. Subtract 480. Write the remainder below. Raise your hand when you're finished. √
- (Write to show:)

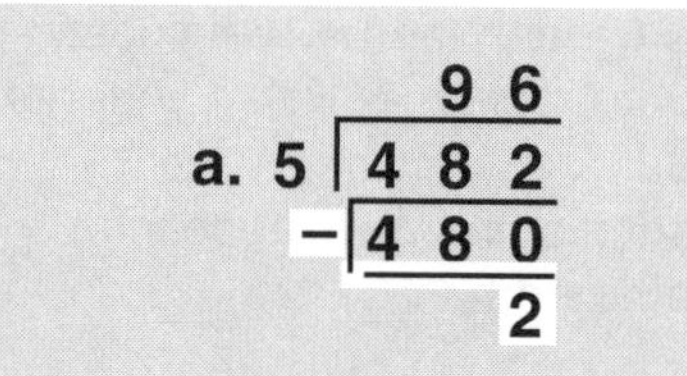

- Here's what you should have. The remainder is 2. The problem divides by 5. Say the fraction for the answer. (Signal.) *2-fifths.*
- Write it after 96. √
- (Write to show:)

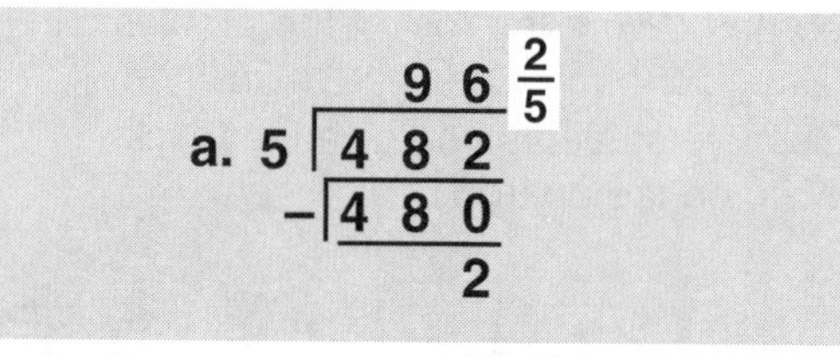

Teaching note: Here are the more common mistakes that students make:

- They forget the subtraction sign.
- They forget to write the fraction in the answer.
- They may have trouble writing the correct fraction. Sometimes, they have a reversal.

Here's a good way to prompt students so they will avoid these mistakes:

"What do you do after you multiply?" *Subtract.*

"Did you show all the work for your subtraction?" *Yes.*

"What's the remainder?" *2.*

"What are you dividing by in this problem?" *5.*

"Say the fraction for 2 divided by 5." *2-fifths.*

After students work on problems of this type for several lessons, they figure out the remainder for problems that divide by a two-digit value. Students write the multiplication problem with the **two-digit value on top.**

Here's part of the introduction from Lesson 46:

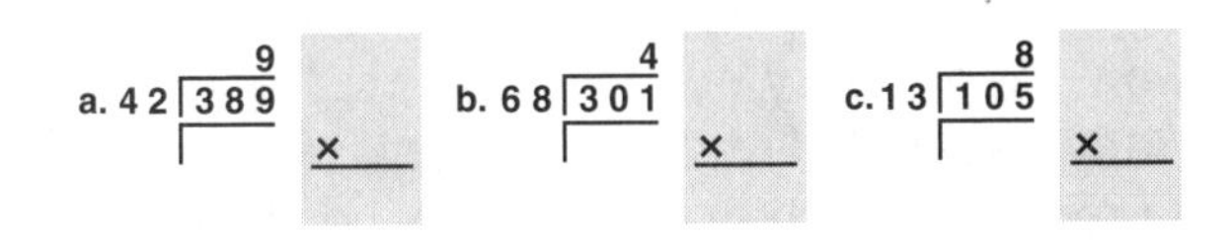

c. Problem B. Start with the 2-digit value and say the multiplication problem you'll work. (Signal.) *68 times 4.*

- Work that problem; subtract; then write the remainder as a fraction in the answer. Raise you hand when you're finished.
  (Observe students and give feedback.)
- (Write on the board:)

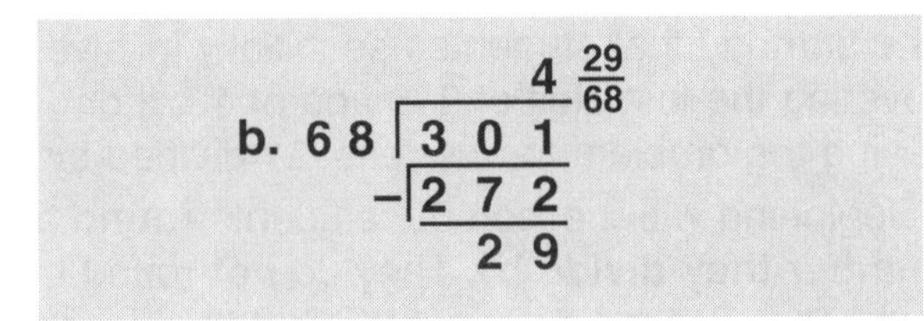

- Here's what you should have. When you multiply 68 by 4, you get 272. When you subtract, you get 29. So the fraction is 29/68. Raise your hand if you got everything right.

d. Your turn: Work problem C. Raise your hand when you're finished.
  (Observe students and give feedback.)

- (Write on the board:)

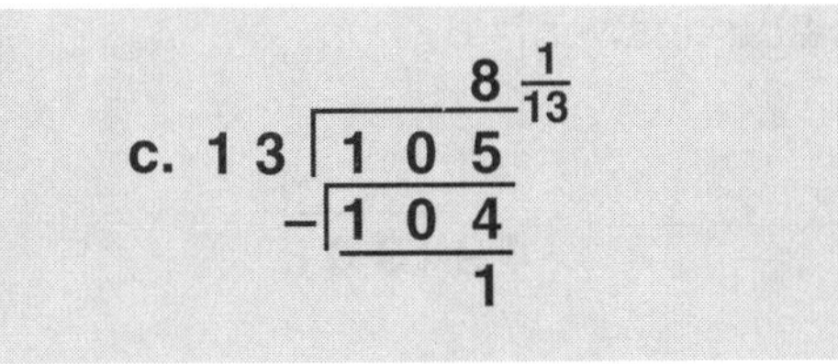

- Here's what you should have for problem C. 13 times 8 is 104. The fraction is 1/13. Raise your hand if you got everything right.

> ***Teaching note:*** Praise students who follow the new procedure without undue prompting. Use the same basic corrections that you used when students worked problems that divide by a single-digit number.

Following the introduction, students work with answers that are either too big or are correct. Students determine whether the answer is appropriate by multiplying and then subtracting. If the answer is too big, they are unable to subtract. They make the answer 1 smaller and do the multiplication for that answer.

Here's the introduction from Lesson 51:

a. For some of these problems, the whole number part of the answer is too big. For other problems, the whole number part is right. You're **not** going to work all the problems. If the answer is too big, you'll work the **second problem.** You'll write a whole number answer that is 1 smaller and figure out the complete answer.

b. We'll work the sample problem together.

- (Write on the board:)

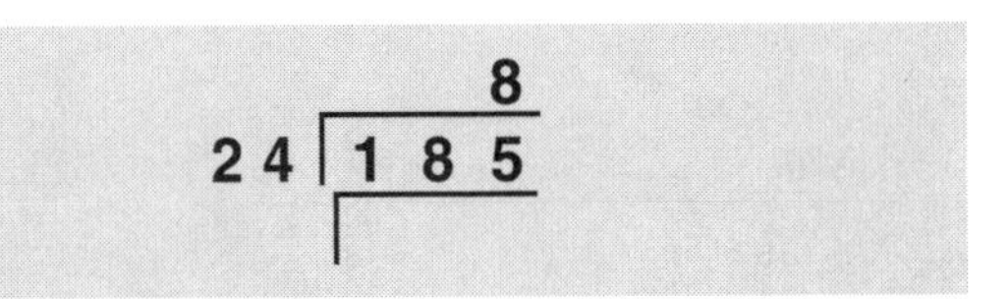

- Say the multiplication problem you'll work. (Signal.) *24 times 8.*
- The answer is 192.
- (Write to show:)

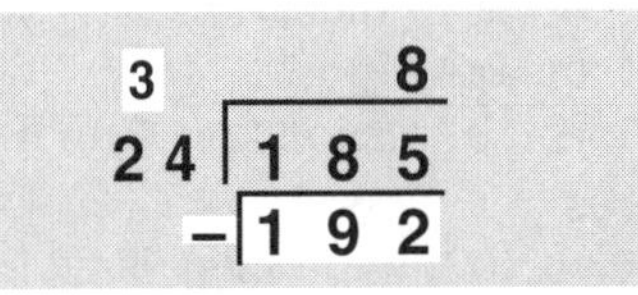

- 192 is too big. So the answer—8—is too big. What's the correct answer? (Signal.) *7.*
- So we work the same problem with an answer of 7.
- (Write to show:)

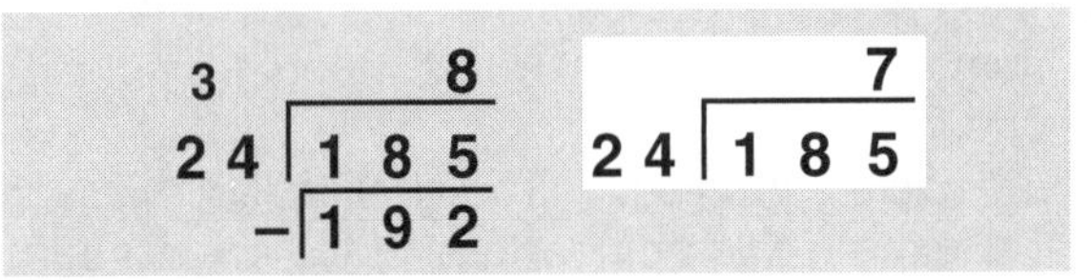

- When we work this problem, we should get a remainder that is right. Do it. Copy the work for the first problem. Write the answer of 7 for the second problem. Figure out the remainder and complete the answer. Raise your hand when you're finished.
  (Observe students and give feedback.)
- (Write to show:)

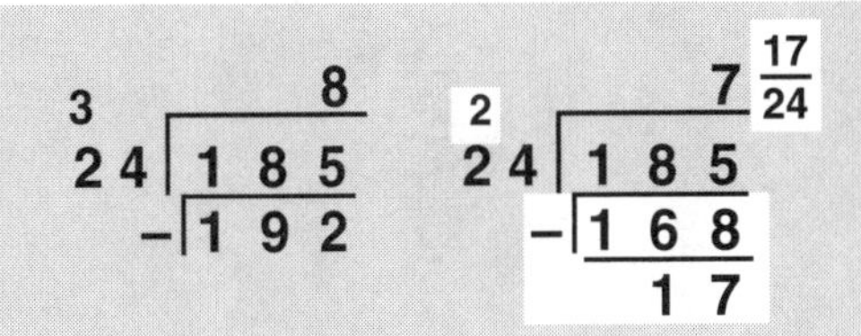

- Here's what you should have.
- Remember, do the multiplication for the first problem in the item. If the answer is too big, write the answer that is **1 smaller** and work the second problem.

In Lesson 58, problems with remainders that are **too large** are introduced. Students are first shown problems that have answers. The fractions in some answers are more than 1. Those fractions indicate that the whole number part of the answer is too small. Students work the problem with an answer that is 1 larger. The fraction in their answer is less than 1, indicating that the whole number part of the answer is correct.

Here's part of the introduction from Lesson 58:

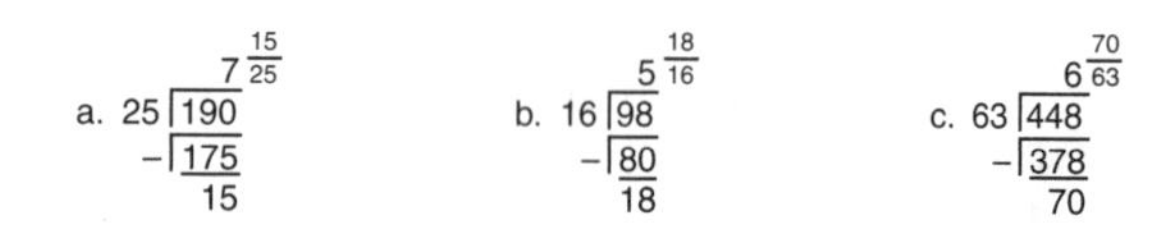

a. The answers are shown for the problems in part 5. The answers for some problems are silly. They show a fraction that is more than 1. The fraction in the answer must be less than 1. If the fraction is not less than 1, you must make the whole-number part of the answer **bigger.**

b. Problem A. Is the fraction less than 1? (Signal.) *Yes.*
- So the answer to that problem is all right.
- Problem B. Is the fraction less than 1? (Signal.) *No.*
- The fraction is more than 1. So the whole-number part of the answer is wrong. It's not big enough.
- Problem C. Is the fraction less than 1? (Signal.) *No.*
- The fraction is not less than 1. So the whole-number part of the answer is wrong. It's not big enough.

c. Go back to problem B. The fraction is not less than 1. So the whole-number part of the answer is not big enough. What is the whole number shown in the answer? (Signal.) *5.*
- Copy the problem and work it with an answer of 6. See if you get a fraction that is less than 1. Raise your hand when you're finished. (Observe students and give feedback.)
- (Write on the board:)

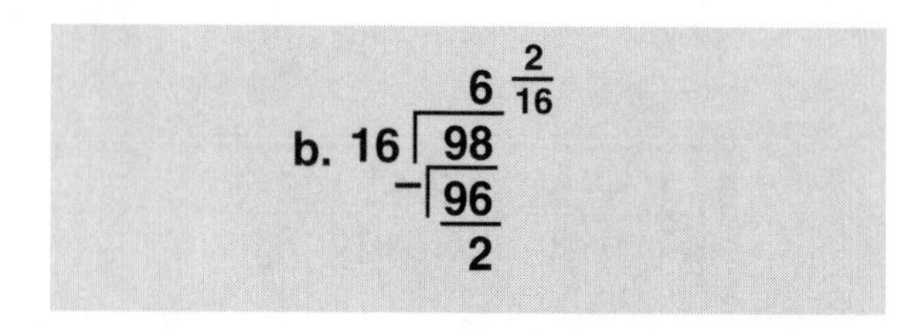

- Here's what you should have. The fraction is less than 1, so the answer is correct.

Teaching note: This exercise has a lot of teacher talk. A good practice for presenting exercises of this type is to move fast. If students make a mistake, correct it quickly by giving the correct answer and then going on. It's probably not necessary to "repeat any step until firm." The students work a problem in step c. At that time, you'll get good information about any difficulties.

In Lesson 66, students work division problems that do not have any part of the answer shown. For example:

43 | 218

The strategy that students use initially involves covering the last digit of 218 and of 43, then saying the problem for the tens: 21 divided by 4.

Beginning with Lesson 68, students **round the number they divide by.** They do **not** round the number under the division sign, but they ignore the final digit and work the problem for the tens. For example:

49 | 308

Students round 49 to 5 tens. They work the estimation problem: 30 divided by 5. The estimated answer is 6:

Here's part of the exercise from Lesson 68:

a. 47 | 208   b. 29 | 241   c. 52 | 368

a. For each problem, you'll say the estimation problem for the tens. You'll first round the number you divide by—just the number you divide by.

b. Problem A. What are you dividing by? (Signal.) *47.*
- How many tens does 47 round to? (Signal.) *5.*
- Say the problem that divides by 5. (Signal.) *20 divided by 5.*
- Problem B. What are you dividing by? (Signal.) *29.*
- How many tens does 29 round to? (Signal.) *3.*

- Say the problem that divides by 3. (Signal.) *24 divided by 3.*
  (Repeat step b until firm.)

c. Problem C. What are you dividing by? (Signal.) *52.*

- How many tens does 52 round to? (Signal.) *5.*
- Say the problem that divides by 5. (Signal.) *36 divided by 5.*

d. Work problem A. Say the estimation problem to yourself. Write the answer above the ones digit of 208. Then complete the problem. Raise your hand when finished.
  (Observe students and give feedback.)

- (Write on the board:)

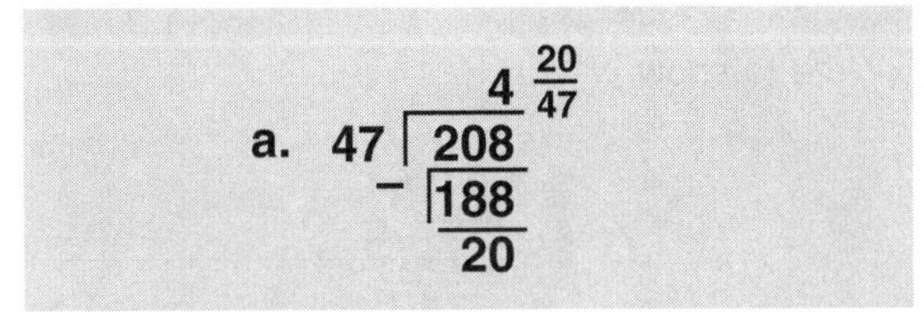

- Here's what you should have. The estimation problem is 20 divided by 5. That's 4. 47 times 4 is 188. The fraction is 20/47. Raise your hand if you got it right.
- Remember, round the number you're dividing by to the nearest ten. Then work the estimation problem.

Teaching note: Step b provides relevant practice on key discriminations students must make to work the problems—rounding the number they divide by and saying the problem for the tens. This step should be repeated until the students are absolutely firm. If they are firm in the procedure, they will be able to work quickly and confidently when working the problems. You won't have to prompt them individually on the procedure.

All the problems students work initially generate estimates that work. The answer is neither too large nor too small. During the lesson span that students work these problems, they continue to test partially-worked problems that have trial answers that are too large or too small.

In Lesson 71, the second division sign is dropped and students work the problems in a conventional manner:

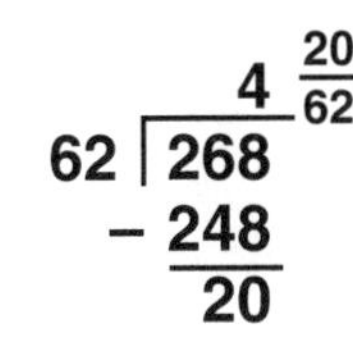

In Lesson 86, all the component skills come together and students work problems that generate estimates that are either too large, too small, or correct. This is where the hard work in earlier lessons pays off. Students should not have serious difficulties if they performed adequately on the earlier exercises. They should know how to estimate the answer, how to adjust the answer if the remainder is more than the number of the problem divides by, and how to adjust the answer if they can't subtract.

Here's part of the introduction from Lesson 86:

a. 82⟌240 b. 68⟌152 c. 25⟌185 d. 90⟌673

a. For some of these problems, the estimation problem won't give you the right answer. When you multiply, you'll get a value that is either too big or too small.

b. Remember, if you can't subtract, you have to change the answer.

- Everybody, how do you change it? (Signal.) *Make it smaller.*
- Yes, if you can't subtract, the answer is too big and you make it smaller.
- If you get a remainder that's bigger than the number you divide by, you have to change the answer. How do you change it? (Signal.) *Make it bigger.*
- Yes, if the remainder is too big, you make the **answer** bigger.
  (Repeat step b until firm.)

c. Problem A says: 240 divided by 82. Say the estimation problem. (Signal.) *24 divided by 8.*

- What's the answer? (Signal.) *3.*
- Write that answer. Then multiply and figure out if the estimation answer is the right size. Raise your hand when you know it's correct.
- (Write on the board:)

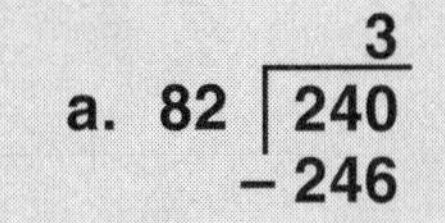

- Here's what you should have. You couldn't subtract. So what do you know about the estimation answer? (Signal.) *It's too big.*
- Fix up the answer and rework the problem. You don't need to copy the problem. Just change the answer and rework it. Raise your hand when you're finished.

- (Change to show:)

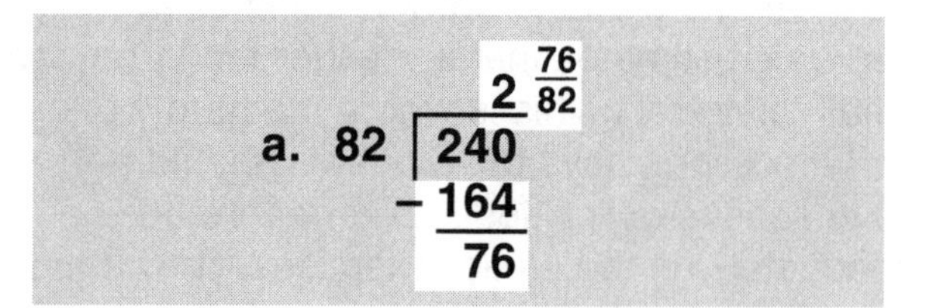

- Here's what you should have.

d. Your turn: Work the rest of the problems in part 1. Remember, the estimation problem may give you an answer that's too big or too small.

Teaching note: The discrimination that is presented in step b is tricky. A good idea is to present the questions in a way that provides the students with thinking time. "Remember, if you can't subtract, you have to change the answer. (Pause) Everybody, how do you change it?" If you pause, students have time to recall what they do. After students receive modest prompting for the first problem, they work the rest of the problems without prompts. They should not have serious difficulties if the earlier instruction has been careful.

The final extension in the division track involves problems that have two-digit answers. The work begins in Lesson 97. The procedure is to underline the part of the problem that is at least as large as the number the problem divides by, do the work for that part, bring down the next digit, and work a second problem. For the introduction, the underlining for the first digit of the answer is provided.

Here's part of the introduction:

b. Problem A: 1473 divided by 39. Here's the problem for the underlined part: 147 divided by 39. Say the problem. (Signal.) *147 divided by 39.*

- Say the **estimation** problem for that part. (Signal.) *14 divided by 4.*
- Write the answer above the last digit of the underlined part. Then multiply and write the number you get below the underlined part. Then subtract. Raise you hand when you've done that much.
- (Write on the board:)

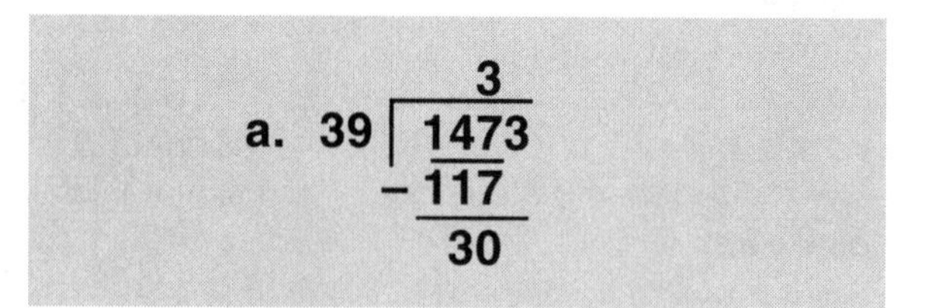

- Here's what you should have. 117 is right under 147. The remainder is **30.** Fix up any mistakes.
- You've worked the problem for the tens. Now you'll work the problem for the ones. The first thing you do is bring down the ones digit that's under the division sign. What digit is that? (Signal.) *3.*
- (Write to show:)

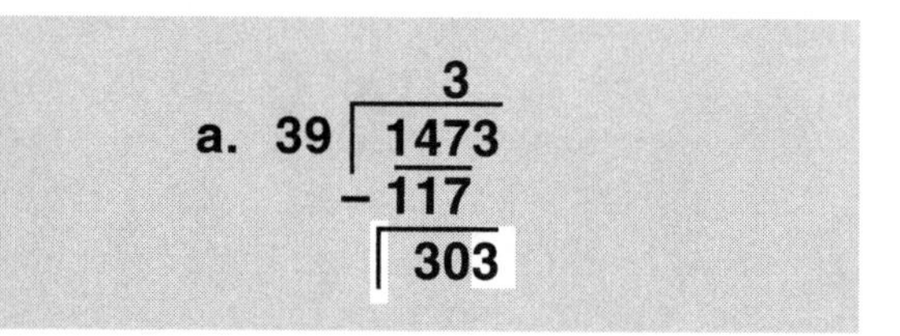

- Write it after the **30** and show the division sign for the problem: 303 divided by 39. Say the estimation problem for 303 divided by 39. (Signal.) *30 divided by 4.*
- Write the answer in the ones column. Then multiply, subtract and complete the answer. Raise your hand when you are finished.
(Observe students and give feedback.)
- (Write to show:)

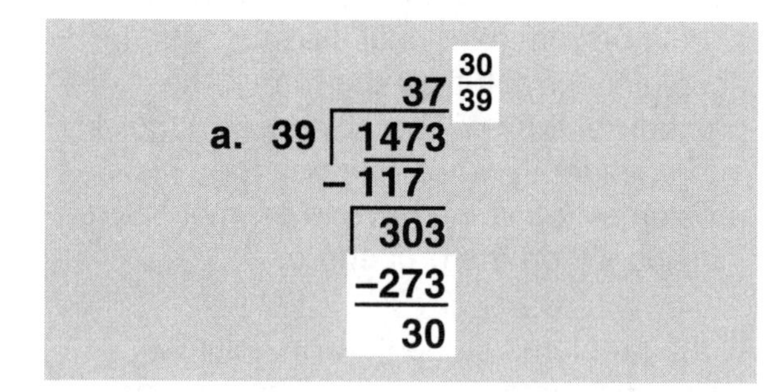

- Here's what you should have. The answer for the estimation problem is **7.** When you multiply, you get 273. The remainder is **30.** Raise your hand if you got everything right.

Teaching note: In step b, you provide students with subtle but important information. Make it clear. "Multiply and write the answer you get **below the underlined part.**" This is the step that most likely will give students trouble. The underlined part provides a prompt for the last digit of the answer to the multiplication problem. The last digit of the answer goes under the last underlined digit. If you stress the rule of writing the answer under the underlined part, students will perform appropriately.

In Lesson 101, students work problems of this type that do not have underlined parts. By Lesson 104, students work a mixture of short division and long division problems, some of which have two-digit answers. Practice in working division problems continues through Lesson 105, after which it is reviewed in independent-work activities.

Calculator Skills

Throughout Level E, students use calculators to work specified problems. All students need a calculator. They are to use it only for tasks that are signaled with the calculator icon:

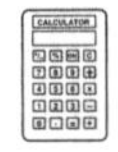

Calculators are used for:

1) New problem-solving procedures in which calculation interferes with applying the steps in the procedure.

2) Problems that are elegantly demonstrated with a calculator. For instance, the relationship between .50 and .5 is shown elegantly with a calculator. Enter .50 and =. The calculator displays the equivalent value: .5.

3) Checks of longhand calculation. Different methods of checking are possible for different problem types.

Note that **calculators are not a substitute for longhand calculation.** Furthermore, the use of calculators is inappropriate for many problem types—such as ratio problems that terminate in **mixed-number answers.** For some of those answers, the calculator would display a decimal value with up to seven places.

Calculators are specified for some tests. The parts of the test that require calculators are at the end of the test. Students are not to use calculators for any other parts of the test.

Follow these calculator rules to ensure that the work with calculators goes smoothly:

1) Make sure that every student has a calculator available for the lesson. Calculators should be in assigned places or should be picked up by students before beginning the lesson—not during the lesson.

2) For parts of the lesson that do not specify calculator use, calculators should either be stored in a desk or placed face down on the desk.

3) For parts of the lesson that specify calculator use, students should do the calculator work quickly. Calculators should generally SAVE time, not require more time than longhand calculation requires.

4) For independent work that requires a calculator, students should have access to a calculator. If they do not own one, specify a time or a checkout procedure that permits them to take a calculator home. Generally, a better procedure is to identify the part of the independent work that involves calculators and permit students to work that part in school, possibly during a study period.

Work with calculators is structured in Lessons 3 and 4. Students practice whole number operations—addition, subtraction, multiplication, and division. The basic procedure that students follow is to enter the digits of the first numbers in the problem; enter the appropriate operational sign: +, –, ×, ÷; enter the digits of the second number, then press =. If students make a mistake, they are to press clear and rework the problem.

In Lesson 4, students use a calculator to show the relationship between multiplication and division. Students express problems such as:

$$5 \times \blacksquare = 560$$

as division problems. For example:

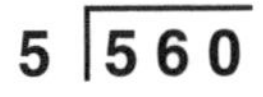

Students work each division problem with their calculators, then write the answer to the multiplication problem. In this situation, the calculator facilitates the demonstration of the relationship.

In Lesson 8, the calculator is used in the context of problem solving. Students say the addition or subtraction problem they'll work and then work the problem with their calculators and write the answers. ***Note:*** Students are **not** required to write the problems they'll work with the calculator, just the answer.

In this situation, the calculator removes interference that lengthy calculation would impose. As students progress through the program, calculators are used with increased frequency to explore relationships and check work.

Number Relationships

For students to progress smoothly in math, they are expected to understand relationships between numbers that are expressed in different ways. 6/3 is 2. It is also 200%. It is also 2.00. It is also a series of fractions that equals 2—8/4, 12/6, etc.

Level E provides extensive work on these relationships. The principal vehicle for students to express the relationships is a table that has columns for different notations. For each row, students convert values from one notation to another. Here are some of the table formats that are presented in Level E:

Fraction	Division
$\frac{28}{4}$	$\overline{)}$
	$6\overline{)42}$

Fraction	Decimal	%
$\frac{156}{100}$		
	.05	
		300%

Mixed Number	Fraction	Decimal
	$\frac{125}{100}$	
$3\frac{5}{1000}$		
		2.8

Relationships between whole numbers, mixed numbers, and fractions are also illustrated on the number line.

FRACTIONS/WHOLE NUMBERS

A relationship that is reviewed early in Level E is that between fractions and whole numbers. The relationship is twofold: any whole number can be expressed as a fraction with a particular denominator, and any fraction for a whole number can be expressed as other, equivalent fractions.

Beginning in Lesson 5, students write fractions for points shown on a number line.

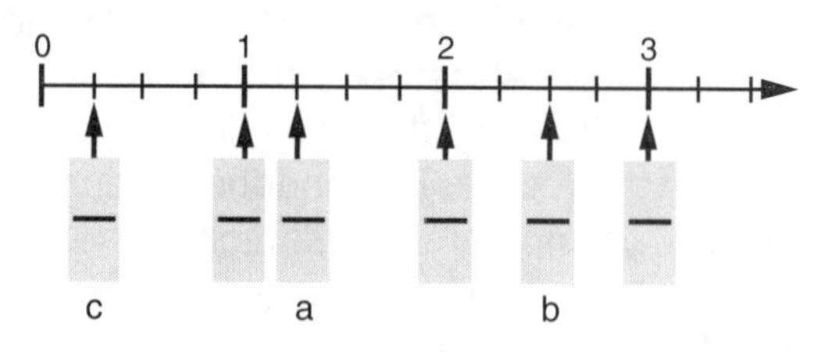

Students first determine the denominator of the fraction. All fractions on the same number line have the same denominator (4 in the example above). The numerator of each fraction indicates the number of parts from the beginning of the number line. Fraction **a** is 5/4. Fraction **b** is 10/4.

Students later focus on the relationship between the numerators and denominators of fractions that equal whole numbers. If the fraction equals a whole number, the numerator is a multiple of the denominator. If the denominator is 5, the numerators for whole numbers are 0, 5, 10, 15, and so forth. Students apply this relationship to number lines.

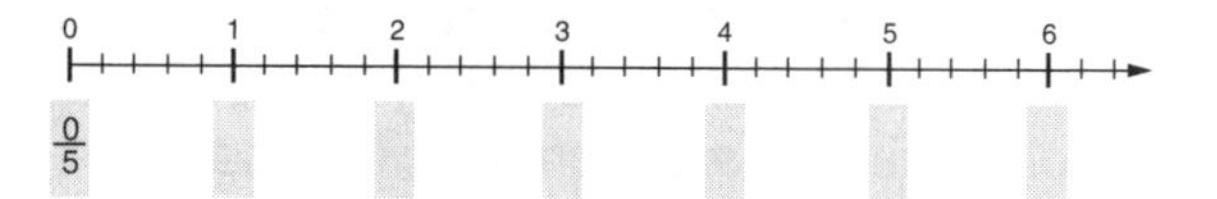

Students later work with equations that reinforce the relationship between the various fractions that equal a whole number.

For example:

$$8 = \frac{\blacksquare}{3} = \frac{\blacksquare}{1} = \frac{\blacksquare}{8} = \frac{\blacksquare}{7} =$$

Equations of this form are first introduced in Lesson 25. Here's the first part of the exercise:

a. Each problem has a whole number and a series of fractions that equal the whole number.

b. For equation A, the whole number is 4. So all the fractions have a top number that is 4 times the denominator. The denominators are shown.

- What's the first denominator? (Signal.) *3.*
- The fraction equals 4. So you multiply 3 times 4 to find the top number.
- Your turn: Complete equation A. Raise your hand when you're finished.
  (Observe students and give feedback.)

- (Write on the board:)

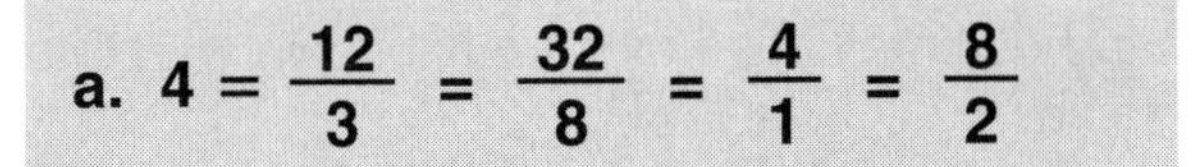

- Here's what you should have. 4 equals 12-thirds, equals 32-eighths, equals 4 over 1, equals 8-halves. Raise your hand if you got everything right.

FRACTIONS/DIVISION/MIXED NUMBERS

Another relationship links fractions and division. The relationship is most easily expressed by reading a fraction as a division problem. For example: 40/5 is 40 divided by 5. That's 8.

Here's part of the exercise from Lesson 8:

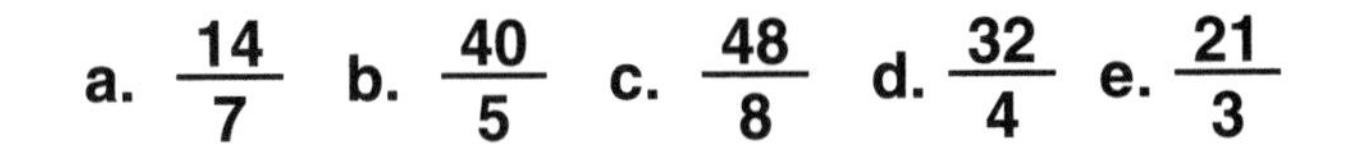

b. For each fraction, you'll write the division problem and the answer. Remember, you can read a fraction as a division problem by starting with the top number.

c. Fraction A. Read it as a division problem. (Signal.) *14 divided by 7.*

- Fraction B. Read it as a division problem. (Signal.) *40 divided by 5.*
- Fraction C. Read it as a division problem. (Signal.) *48 divided by 8.*

d. Your turn: Write the division problem and the answer for each fraction. Raise your hand when you're finished.
(Observe students and give feedback.)

e. Check your work. I'll say each fraction. You'll say the division problem and the answer.

- Fraction A: 14-sevenths. (Signal.) *14 divided by 7 equals 2.*
- Fraction B: 40-fifths. (Signal.) *40 divided by 5 equals 8.*
- Fraction C: 48-eighths. (Signal.) *48 divided by 8 equals 6.*
- Fraction D: 32-fourths. (Signal.) *32 divided by 4 equals 8.*
- Fraction E: 21-thirds. (Signal.) *21 divided by 3 equals 7.*

Starting in Lesson 11, students complete tables that express the relationship between fractions and division.

Fraction equation	Division
a. $\frac{40}{8}$ =	$\overline{)\quad}$
b.	$7\overline{)56}$
c. $\frac{48}{8}$ =	$\overline{)\quad}$
d.	$4\overline{)32}$
e. $\frac{18}{9}$ =	$\overline{)\quad}$

For each row, students complete the equation to show the whole number the fraction equals and the corresponding division statement.

An extension of the relationship between fractions and division is the relationship between fractions and mixed numbers. Mixed numbers are an expression of improper fractions that do not equal whole numbers. If the numerator is not a multiple of the denominator, the fraction can be expressed as a mixed number—a whole number plus leftover parts. The work with this relationship begins in Lesson 19. Students express mixed numbers as fractions.

In Lesson 39, students convert fractions into mixed numbers. Students are presented with fractions that are more than one. Students write the fraction as a division problem, work it, and express the remainder as a fraction. The answer to the problem is the mixed number that equals the original fraction.

Here's part of the exercise from Lesson 39:

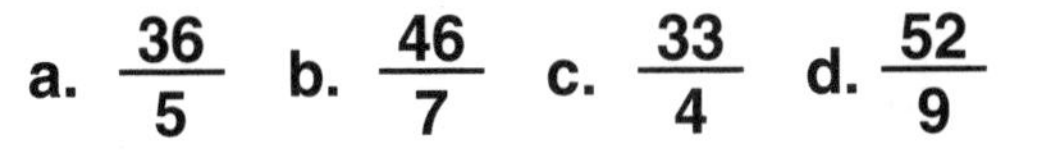

c. Fraction A. Read it as a division problem. (Signal.) *36 divided by 5.*

- Fraction B. Read it as a division problem. (Signal.) *46 divided by 7.*
- Fraction C. Read it as a division problem. (Signal.) *33 divided by 4.*

d. Your turn: Write the division problem and the answer for each fraction in part 5. Show each answer as a mixed number. Raise your hand when you're finished.
(Observe students and give feedback.)

e. Check your work.

- Problem A: 36-fifths. Say the division problem and the whole answer. (Signal.) *36 divided by 5 equals 7 and 1-fifth.*
- So 7 and 1-fifth equals the fraction you started with—36-fifths.
- Problem B: 46-sevenths. Say the division problem and the whole answer. (Signal.) *46 divided by 7 equals 6 and 4-sevenths.*
- So 6 and 4-sevenths equals the fraction you started with—46-sevenths.
- Problem C: 33-fourths. Say the division problem and the whole answer. (Signal.) *33 divided by 4 equals 8 and 1-fourth.*
- So 8 and 1-fourth equals the fraction you started with—33-fourths.
- Problem D: 52-ninths. Say the division problem and the whole answer. (Signal.) *52 divided by 9 equals 5 and 7-ninths.*
- What fraction does that equal? (Signal.) *52-ninths.*

Starting in Lesson 44, students complete tables that have columns for fractions and mixed numbers. Here's an example from Lesson 44:

	Fraction	Mixed Number
a.	$\frac{40}{9}$	
b.		$7\frac{3}{5}$
c.		$10\frac{1}{2}$
d.	$\frac{29}{3}$	
e.	$\frac{47}{8}$	

That mixed number equals the missing value in the multiplication equation.

DECIMAL VALUES

The main relationships involving decimal values that students learn in Level E are:

1) Fractions with denominations of 10, 100, or 1000 can be expressed as decimal values and conversely, any decimal value can be expressed as a fraction or a mixed number.

2) Any fraction can be converted into a decimal value through division.

In Lesson 17, students are presented with the relationship between whole numbers, fractions and decimals. The system is shown with this table:

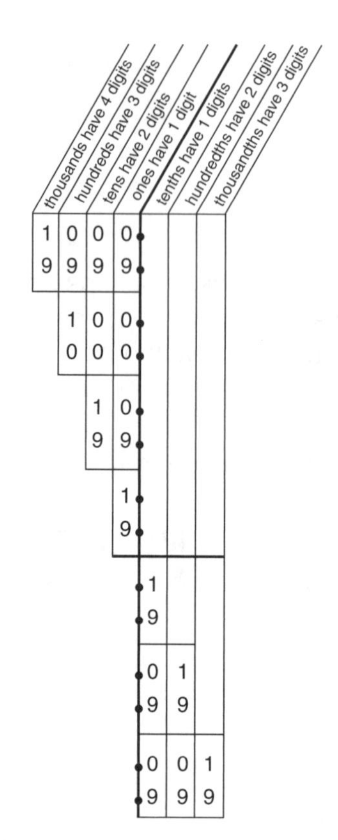

Any value to the left of the decimal point is a whole number. Any value to the right of the decimal point can be expressed as a fraction that is less than one. Reading the decimal value identifies the fraction that equals the decimal value—**the number of places after the decimal point** indicates the fraction.

If a decimal value ends one place after the decimal point, it tells about tenths.

If a value ends two places after the decimal point, it tells about hundredths.

If a value ends three places after the decimal point, it tells about thousandths.

Starting with Lesson 22, students work with tables, each row of which has places for a decimal value and the equivalent fraction. In Lesson 22, the fractions are less than one. In Lesson 24, the decimal values are more than one; students express them as mixed numbers.

Here are the tables from Lessons 22 and 25.

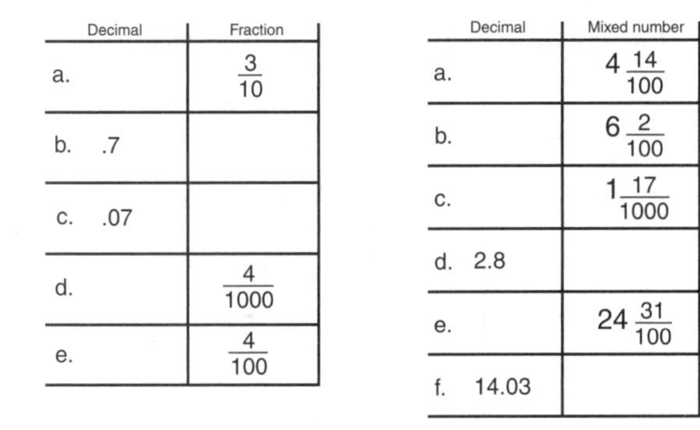

	Decimal	Fraction
a.		$\frac{3}{10}$
b.	.7	
c.	.07	
d.		$\frac{4}{1000}$
e.		$\frac{4}{100}$

	Decimal	Mixed number
a.		$4\frac{14}{100}$
b.		$6\frac{2}{100}$
c.		$1\frac{17}{1000}$
d.	2.8	
e.		$24\frac{31}{100}$
f.	14.03	

By reading either the decimal value or the mixed number, the student says the same thing, for example, 1 and 17-thousandths. For the decimal value, the word **and** indicates where the decimal point goes. The word **thousandths** indicates that the value is to **end three places after the decimal point.**

In Lesson 28, students learn the procedure for converting an **improper fraction** into a decimal value. The fractions have denominators of 10, 100, or 1000. The decimal value has the same digits as the numerator of the fraction. Students first write the digits from the numerator, then place the decimal point according to the denominator. If the denominator is 10, there's one place after the decimal point. If the denominator is 100, there are two places after the decimal point. If the denominator is 1000, there are three places after the decimal point.

For example:

$$\frac{237}{100}$$

The digits are 2, 3, and 7. Those are the digits for the decimal notation. The denominator is 100. So there are two places after the decimal point: 2.37.

After the introduction in Lesson 28, students work with tables that require them to express the relationship between improper fractions, mixed numbers, and decimal values.

Here's an example from Lesson 39:

	Fraction	Decimal	Mixed number
a.			$3\frac{9}{100}$
b.		15.4	
c.		8.07	
d.	$\frac{17}{10}$		

Beginning with Lesson 41, students expand what they have learned about the relationship between fractions and decimal values. They learn that **fractions with any denominator can be converted into decimal values by working a division problem.** For the demonstration in Lesson 41, they use their calculators to work the division problems. To convert a mixed number, for example:

$$7\frac{3}{4}$$

They work the division problem for the fraction, then add the whole number. The division for 3/4 is $3 \div 4 = .75$. The whole number is 7. The complete decimal value is: 7.75.

Here's part of the introduction:

d. Item A: 3/12. It's less than 1. Say the division problem. (Signal.) *3 divided by 12.*
- Work the division problem and write the **complete equation** that starts with 3/12. Raise your hand when you're finished.
  (Observe students and give feedback.)
- (Write on the board:)

$$\textbf{a. } \frac{3}{12} = 0.25$$

- Here's what you should have: 3/12 equals zero and 25-hundredths.

e. Item B: 14/8. That fraction is more than 1. Say the division problem. (Signal.) *14 divided by 8.*
- Work the division problem and write the complete equation. Raise your hand when you're finished.
  (Observe students and give feedback.)
- (Write on the board:)

$$\textbf{b. } \frac{14}{8} = 1.75$$

- Here's what you should have: 14/8 equals 1 and 75-hundredths.

f. Item C: 7 and 4/50. Work the division problem **for the fraction.** Then add 7 and write the complete equation. Show the mixed number, an equal sign and the decimal number that equals 7 and 4/50. Raise your hand when you're finished.
(Observe students and give feedback.)

- (Write on the board:)

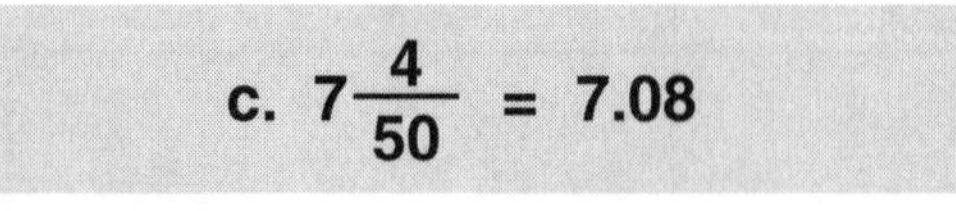

$$c.\ 7\frac{4}{50} = 7.08$$

- Here's what you should have: 7 and 4/50 equals 7 and 8-hundredths. Raise your hand if you got it right.

g. Remember, you can work any fraction as a division problem. Your calculator will show the decimal value that equals the fraction.

Teaching note: The steps involved in this procedure are ones that have been applied to working other problems. For problems a and b, students read the fraction as a division problem, work the division problem on their calculator, and write the equation that shows the fraction and equivalent decimal value. For problem c, students first convert the fraction. Then they add the whole number and write the complete equation:

$$7\frac{4}{50} = 7.08$$

PERCENTS

The final conversion that students learn relates **percents to fractions.** A percent number is a hundredths fraction. Procedurally, this relationship means that the percent number has the same digits as the **numerator** of the fraction. The percent sign is a substitute for the denominator of 100.

For example:

$$\frac{6}{100} = 6\% \qquad \frac{210}{100} = 210\%$$

Here's the table that students work in the first lesson (Lesson 92) that presents the relationship between fractions and percents:

	Decimal	Fraction	Percent
Sample row	.04	$\frac{4}{100}$	4%
a.		$\frac{206}{100}$	
b.		$\frac{80}{100}$	
c.		$\frac{7}{100}$	
d.		$\frac{15}{100}$	

The first row is completed. For the other rows, the fraction is shown. It generates the decimal value and the percent value. Some of the examples are more difficult than they may seem because the conversion to decimal places requires two places to show hundredths. For values like 7/100, this stipulation means that the student must insert a zero immediately after the decimal point: .07. The corresponding percent value does **not** require an additional zero: 7%.

In subsequent lessons, students complete tables with rows that show either the fraction, decimal, or corresponding percent.

Here's an example from Lesson 94:

	Decimal	Fraction	Percent
a.		$\frac{100}{100}$	
b.			802%
c.	4.03		
d.			8%
e.		$\frac{90}{100}$	

Various types of problems that advanced-math students work assume that they know the relationship between fractions, decimals, mixed numbers, whole numbers, and percents. Students who complete Level E know the fundamental relationships and also receive practice in applying their knowledge to problem-solving activities. For instance, immediately after they have learned the percent-fraction conversion, they work ratio and proportion problems that involve percents. (See **Ratios and Proportions** track of the Applications section on page 94.)

Operational Relationships

INVERSE OPERATIONS

In Level E, students learn about the inverse operations of addition-subtraction and multiplication-division.

The relationship between multiplication and division is introduced in Lesson 1. Students complete a table that shows multiplication problems of the form: 9 × ■ 63.

Multiplication	Division
a. 7 × ▢ = 35	⟌
b. 9 × ▢ = 63	⟌
c. 1 × ▢ = 9	⟌

Students write the missing value, then write the corresponding division fact.

In Lesson 4, students work problems of the same form but that are not simple fact relationships. Here's part of the table from Lesson 4:

Multiplication	Division
a. 8 × ▢ = 168	⟌
b. 6 × ▢ = 114	
c. 5 × ▢ = 560	

For these problems, the relationship between multiplication and division is necessary because students don't know the answer to the multiplication problem. They work the corresponding division problem, then complete the multiplication problem.

The relationship between multiplication, fractions, and division is made explicit in Lesson 45. Students work problems of the form:

9 (■) = 369

Instead of writing the **division problem** to figure out the missing value, students write the missing value as a **fraction.** They then convert the fraction into a division problem and express the missing value as a whole number.

Here's part of the exercise from Lesson 45. It follows a review of the relationship between division and fractions.

a. For each problem, you'll tell me the **fraction** for the missing value.

b. Problem A: 5 times some value equals 345. Everybody, say the fraction for the missing value. (Signal.) *345-fifths.*

- Problem B: 4 times some value equals 344. Everybody, say the fraction. (Signal.) *344-fourths.*
- Problem C: 4 times some value equals 560. Everybody, say the fraction. (Signal.) *560-fourths.*

c. Your turn: Complete each equation. Show the missing value written as a fraction. Raise your hand when you're finished.
(Observe students and give feedback.)

- (Write on the board:)

a. $5\left(\frac{345}{5}\right) = 345$ **b.** $4\left(\frac{344}{4}\right) = 344$

c. $4\left(\frac{560}{4}\right) = 560$ **d.** $7\left(\frac{504}{7}\right) = 504$

d. Check your work. Here's what you should have for each equation.

- Everybody, read equation A. (Signal.) *5 times 345-fifths equals 345.*
- Read equation B. (Signal.) *4 times 344-fourths equals 344.*
- Read equation C. (Signal.) *4 times 560-fourths equals 560.*
- Read equation D. (Signal.) *7 times 504-sevenths equals 504.*

e. Use your calculator to figure out what the fraction equals in problem A. On the line below problem A, write the whole equation with a number in place of the fraction. Raise your hand when you're finished.
(Observe students and give feedback.)

- (Write to show:)

a. $5\left(\frac{345}{5}\right) = 345$ **b.** $4\left(\frac{344}{4}\right) = 344$

5 (69) = 345

- Here's what you should have. 345 divided by 5 is 69. So the equation you should have written below is: 5 times 69 equals 345.

Working the multiplication problem 5 times 69 would verify that the value in parentheses is correct.

Starting in Lesson 48, students follow the same procedure to work problems in which the missing fraction does not equal a whole number, such as:

$$4(\blacksquare) = 7$$

Students express the missing value as a fraction: 7/4. This conversion suggests the complete relationship between fractions, multiplication, division, and mixed numbers. Students start with a multiplication problem. They express the missing value as a fraction. They know how to write the fraction as a division problem $(4\overline{)7})$ and how to express the answer as a mixed number $(1\frac{3}{4})$.

The work with the relationship between addition and subtraction begins in Lesson 11. Students work an addition problem, then check the answer by working a subtraction problem that starts with the answer of the addition problem and ends with the first number of that problem. Students use their calculator for these checks.

Here's a completed exercise from Lesson 12:

a. 425 + 329 = 754
754 – 329 = 425

b. 38 + 597 = 635
635 – 597 = 38

c. 325 + 78 = 403
403 – 78 = 325

d. 172 + 568 = 740
740 – 568 = 172

In Lesson 13, students work subtraction problems with their calculator, then check the answer by working addition problems that start with the answer of the subtraction problem and end with the first number of that problem.

For example, students work the problem:

528 – 175 = 353

They check their answer by working the problem:

353 + 175 =

The answer should be the first number in the subtraction problem: 528.

In Lesson 14, students work a mixed set of problems that has both addition and subtraction problems. Students use inverse operations to check the problems.

The work with inverse operations is applied to a variety of word problems beginning with Lesson 109. (See **Problem-Solving** applications, page 82.)

Place Value and Rounding

In Level E, students learn the place names of digits up to millions. They learn to express the value of a digit and learn procedures for rounding to a specified place (e.g., ten, hundred, thousand). The work begins in Lesson 71 with the rules for place value. Students are presented with a model that shows the place names for millions numbers.

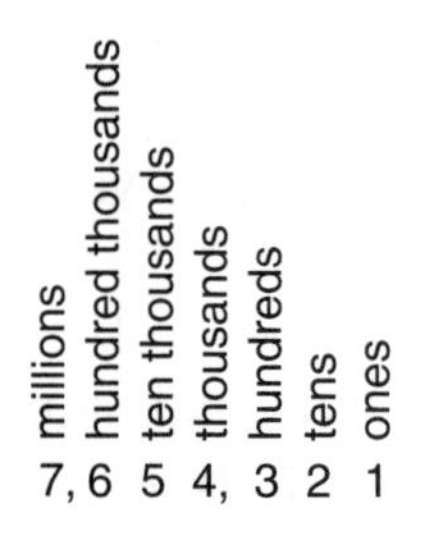

The digits are related to the place names. If the number has seven places, it's a millions number. If it has five places, it's a ten-thousands number. The place-name rule also relates to the procedure for putting commas in larger numbers. Starting from the right, a comma goes after columns 3, 6, and so forth. ***Note:*** Prior to Lesson 71, commas are used only for numerals with five or more digits. After Lesson 71, commas are optional for four-digit numerals.

The initial exercises involve arrowed digits. Students write the "column name" for the digit.

Here are some of the examples from Lesson 71:

a. 5,743,214   b. 6,394,172   c. 8,569,421   d. 9,123,617

For item a, students write: **thousand.**

For item b, students write: **million.**

Starting with Lesson 73, students write **the value** for the arrowed digits.

a. 5,803,649   b. 24,539   c. 56,791   d. 157,264   e. 91,325

For numeral a, they write: **600;** for numeral c, they write: **50,000.**

The work with rounding is a simple extension of the place-value activities. Students round to the arrowed digit. The procedure is to look at **the digit after the arrowed digit.** If that digit is 5 or more, the arrowed digit rounds up. If the digit after the arrowed digit is less than 5, the arrowed digit does not round up.

Here's part of the introduction from Lesson 76:

a. 94,833 ↑ b. 78,399 ↑ c. 43,645 ↑

c. Item A: The arrowed digit is thousands. Is the digit after thousands 5 or more? (Signal.) *Yes.*
- So you round the **arrowed digit** up. What will you write in place of 4? (Signal.) *5.*
- And all the digits after the 5 will be zeros. Write the numeral for 94,833 rounded to thousands. Raise your hand when you're finished. √
- (Write on the board:)

a. 95,000

- Here's what you should have. The numeral rounded to thousands is 95,000.

d. Item B. The arrowed digit is thousands. Is the digit after thousands 5 or more? (Signal.) *No.*
- So you don't round up. Write numeral B rounded to thousands. Raise your hand when you're finished. √
- (Write on the board:)

b. 78,000

- Here's what you should have. 78,399 rounds to 78,000.

e. Item C. The arrowed digit is hundreds. Is the digit after hundreds 5 or more? (Signal.) *No.*
- So you don't round up. Write the numeral rounded to hundreds. Raise your hand when you're finished. √
- (Write on the board:)

c. 43,600

- Here's what you should have. 43,645 rounds to 43,600.

Teaching note: The context for rounding these values requires students to show the digits before the arrowed digit and show zeros after the arrowed digit. This is close to the context that occurs in problem-solving situations where values are to be rounded to specified places. When rounding 94833 to thousands, students write: 95000.

Beginning with Lesson 78, students follow written directions for rounding values. For example: **Round 8743 to the nearest hundred.** This type of activity requires students to apply what they have learned about the column names.

Beginning with Lesson 90, students extend the rounding rules to decimals. The procedure is different because zeros after the last decimal digit do not change the value of the number. Therefore, students do not write zeros after the rounded digit.

For example:

4.3261
↑

Students round to the tenths place. They show no zeros after the tenths: 4.3.

The progression of activities parallels that for whole numbers. Students first round the value to the arrowed digit. Problems are of the form:

a. 19.249 ↑ b. 23.471 ↑ c. 2.5380 ↑

Later, they round from written directions that name the place. Here is part of the exercise from Lesson 92:

a. Round 3.05882 to the nearest thousandth.
b. Round 20.3102 to the nearest tenth.

a. You're going to round decimal values. The directions tell which decimal place to round to. Remember, you look at the digit **after** the digit you'll round. You round up if the digit **after** is 5 or more. You don't show any zeros after the rounded digit.

b. Round the values in part 4. Raise your hand when you're finished.
(Observe students and give feedback.)

c. (Write on the board:)

a. 3.059
b. 20.3
c. 6.778
d. 14.85
e. 4.20

- Here's what you should have for values A through E. Raise your hand if you got all of them right.

Students later apply what they have learned about rounding to dollar amount problems. If the problem involves a dollar amount, they round the answer to the nearest hundredth.

For example:

$$\begin{array}{r} \overset{2\,1}{\$\,4.75} \\ \times\ 3.3 \\ \hline 1425 \\ +\ 14250 \\ \hline \$\ 15.675 \end{array}$$

Students round the answer to $15.68.

Fractions

In Level E, students work problems that add, subtract, and multiply fractions. The fraction skills are then used in problem-solving situations. Here is a summary of the main objectives involving fractions, operations, and relationships that are taught in Level E:

FRACTION OPERATION/CONCEPT	BEGINS IN LESSON
Add and subtract fractions with like denominators	4
Multiply fractions	9
Add and subtract whole numbers and fractions	19
Multiply whole numbers and fractions	32
Apply the fraction multiplication rule: If you multiply by more than 1, you end up with more than you started with	31
Equivalent fractions	14
Add and subtract fractions with unlike denominators	67
Compare fractions	111
Simplify fractions	31

ADDITION AND SUBTRACTION: LIKE DENOMINATORS

Work with addition and subtraction of fractions with like denominators begins in Lesson 4. Students copy the denominator in the answer and operate on the numerators according to the operational sign (+ or −). Students also discriminate between problems that can be worked the way they are written and those that cannot.

Here's a set of problems from Lesson 4:

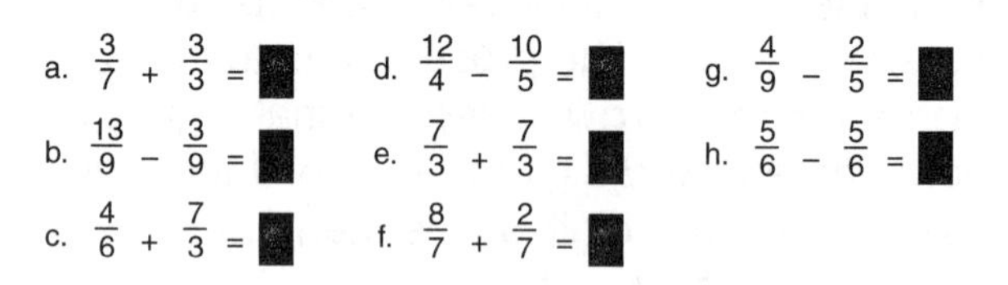

Students copy the problems they can work as written and work them.

ADDITION AND SUBTRACTION: WHOLE NUMBER AND FRACTION

Addition of whole numbers and fractions begins in Lesson 19. Problems present mixed numbers. Students rewrite the mixed number as an addition problem, then change the whole number into a fraction with the same denominator as the other fraction.

Here's part of the exercise that follows the textbook introduction:

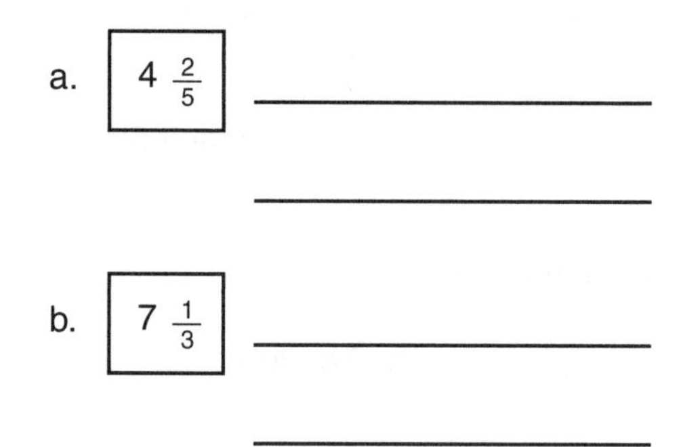

b. Problem A: 4 and 2-fifths. That's 4 **plus** 2-fifths. We change 4 into a fraction that has the same denominator as 2-fifths. What denominator? (Signal.) *5.*

- So what will you multiply 4 by to change 4 into a fraction? (Signal.) *5.*
- Problem B: 7 and 1-third. That's 7 plus 1-third. What will both denominators be? (Signal.) *3.*
- Problem C: 9 and 5-sixths. That's 9 plus 5-sixths. What will both denominators be? (Signal.) *6.*
- What will you multiply 9 by? (Signal.) *6.* (Repeat step b until firm.)

c. Your turn: Write mixed-number A as an addition problem. Write that on the top line. 4 plus 2-fifths. Below, show the fractions 20-fifths plus 2-fifths and write the answer. Raise your hand when you're finished.

- (Write on the board:)

$$\text{a. } 4 + \frac{2}{5}$$

$$\frac{20}{5} + \frac{2}{5} = \frac{22}{5}$$

- Here's what you should have. 20-fifths plus 2-fifths equals 22-fifths. So 4 and 2-fifths equals 22-fifths.

d. Problem B. Write the addition problem for the mixed number. That's 7 plus 1-third. Below, write the fraction for the whole number, add 1-third and write the answer. Raise your hand when you're finished.

- (Write on the board:)

$$\text{b. } 7 + \frac{1}{3}$$

$$\frac{21}{3} + \frac{1}{3} = \frac{22}{3}$$

- Here's what you should have.

Teaching note: Students are lead through the first problem. The reason is to show the "mechanical steps" involved in the solution. For the remaining problems, students are not lead. The only reason for the initial leading is to obviate difficulties that students have in understanding what they are to write and how to write it.

In Lesson 29, the set of examples is expanded to include: a) problems that have a whole number as the second value in the problem and b) problems that require subtraction.

Here are the items from Lesson 29:

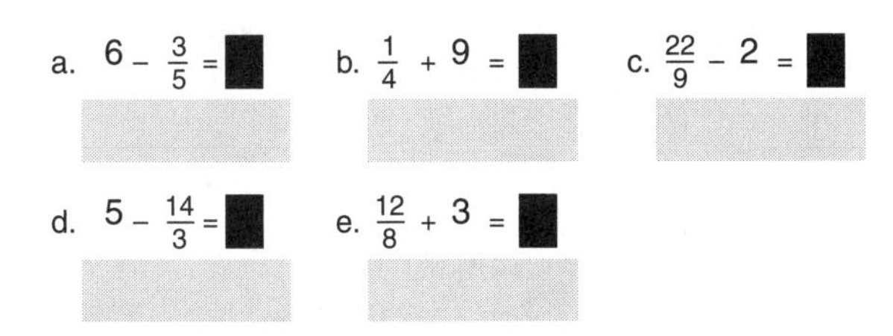

MULTIPLICATION

Students are introduced to multiplying fractions in Lesson 9. Students multiply the numbers on top and write the answer on top, then multiply the numbers on the bottom and write the answer on the bottom.

In Lesson 12, students work a mixed set of problems that includes addition, subtraction, and multiplication. Some of the addition and subtraction problems cannot be worked the way they are written. Students first determine the operation (add, subtract, or multiply). If the problem multiplies, they operate on both the numerators and the denominators; if the problem adds or subtracts, they operate on the numerators and simply copy the denominator. If the denominators are not the same, however, they do not work the problem. Problem sets of this type are very important for shaping student understanding of the operations and how they are different from each other.

MULTIPLICATION: WHOLE NUMBER AND FRACTION

In preparation for problems that multiply a whole number and a fraction, students learn that they can convert a whole number into a simple fraction. That fraction has a denominator of 1: 5 = 5/1; 8 = 8/1. This skill is introduced in Lesson 32.

In Lesson 32, students work a mixed set of problems. Some of the problems multiply a whole number and a fraction. Students first change the whole number into a simple fraction, then multiply. For problems that add or subtract, students first change the whole number into a fraction with the same denominator as the other fraction.

Here's part of the exercise from Lesson 32:

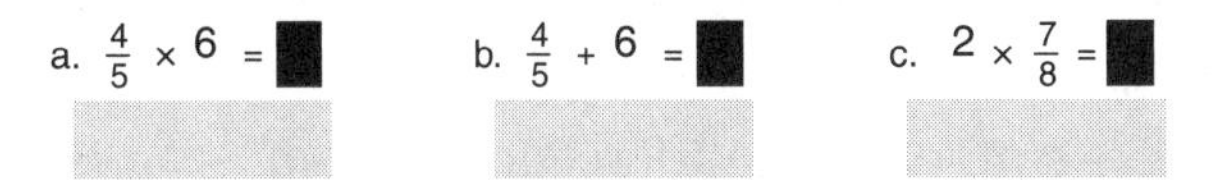

a. Some of these problems multiply, some add, and some subtract. You're going to work each problem. Remember, when you multiply, change the whole number into a simple fraction.

b. Problem A: 4-fifths times 6. You're multiplying. So what simple fraction can you write for 6? (Signal.) *6 over 1.*

- Problem B: 4-fifths **plus** 6. You're not multiplying. So you don't change 6 into a simple fraction. You have to change it into the fraction that has 5 as the denominator. What fraction will you write for 6? (Signal.) *30-fifths.*
- Problem C: Are you multiplying? (Signal.) *Yes.*
- So you can write the fraction as 2 over 1.
- Problem D: Are you multiplying? (Signal.) *No.*
- So you can't write the fraction as 9 over 1.

c. Your turn: Rewrite problem A and work it. Raise your hand when you're finished.

(Observe students and give feedback.)

- (Write on the board:)

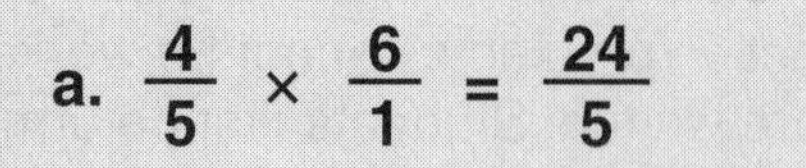
$$a.\ \frac{4}{5} \times \frac{6}{1} = \frac{24}{5}$$

- Here's what you should have. You changed 6 into 6 over 1. The answer is 24-fifths.

d. Work problem B. Raise your hand when you're finished. (Observe students and give feedback.)

- (Write on the board:)

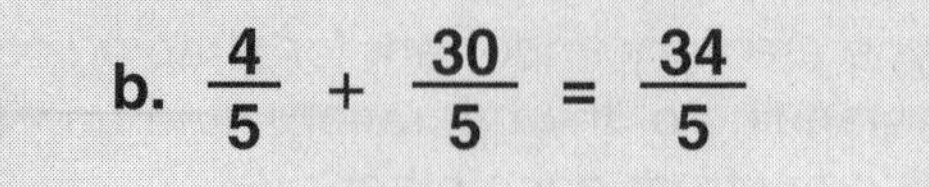
$$b.\ \frac{4}{5} + \frac{30}{5} = \frac{34}{5}$$

- Here's what you should have. You changed 6 into 30-fifths. The answer is 34-fifths. Raise your hand if you got everything right.
- Remember, if you add or subtract, the denominators must be the same. If you multiply, the denominator can be 1, but you must have a denominator.

FRACTION MULTIPLICATION RULES

In Lesson 31, students first review what they know about multiplication (when you multiply by more than 1, you end up with more than you started with: $5 \times 2 = 10$; when you multiply by 1, you end up with the same value you start with: $5 \times 1 = 5$). These rules are important for much of what students do in the program. They provide the basic rationale for equivalent fractions and for working ratio and proportion problems, which involve equivalent fractions.

Here's an equivalent-fraction problem:

$$\frac{2}{3} = \frac{18}{\square}$$

The goal is to figure out the value that goes in the box. If the values are equivalent, you multiply the first value by 1.

$$\frac{2}{3} \times \frac{9}{9} = \frac{18}{\boxed{27}}$$

The new rule students learn in Lesson 31 is that when you multiply by less than 1, you end up with less than you started with:

$$5 \times \frac{1}{2} = \frac{5}{2}$$

Students apply the rule to a set of problems.

Here's part of the exercise:

a. $4 \times \frac{6}{5} = \blacksquare$ b. $4 \times \frac{5}{6} = \blacksquare$ c. $4 \times 6 = \blacksquare$ d. $4 \times \frac{1}{2} = \blacksquare$

c. Problem A. Are you multiplying 4 by more than 1 or less than 1? (Signal.) *More than 1.*

- So will the answer be more than 4 or less than 4? (Signal.) *More than 4.*
- Problem B. Are you multiplying 4 by more than 1 or less than 1? (Signal.) *Less than 1.*
- So will the answer be more than 4 or less than 4? (Signal.) *Less than 4.*
- Problem C. Are you multiplying 4 by more than 1 or less than 1? (Signal.) *More than 1.*
- So will the answer be more than 4 or less than 4? (Signal.) *More than 4.*

d. Your turn: Don't copy the problems. Just write **more than 4** or **less than 4** to tell about the answer to each problem. Write each answer on a new line. Raise your hand when you're finished. (Observe students and give feedback.)

e. Check your work.

- Problem A: 4 times 6-fifths. Tell me about the answer. (Signal.) *More than 4.*
- Problem B: 4 times 5-sixths. Tell me about the answer. (Signal.) *Less than 4.*
- Problem C: 4 times 6. Tell me about the answer. (Signal.) *More than 4.*
- Problem D: 4 times 1-half. Tell me about the answer. (Signal.) *Less than 4.*

f. Your turn: Next to each answer you wrote for part 6, copy the problem and work it. Remember to write 4 as 4 over 1 when you multiply 4 by a fraction. Raise your hand when you're finished. (Observe students and give feedback.)

g. Check your work.

- Problem A: 4 times 6 fifths. Everybody, what's the answer? (Signal.) *24-fifths.*
- Is that more than 4? (Signal.) *Yes.*
- Problem B: 4 times 5-sixths. Everybody, what's the answer? (Signal.) *20-sixths.*
- Is that more than 4? (Signal.) *No.*
- Problem C: 4 times 6. Everybody, what's the answer? (Signal.) *24.*
- Is that more than 4? (Signal.) *Yes.*
- Problem D: 4 times 1-half. Everybody, what's the answer? (Signal.) *4-halves.*
- Is that more than 4? (Signal.) *No.*

Teaching note: In steps e and g, you check the students' work. Make sure that students do well. If they get off to a weak start, they may have serious difficulties later when they apply the rule about multiplying a value by more than 1 or less than 1. If students make a lot of mistakes, direct them to start with a new piece of paper. Repeat the exercise and hold students to a very high criterion of performance—virtually no mistakes. It will be time well spent, and it will communicate to the students that understanding the multiplication rule is very important.

In Lesson 32, students apply the rule to problems that are not intuitively obvious. Students first multiply, then circle the last value if it is more than the starting value.

Here's the part of the exercise that is presented after students have worked a set of problems:

Key:

a. $\frac{3}{1} \times \frac{7}{8} = \frac{21}{8}$ b. $\frac{1}{5} \times \frac{9}{1} = \frac{9}{5}$

c. $\frac{7}{3} \times \frac{4}{5} = \frac{28}{15}$ d. $\frac{20}{5} \times \frac{4}{3} = \frac{80}{15}$

f. In each problem you worked, the value you end up with is not the same as the value you start out with. Remember, if you multiply by more than 1, you end up with more than you start with.
- Listen: Circle the last value if it is more than the value you start with. Look at the number you multiply by. If it's more than 1, circle the last value. If the number you multiply by is not more than 1, don't circle the last value. Raise your hand when you've circled all the last values that are more than the starting values.
  (Observe students and give feedback.)

g. Check your work.
- Problem A. Did you circle the last value? (Signal.) *No.*
- Right. You didn't multiply 3 by more than 1. So 21-eighths is not more than 3 over 1. It's less.
- Problem B: Did you circle the last value? (Signal.) *Yes.*
- Yes. You're multiplying by a lot more than 1. So the answer is a lot more than 1-fifth.
- Problem C. Did you circle the last value? (Signal.) *No.*
- Right. You didn't multiply by more than 1. So 28-fifteenths is not more than 7-thirds. It's less.
- Problem D. Did you circle the last value? (Signal.) *Yes.*
- Yes. You're multiplying by more than 1. So 80-fifteenths is more than 20-fifths.

Teaching note: When you observe and give feedback in step f, correct mistakes by requiring students to use what they have been told about multiplying. For example: A student has circled 28/15 in this problem:

c. $\frac{7}{3} \times \frac{4}{5} = \frac{28}{15}$.

Here's a good correction: "Touch the fraction you're multiplying by in this problem."

(If the student touches the first value, say: "That's wrong. You're touching the starting value. Touch the fraction you are multiplying by.")

"Is that value more than 1 or less than 1?" *Less than one.*

"So will you end up with more than the starting value or less than the starting value?" *Less than the starting value.*

"You end up with less than you start with, so you should not have circled anything."

If a student has not circled 80/15 in the problem: **d.** $\frac{20}{5} \times \frac{4}{3} = \frac{80}{15}$, use a variation of the correction above:

"Touch the fraction you're multiplying by in this problem. Is that value more than 1 or less than 1?" *More than 1.*

"So will you end up with more than the starting value or less than the starting value?" *More than the starting value.*

"You end up with more than you start with, so you should have circled the ending value."

A variation of this activity appears first in Lesson 38. Students circle either the starting value or the ending value to indicate which is larger. Finally, in Lesson 54, students work a full range of problems including problems that multiply by a fraction equal to 1. For these problems, students circle the equal sign.

The discrimination between problems that multiply by more than 1 or by less than 1 is important for student understanding of many problem types that they'll work later, such as: What's 5/3 of 90? Students should understand that the answer will be more than 90.

EQUIVALENT FRACTIONS

The creation of a pair of equivalent fractions implies multiplying fractions. The first fraction is multiplied by 1 to generate the second fraction. So the second fraction equals the first fraction. Equivalent fractions are extremely important because they provide the mathematical underpinning for problems involving ratios and proportions.

Before students apply the rule that equivalent fractions are created by multiplying by 1, they work with a variety of tasks that represent equivalent fractions. For example, starting in Lesson 14, students refer to pictures to write an equation that shows a series of equivalent fractions.

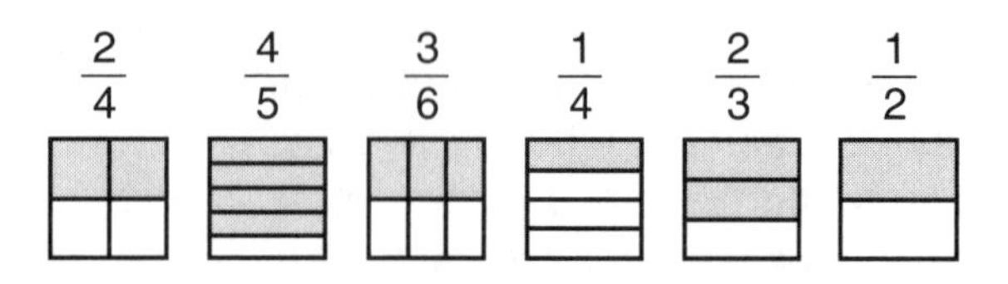

Students construct the equation: $2/4 = 3/6 = 1/2$.

In subsequent lessons, students work similar problems, some of which involve the number line.

Students construct the equation for the two number lines that show the same value: $5/3 = 10/6$.

In Lesson 17, students apply the rule that if fractions are equivalent, the first fraction is multiplied by 1. Students are presented with pictures of equivalent fractions:

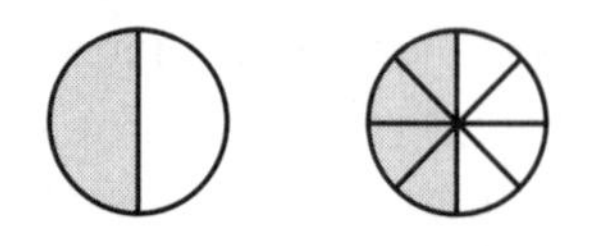

They write the simple equation that shows the two fractions:

$$\frac{1}{2} \qquad = \frac{4}{8}$$

Students then figure out the fraction that equals 1:

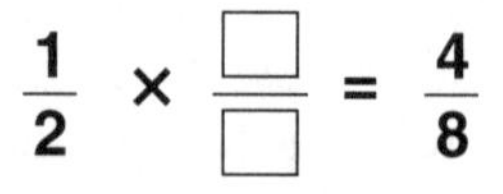

$$\frac{1}{2} \times \frac{\square}{\square} = \frac{4}{8}$$

They do that by working the problem for the top numbers ($1 \times \blacksquare = 4$) and the problem for the bottom numbers ($2 \times \blacksquare = 8$) The answer is the same: 4. The fraction that equals 1 is 4/4:

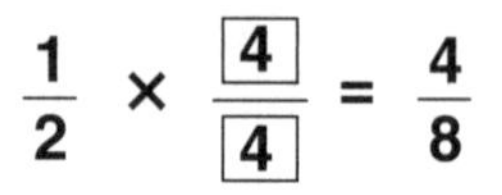

$$\frac{1}{2} \times \frac{\boxed{4}}{\boxed{4}} = \frac{4}{8}$$

Here's part of the exercise from Lesson 17:

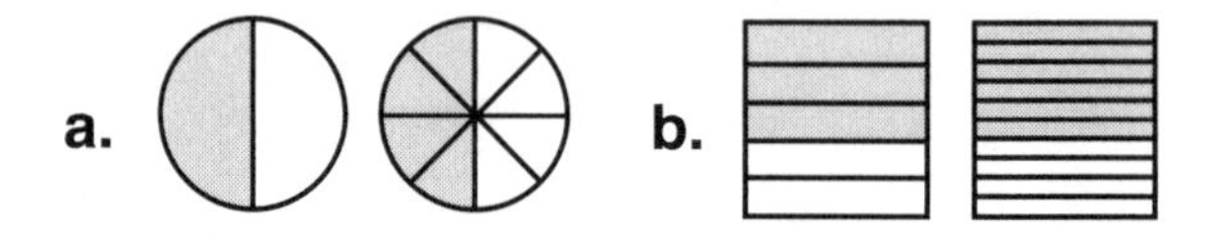

d. The fractions shown in each item are equal. Write the two fractions shown in item A. Show the equal sign, but leave a space before the equal sign. √

- (Write on the board:)

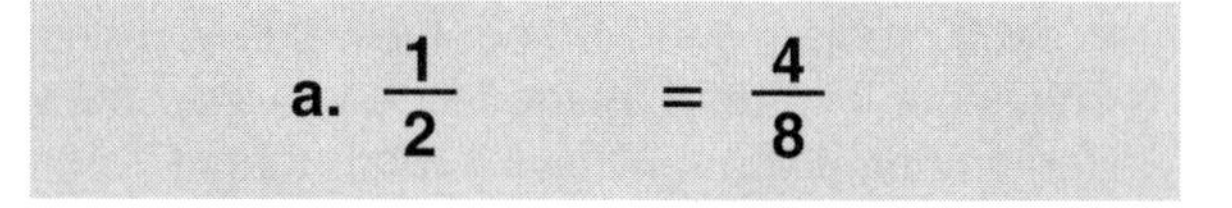

$$\text{a. } \frac{1}{2} \qquad = \frac{4}{8}$$

- You should have written the equation: 1-half equals 4-eighths.
- If the fractions are equivalent, you can multiply by 1 to show they are equivalent. You'll multiply by a fraction that equals 1.
- (Write to show:)

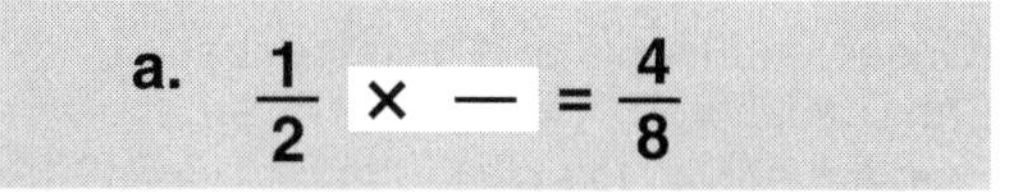

$$\text{a. } \frac{1}{2} \times \text{—} = \frac{4}{8}$$

e. Start with the bottom. Remember, that's the number of parts in each unit. Figure out what you multiply by to get from 2 to 8. Then check the top. See what you multiply 1 by to get 4. Write the missing fraction. Raise your hand when you're finished.

- Everybody, what fraction do you multiply 1-half by to get 4-eighths? (Signal.) *4-fourths.*
- (Write $\frac{4}{4}$.)
- Yes, 4-fourths equals 1. It tells you that if you multiply the parts in each unit by 4, and multiply the parts that are shaded by 4, you'll end up with a fraction that equals 1-half.

f. Your turn: Write the complete equation for B. First write the fractions that are equal. Remember the equal sign. Then figure out the fraction you multiply by. That fraction should equal 1. Raise your hand when you're finished.
(Observe students and give feedback.)
- (Write on the board:)

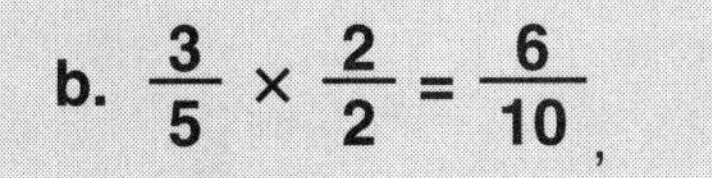

- Here's what you should have. The fractions are 3-fifths and 6-tenths. You multiply by 2-halves. 2-halves equal 1.

> ***Teaching note:*** If students have trouble identifying the answer to the problem on the bottom or top, use this correction:
> Example:
>
> $$\frac{2}{9} \times \frac{\square}{\square} = \frac{14}{63}$$
>
> "Touch the bottom numbers. Say the problem for the bottom numbers." *9 times what number equals 63?*
> "What's the answer?" *7.*
> "Touch the top numbers. Say the problem for the top." *2 times what number equals 14?*
> "What's the answer?" *7.*
> "Write the fraction that equals 1."
> (Students write: **7/7.**)

In Lesson 21, students determine whether pairs of fractions are equivalent. Problems are of the form:

a. $\frac{2}{3} \times \square = \frac{6}{12}$ b. $\frac{2}{3} \times \square = \frac{8}{12}$

Students work the problem on the top and on the bottom. They write the missing fraction. If the fraction equals 1, the other values in the problem are equivalent. Students write a simple equation below:

$\frac{2}{3} \times \boxed{\frac{3}{4}} = \frac{6}{12}$ b. $\frac{2}{3} \times \boxed{\frac{4}{4}} = \frac{8}{12}$

$$\frac{2}{3} = \frac{8}{12}$$

Exercises that present this relationship are particularly important because they suggest the relationship between equivalent fractions that are expressed this way:

$$\frac{5}{4} \times \frac{8}{8} = \frac{40}{32}$$

and this way:

$$\frac{5}{4} = \frac{40}{32}$$

When the fraction that equals 1 is not shown, students have a simple equation that expresses the equivalence.

In Lesson 43, students work division problems to figure out the fraction that equals 1.

Here's part of the exercise:

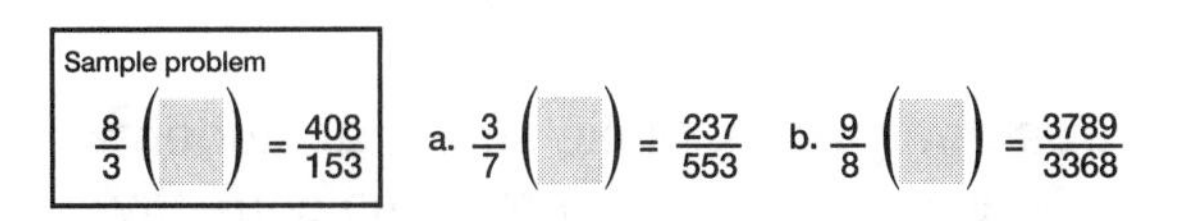

b. The sample problem shows a pair of equivalent fractions.
- Say the **division** problem for the top. (Signal.) *408 divided by 8.*
- Say the division problem for the bottom. (Signal.) *153 divided by 3.*
- Work both problems with your calculator. You should get the same answer for each problem. Raise your hand when you know both answers. √
- Everybody, what's the answer to the problem 408 divided by 8? (Signal.) *51.*
- What's the answer to the problem 153 divided by 3? (Signal.) *51.*
- (Write on the board:)

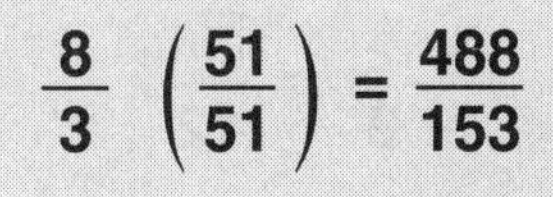

- 8/3 times 51/51 equals 408/153.

c. Problem A: 3/7 equals 237/553. Say the division problem for the top. (Signal.) *237 divided by 3.*
- Say the division problem for the bottom. (Signal.) *553 divided by 7.*
- Work the division problem for the top and for the bottom. Write the fraction that equals 1. Raise your hand when you have the complete equation for problem A.
(Observe students and give feedback.)

- (Write on the board:)

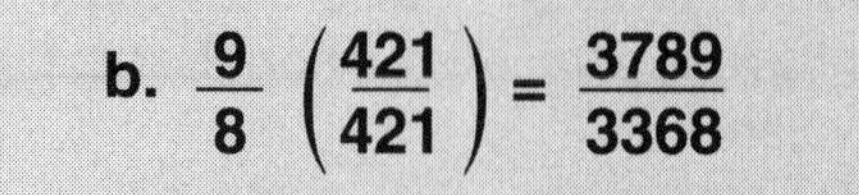

- Here's what you should have: On top, 237 divided by 3 equals 79. On the bottom, 553 divided by 7 equals 79. The fraction that equals 1 is 79/79.

d. Your turn: Work problem B. Raise your hand when you're finished.
(Observe students and give feedback.)

- (Write on the board:)

$$\text{b. } \frac{9}{8}\left(\frac{421}{421}\right) = \frac{3789}{3368}$$

- Check your work. Here's what you should have: 3789 divided by 9 is 421. 3368 divided by 8 is 421. The fraction that equals 1 is 421/421.

> ***Teaching note:*** Make sure that students are saying the division problems correctly in steps b and c.
>
> The teacher presentation script follows the convention of showing fractions this way: Problem A: 3/7; 237/553.
>
> You may have trouble saying the fraction 237/553. Students most probably will also have trouble. Instead of saying: two-hundred-thirty-seven, five-hundred-fifty-thirds, you may prefer to say the two numbers—for example, 237 over 553.

This exercise shows that the same procedure used for simple problems:

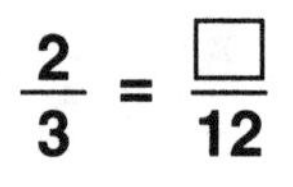

applies to fractions with very large numbers. For these fractions, the problem is expressed as a division problem and requires calculation, but the outcome is the same. The first fraction is multiplied by a fraction that equals 1.

The final type of exercise is introduced in Lesson 54. It requires students to circle the starting value or ending value to indicate which is larger. If the fractions are equivalent, students circle the equals sign.

Here's part of the exercise from Lesson 54:

b. You're going to figure out the missing middle fraction in each problem. Then you'll circle something. If the fractions are not equal, you'll circle the first fraction or the last fraction to show which is larger. If the fractions are equal, you'll circle the equal sign. Remember, circle the larger fraction or the equal sign.

c. Copy problem A and work it. Figure out the missing number. Circle the first fraction, the last fraction, or the equal sign. Raise your hand when you're finished.
(Observe students and give feedback.)

- (Write on the board:)

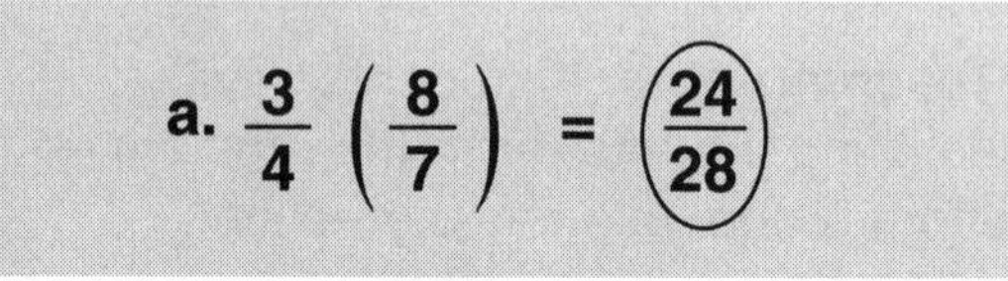

- Here's what you should have. The missing fraction is 8/7. That's more than 1. So you circled the last fraction. It's larger than the first fraction.

d. Work problem B. Raise your hand when you're finished.
(Observe students and give feedback.)

- (Write on the board:)

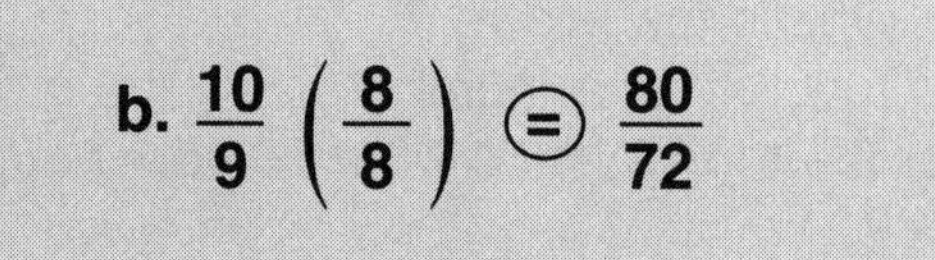

- Here's what you should have. The middle fraction is 8/8. That's 1. So you circled the equal sign because the first fraction and the last fraction are equal. Raise your hand if you got it right.

ADDITION AND SUBTRACTION: UNLIKE DENOMINATORS

The first problems that involve unlike denominators are introduced in Lesson 67. Before that introduction, students learn skills that are prerequisite to the procedure. Beginning in Lesson 61, they learn to work vertical problems that have like denominators:

$$\begin{array}{r} \frac{9}{8} \\ -\ \frac{2}{8} \\ \hline \end{array}$$

Students also learn to find the least common multiple for a pair of values. That's the first common number one reaches when counting by the two values. To show the first common number, they complete a pair of equations.

$$9 \times \square = \square$$
$$6 \times \square = \square$$

To work the problems, students identify the first number they reach when counting by 9 and counting by 6:

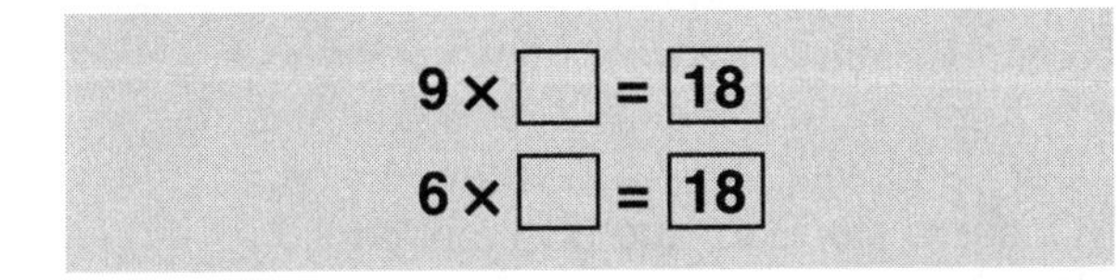

then complete the multiplication equations.

Here's part of the introduction from Lesson 65:

a. Each item shows the first part of two multiplication problems. You're going to complete both problems so they end with the same number. You'll find the **first common number.**

b. Problem A. You're multiplying by 6 in one problem and by 8 in the other. The answer to both problems will be the first number you'd reach counting by 6 and counting by 8.

- The number could **not** be 32 because you don't reach that number counting by 6.
- The number could **not** be 48. You reach 48 counting by 6 and counting by 8, so 48 is a common number, but it's not the **first** common number for counting by 6 and by 8. Raise your hand when you know the first common number you'd reach counting by 6 and by 8.
- Everybody, what's the first common number? (Signal.) *24.*
- (Write on the board:)

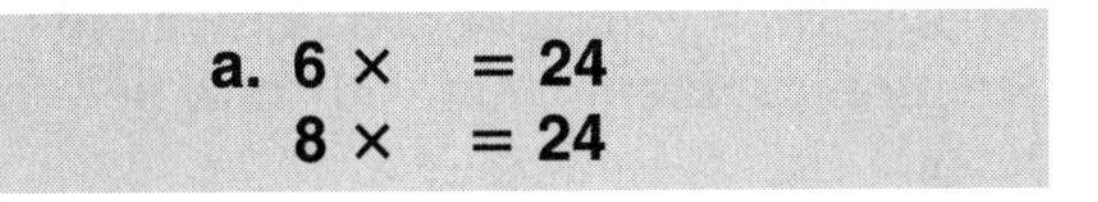

- So both facts will end with 24. Copy and complete each multiplication fact to show the number of times.
- (Write to show:)

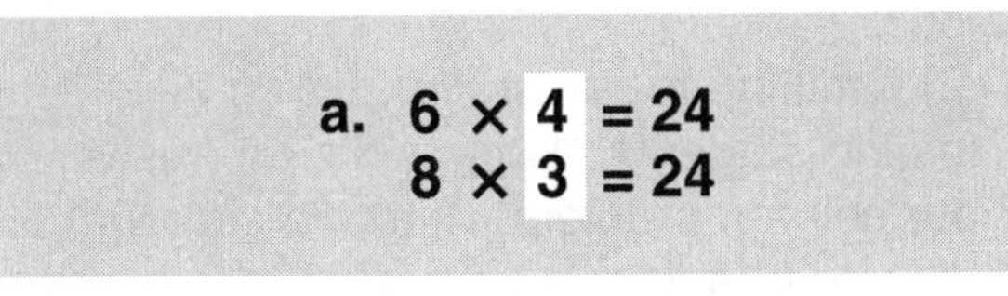

- Here's what you should have: 6 times 4 equals 24 and 8 times 3 equals 24.

Teaching note: If students consistently have difficulty finding the first common number, direct them to write the numbers they count by for each value shown.

Example:

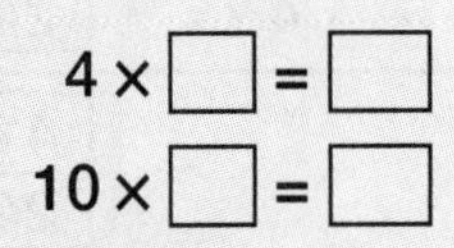

"Write the numbers you say when you count by 4 and the numbers you say when you count by 10." Student writes:
4, 8, 12, 16, 20, 24, 28.
10, 20, 30.

Then: "Circle the first number that is in both rows."

4 8 12 16 (20) 24 28

10 (20) 30

The steps in this procedure are incorporated when working problems that have unlike denominators, which are introduced in Lesson 67.

Here's an example:

$$\frac{7}{8}\left(\quad\right) = \boxed{\frac{\;}{\;}}$$
$$+\frac{5}{6}\left(\quad\right) = +\boxed{\frac{\;}{\;}}$$

Students first identify the least common denominator. That's the first common number for the denominators—24. Students write the denominator for both problems:

$$\frac{7}{8}\left(\quad\right) = \boxed{\frac{\;}{24}}$$
$$+\frac{5}{6}\left(\quad\right) = +\boxed{\frac{\;}{24}}$$

Next, students figure out the fraction that equals 1 and multiply to find the missing numerator in each fraction:

$$\frac{7}{8}\left(\frac{3}{3}\right) = \boxed{\frac{21}{24}}$$
$$+\frac{5}{6}\left(\frac{4}{4}\right) = +\boxed{\frac{20}{24}}$$

Finally, the students add:

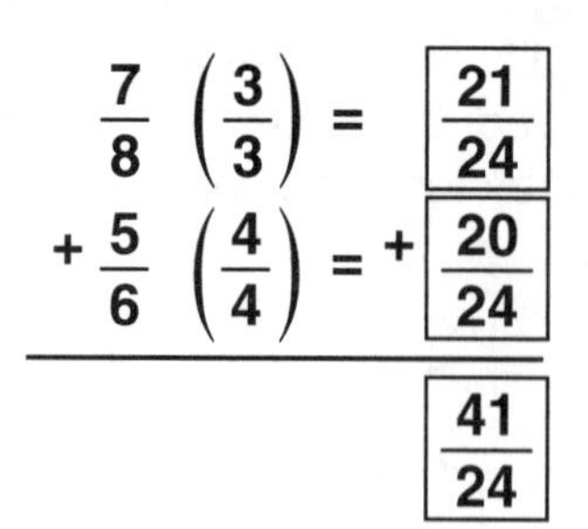

Here's part of the introduction from Lesson 67:

a. There were used cars and new cars on a lot, $\frac{3}{7}$ of the cars were used. There were 64 new cars on the lot.

1. How many used cars were on the lot?
2. How many total cars were on the lot?

c. We'll work the problem in part 5 together.

- (Write on the board:)

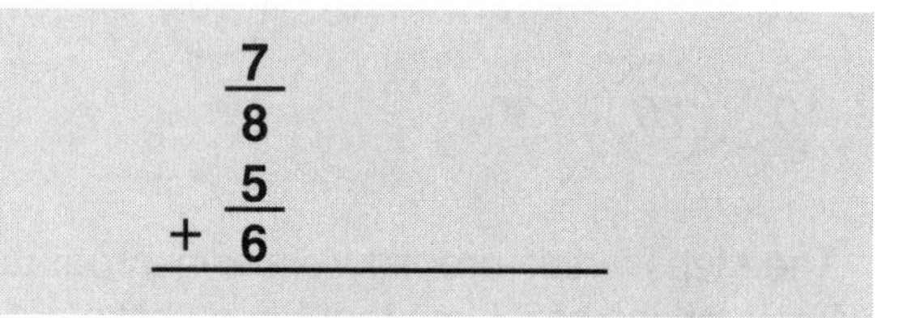

- You can't add these fractions because the denominators are not the same. So you find the first common number for counting by 8 and counting by 6. Raise your hand when you know the first common number.
- Everybody, what's the first common number? (Signal.) *24.*
- So we write 24 as the denominator of each fraction. We write an equal sign to show that we'll work a pair of equivalent fractions.
- (Write to show:)

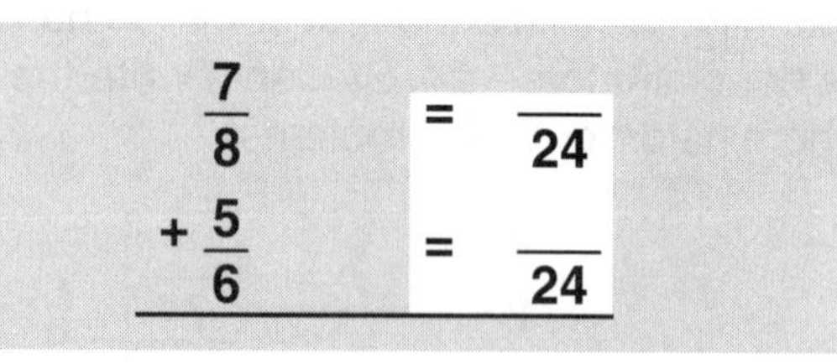

- Your turn: Copy this much of the problem. √
- Now we work an equivalent-fraction problem for 7/8. Do it. Write the missing fraction that equals 1 and complete the fraction that equals 7/8. Raise your hand when you've done that much. (Observe students and give feedback.)
- (Write to show:)

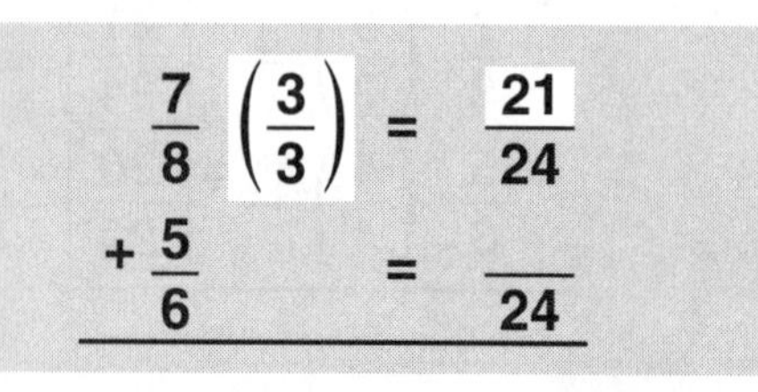

- Here's what you should have so far. 7/8 equals 21/24. Now work the equivalent-fraction problem for 5/6. Raise your hand when you're finished. (Observe students and give feedback.)
- (Write to show:)

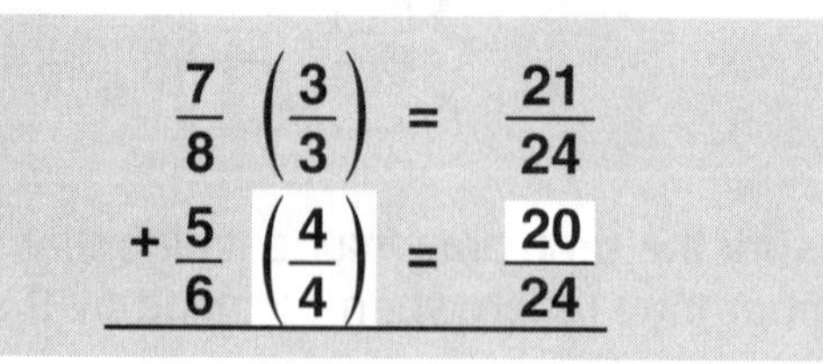

- Here's what you should have. 5/6 equals 20/24. The denominators are the same. So you can add. Do it and write the answer as a fraction. Raise your hand when you're finished. (Observe students and give feedback.)
- (Write to show:)

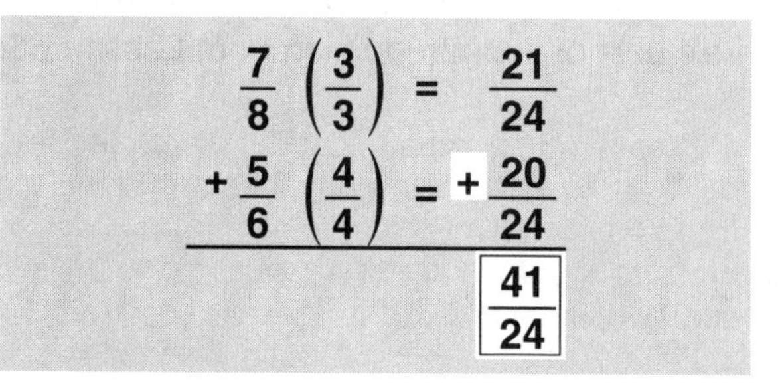

- Here's what you should have. The answer is 41/24. Raise your hand if you got it right.

Teaching note: Although the procedure involves several steps, all the component steps are familiar once students take the first step. When observing students and providing feedback, make sure students see that they are working a pair of equivalent-fraction problems. "Find the first common number for the denominators and write it. Then you have **two equivalent-fraction problems** that you know how to work."

Expect students to make the following mistakes:

1) Omitting equals signs. Remind students: "You're working two equivalent fraction problems. Remember the equal signs."

2) Omitting the operational sign (+ or –). Remind students: "Don't write an answer to your column problem without a sign that tells you to add or subtract."

3) Attempting to write an answer below the original equation. The workbook setup is designed to discourage this type of mistake; however, if you stress that students must work two equivalent-fraction problems, it will be easier for students to set up the equations and, therefore, write the answer in the appropriate place.

By Lesson 71, students have practiced with various forms of unlike denominators:

a) the first common number is the product of the denominators:

$$\begin{array}{rl} \frac{3}{4} & = \frac{\quad}{20} \\ + \frac{1}{5} & = \frac{\quad}{20} \\ \hline \end{array}$$

b) the first common number is the denominator of one of the fractions:

$$\begin{array}{rl} \frac{3}{4} & = \frac{\quad}{8} \\ + \frac{1}{8} & = \frac{\quad}{8} \\ \hline \end{array}$$

c) the first common number is neither the product of the denominators nor one of the denominators:

$$\begin{array}{rl} \frac{3}{4} & = \frac{\quad}{12} \\ + \frac{1}{6} & = \frac{\quad}{12} \\ \hline \end{array}$$

Here's the set of examples from Lesson 71:

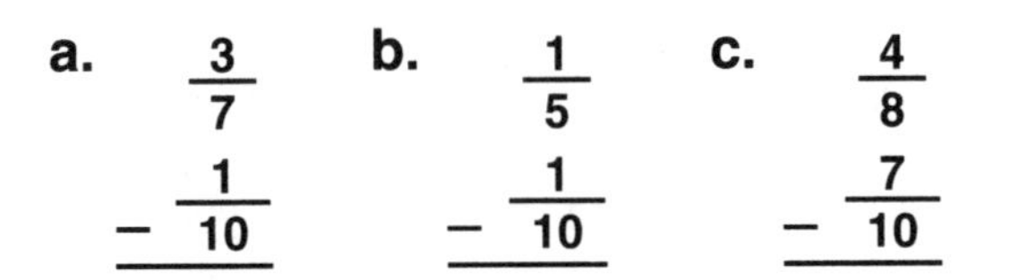

COMPARING FRACTIONS

Students compare fractions with unlike denominators and determine which is larger. Students simply rewrite the fractions with the same denominator.

Example: $\frac{3}{4}$ and $\frac{5}{8}$

Students rewrite the values with a denominator of 8:

$$\frac{6}{8} \quad \frac{5}{8}$$

Then they identify which of the original fractions is larger by writing an inequality statement:

$$\frac{3}{4} > \frac{5}{8}$$

Here's part of the introduction from Lesson 111:

a. Problem A says: Which is more, 2/3 or 3/5?

- Your turn: Write the two fractions in a column; find the lowest common denominator and complete both fractions. Raise your hand when you've done that much.
  (Observe students and give feedback.)
- (Write on the board:)

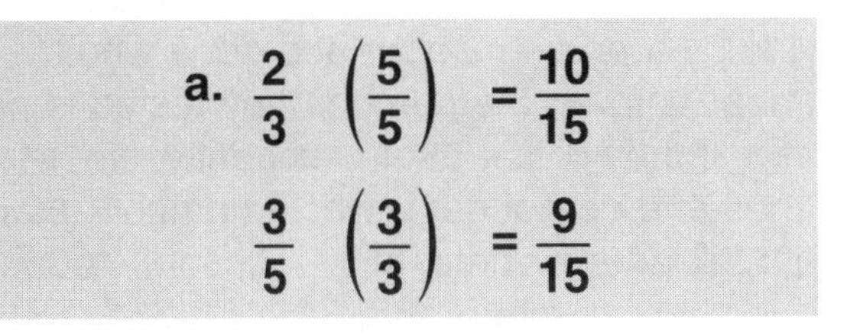

- Here's what you should have so far. The lowest common denominator is 15.
- The problem asks, which is more, 2/3 or 3/5? Write a statement with an inequality sign. Show 2/3 and 3/5 in that order. √
- (Write on board:)

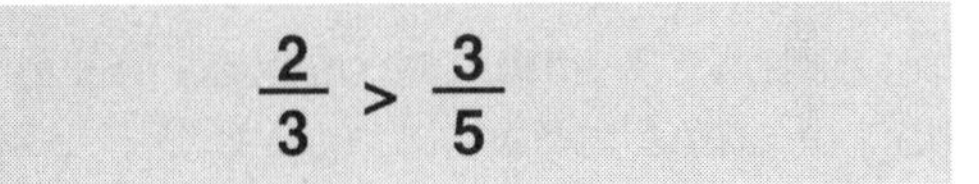

- Here's the answer. 2/3 is more than 3/5.

Teaching note: Step b is particularly important. Students may lose sight of the original question because they are to answer a question about fractions that have been rewritten. Make sure that students are very firm on answering the question the problem asks.

SIMPLIFYING FRACTIONS

Simplifying fractions begins in Lesson 31. The procedure that students follow is to rewrite the numerator and denominator as prime factors:

$$\frac{28}{21} = \frac{2 \times 2 \times 7}{3 \times 7}$$

They then cross out any fractions that equal 1:

$$\frac{28}{21} = \frac{2 \times 2 \times \cancel{7}}{3 \times \cancel{7}}$$

and multiply the remaining factors.

$$\frac{28}{21} = \frac{2 \times 2 \times \cancel{7}}{3 \times \cancel{7}} = \frac{4}{3}$$

Before students simplify fractions, they identify prime factors for various numbers. In Lesson 21, students learn what prime numbers are. (A number is a prime if it has only two factors—1 and the number itself.) Although students are not held accountable for memorizing the prime numbers through 23, they should be able to tell you the prime numbers through 11.

In Lesson 21, students learn to test numbers by dividing by primes through 7. If students divide by a prime number and get a whole number answer, the number they tested is not a prime. If they divide by an exhaustive set of primes and do not get a whole number answer, the number is a prime. In this lesson, students test a set of numbers (83, 346, 41, 351, 53, 55) by dividing by the primes: 2, 3, 5, 7. Students use their calculators for this work. The numbers that are primes are 83, 41, and 53. These numbers are not evenly divisible by 2, 3, 5, or 7. The other numbers are not primes. They result in a whole-number answer when divided by one of the primes.

In Lesson 23, students practice multiplying by a string of prime factors, e.g., $2 \times 3 \times 3 \times 5 = ■$.

In Lesson 24, students rewrite multiplication problems to show only prime factors.

Problems are of the form:

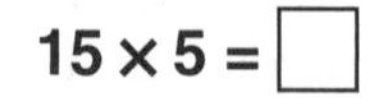

$$15 \times 5 = \square$$

Students rewrite 15:

$$3 \times 5 \times 5 = \square$$

In Lesson 28, students complete an equation that ends with a familiar multiplication-fact number:

$$\square \times \square = 60$$

Students write the fact: $10 \times 6 = 60$. Below, they rewrite the component numbers as primes: $2 \times 5 \times 2 \times 3 = 60$.

> ***Teaching note:*** Students are told that the factors can be written in any order. Checking student work is sometimes difficult because it takes time to find the factors. The answer key shows the factors for any given value in an ascending order: 2, 3, 5. . . .
>
> Examples: $2 \times 2 \times 3 \times 7 = 84$
> $6 \times 10 = 60$
> $(2 \times 3) \times (2 \times 5) = 60$

The procedure of simplifying fractions is an extension of the work with prime factors. It involves the new component, however, of crossing out fractions that equal 1.

The first simplifying exercises show the prime factors for fractions. Students cross out all possible fractions that equal 1. Then they multiply and write the simplified fraction. Below, they write a simple equation showing the starting fraction and the simplified fraction. Initially, students write the answer as a fraction, even if it is more than 1. Later, (starting with Lesson 43) students simplify improper fractions, then write the simplified fraction as a mixed number.

Here's part of the exercise from Lesson 31:

c. Problem B. You're starting with a fraction that is not simplified. What fraction is that? (Signal.) *10-twelfths.*
- You know it's not simplified because you can cross out a fraction that equals 1. Do it and write the simplified fraction that equals 10-twelfths. Raise your hand when you're finished.
- (Write on the board:)

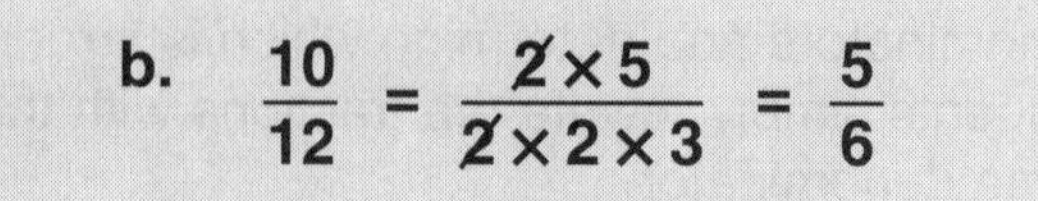

b. $\frac{10}{12} = \frac{\cancel{2} \times 5}{\cancel{2} \times 2 \times 3} = \frac{5}{6}$

- Here's what you should have. You crossed out 2-halves. The simplified fraction that equals 10-twelfths is 5-sixths.

- Below, write the equation that shows the two equivalent fractions. Raise your hand when you're finished.
- (Write to show:)

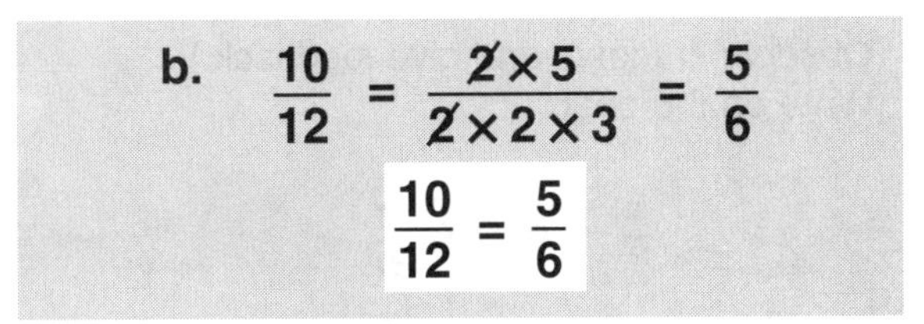

- Here's what you should have. 10-twelfths equals 5-sixths.

d. Problem C. You're starting with a fraction that is not simplified. What fraction? (Signal.). *18-twelfths.*

- You know that 18-twelfths is not simplified because you can cross out a fraction that equals 1. In fact, you can cross out two fractions that equal 1. Do it. Then write what 18-twelfths equals. Below, write the equation that shows the two equivalent fractions. Raise your hand when you're finished.
- (Write on the board:)

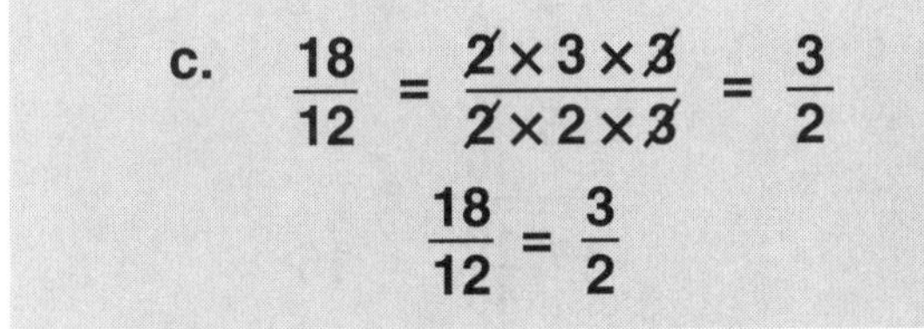

- Here's what you should have. You should have crossed out 2-halves and 3-thirds. The simplified fraction that equals 18-twelfths is 3-halves. Below you should have the simple equation: 18-twelfths equals 3-halves.

> ***Teaching note:*** Students sometimes have trouble identifying the fractions that equal 1 because they look for values that are aligned vertically. Remind them: "You cross out a fraction that equals 1 when you cross out the same number on the top and in the denominator. They don't have to be above or below each other."

In Lesson 32, students learn that if they cross out all the factors in the numerator, they must write 1 in the simplified fraction. Here's part of the exercise:

a. (Write on the board:)

$$\frac{6}{12} = \frac{\cancel{2} \times \cancel{3}}{\cancel{2} \times 2 \times \cancel{3}} =$$

- When you simplify fractions, you might cross out all the factors on top. Here's an example.
- You can see the factors 2 and 3 are crossed out on top.
- Listen: If you cross out all the numbers on top, **you have 1 on top.** The reason is that you've crossed out fractions that equal 1. So when you cross out 2-halves, you really have 1 over 1 in its place. When you cross out 3-thirds, you really have 1 over 1 in its place.
- (Write to show:)

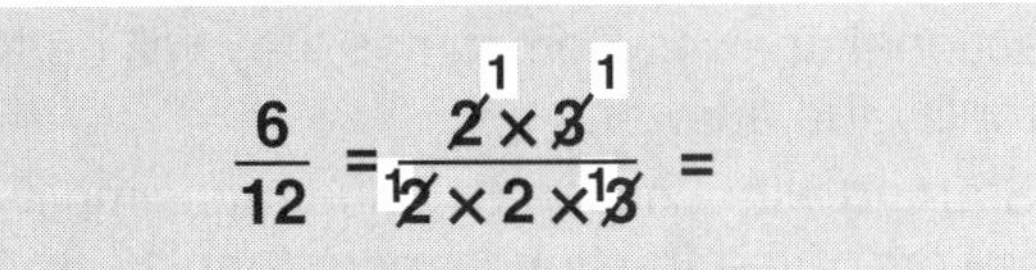

- You can see that when you multiply on top, you have 1 times 1. That's 1.
- (Write to show:)

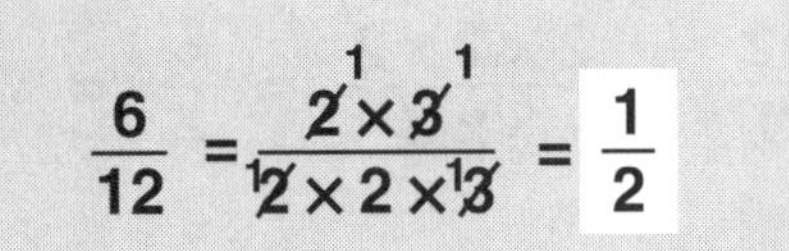

b. Remember, if you cross out everything on top, you still have 1 on top. You **must write that 1 in the answer.**

> ***Teaching note:*** Hold students accountable for writing complete simplified fractions. Do not accept simplified fractions that do not have a number in the numerator:
>
> $$= \frac{\quad}{2}$$
>
> Say: "Look at the prime factors for the numerator. How many do you have on top? . . . Remember, you still have 1 on top. Write that 1 in the answer."

In Lesson 38, students work problems that have 1 in the denominator of the simplified fraction. Writing the 1 in the denominator is optional. Some of the problems that students work in Lesson 38 have 1 in the numerator of the simplified fraction and some have 1 in the denominator.

Finally, in Lesson 41, students are introduced to fractions that cannot be simplified. Students write the prime factors, but since they cannot cross out any fractions that equal 1, students show the "simplified fraction" to be the same as the starting fraction.

Example:

$$\frac{8}{15} = \frac{2 \times 2 \times 2}{3 \times 5} = \frac{8}{15}$$

Following the work on simplified fractions, students follow directions for whether they simplify the answers that they get when working problems from the different tracks. Sometimes they will be instructed not to simplify the fractional answer. Sometimes they will be told to simplify the answer.

Starting with Lesson 61, students simplify answers. If the fraction is more than 1, students first write on the simplified fraction, then the mixed number or whole number it equals. Students should express the work like this:

$$\frac{12}{9} = \frac{2 \times 2 \times \cancel{3}}{3 \times \cancel{3}} = \frac{4}{3} = 1\frac{1}{3}$$

Mixed Number Operations

Adding and subtracting mixed numbers is first introduced in Lesson 74. The basic procedure is: First operate on the fractions, then on the whole numbers. The fractions in the problem have the same denominator:

$$\begin{array}{r} 4\frac{2}{7} \\ +\ 3\frac{4}{7} \\ \hline \end{array}$$

Initially, all the problems that students work have two mixed numbers. In Lesson 76, students work problems that have a whole number and a mixed number. For the problems that are presented initially, students are able to copy the fraction in the answer, then operate on the whole numbers:

$$\begin{array}{r} 45\frac{7}{11} \\ -\ 13 \\ \hline \end{array} \qquad \begin{array}{r} 29 \\ +\ 7\frac{10}{19} \\ \hline \end{array}$$

Later, two special types of problems are introduced: Addition problems in which the sum of the fractions equal 1 and problems that subtract a mixed number from a whole number.

Here's part of the exercise from Lesson 80, where the addition problem type is introduced:

c. Problem A. Work the problem and write the answer with a mixed number. Raise your hand when you've done that much.
(Observe students and give feedback.)

- (Write on the board:)

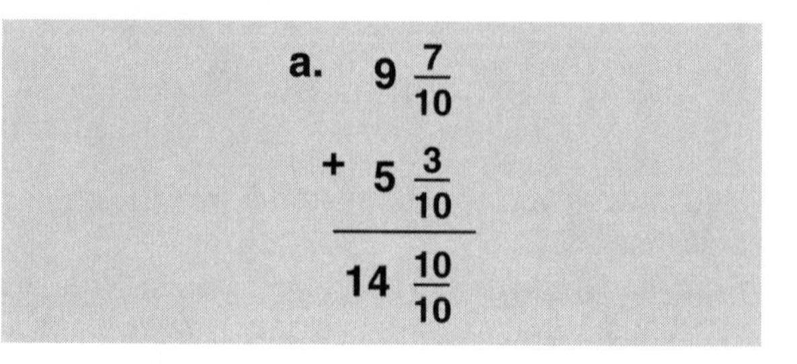

- Here's what you should have. The answer is 14 and 10/10. The **fraction** equals 1. So you can write the answer as a whole number. What number is that? (Signal.) *15.*
- (Write to show:)

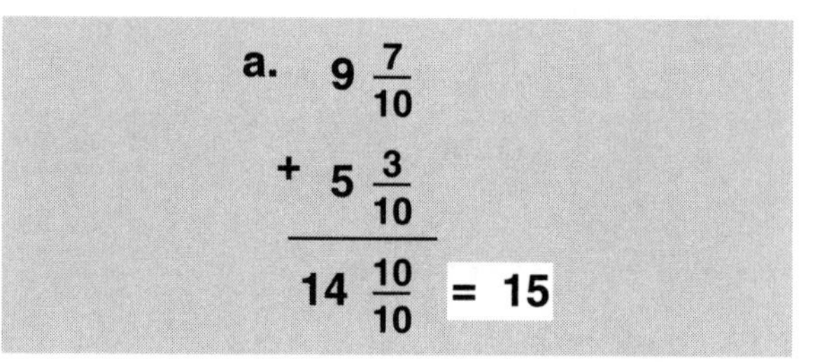

Before students are introduced to this type, they have practice rewriting mixed numbers that have a fraction equal to 1.

For example:

$$5\frac{4}{4} = \square$$

Students write:

$$5\frac{4}{4} = \boxed{6}$$

In Lesson 84, students work the subtraction type. The solution involves "borrowing." Students rewrite the whole number as a mixed number, with a fraction that equals 1.

Here's part of the introduction:

- (Write on the board:)

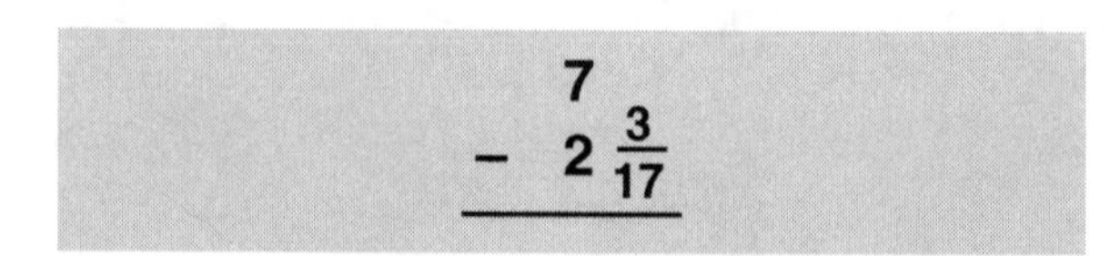

e. I'm going to borrow 1 from the 7. So what do I write above the 7? (Signal.) *6.*
- I'm going to write the 1 I borrowed as a fraction. What fraction? (Signal.) *17-seventeenths.*
- (Write to show:)

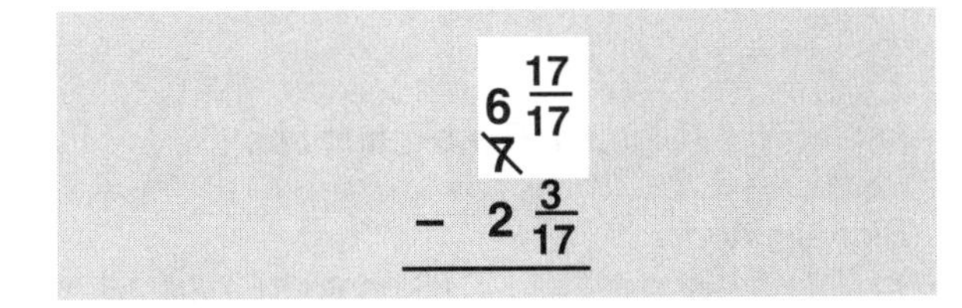

- Now I can subtract, starting with the fractions. What's 17/17 minus 3/17? (Signal.) *14-seventeenths.*
- What's 6 minus 2. (Signal.) *4.*
- (Write to show:)

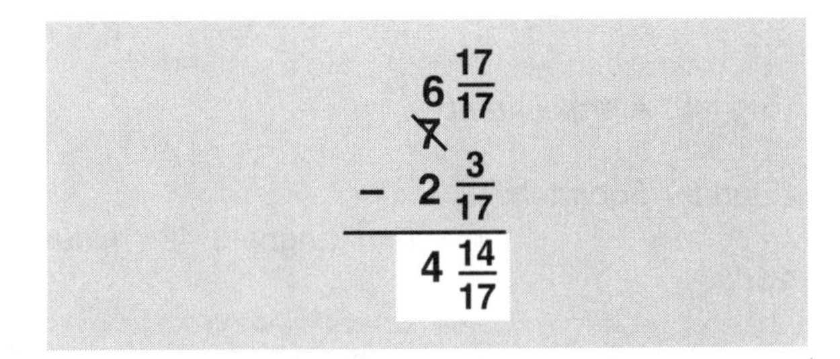

In Lesson 88, students work a mixed set of problems, some of which require rewriting the top number for borrowing or rewriting the answer for addition problems.

c. Work problem A. Raise your hand when you're finished. (Observe students and give feedback.)
- (Write on the board:)

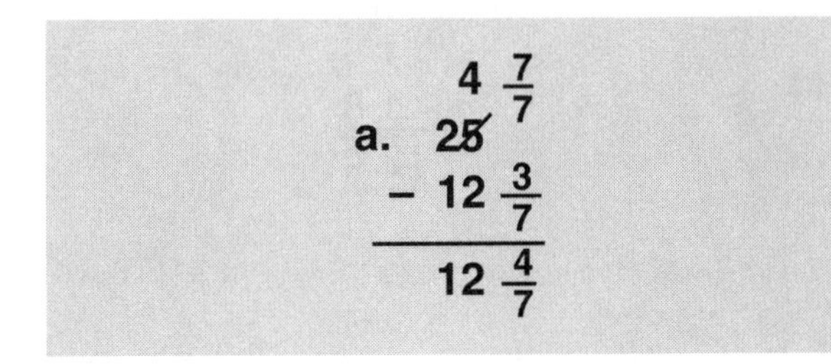

- Here's what you should have. To find the missing value, you subtract 12 and 3/7 from 25. You rewrite 25 as 24 and 7/7. The answer is 12 and 4/7.

d. Work problem B. Raise your hand when you're finished.
- (Write on the board:)

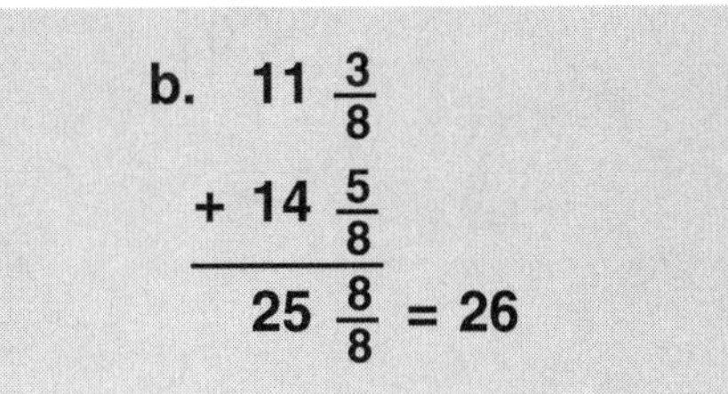

- Here's what you should have. To find the total, you add 11 and 3/8 and 14 and 5/8. The answer is 25 and 8/8. That's 26.

Work with the special types of mixed number problems prepares students for work with ratio tables. When solving some ratio table problems, students will work mixed number problems that require borrowing or that require rewriting the answer.

Number Families and Extensions

Number families are required for much of the work that students do in Level E, including word problems that are difficult for students using traditional problem-solving techniques (not number families). The number family expresses the relationship between three values that are used in related addition-subtraction statements. Here are number families for simple facts:

2 3 → 5	1 8 → 9	3 7 → 10
2 + 3 = 5	1 + 8 = 9	3 + 7 = 10
3 + 2 = 5	8 + 1 = 9	7 + 3 = 10
5 − 3 = 2	9 − 8 = 1	10 − 7 = 3
5 − 2 = 3	9 − 1 = 8	10 − 3 = 7

The number at the end of the arrow is the big number. The other two numbers are the related small numbers. The facts are shown below each family.

Number families with a missing value translate into addition/subtraction problems. The number family always shows the **big number** at the end of the arrow:

To figure out a missing value (the box), first identify whether the box is a small number or the big number; then write the appropriate problem. If the box is a small number, you subtract:

If the box is the big number, you add:

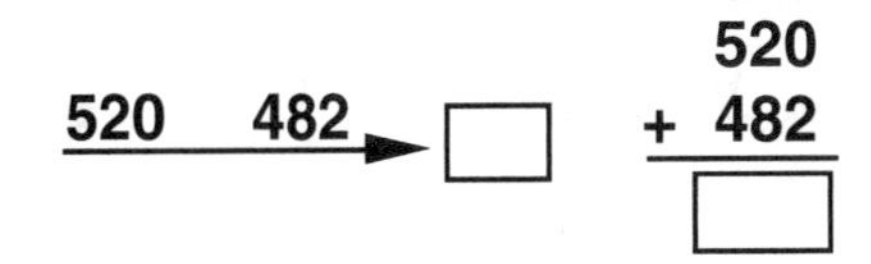

The families become important when working calculation problems that students typically have trouble with, such as:

To work such problems, students first determine which number in the equation is the big number. In a subtraction expression, the starting number is the big number. Therefore, that number goes at the end of the number-family arrow:

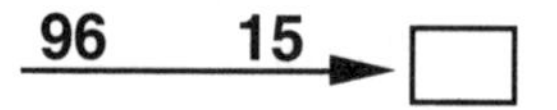

The other two numbers are small numbers. They go on top of the arrow:

96 15 → □

Students now work a problem to figure out the missing value. The box is the big number. To find a missing big number, you add:

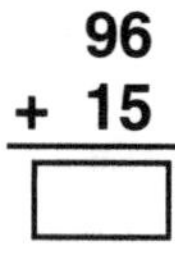

Teaching note: Sometimes students (and teachers) treat number families as busy work. They are not. If students do not understand the relationships that are implied by number families, they will certainly have difficulty with the work in Level E. Remind them that they will use number families to work problems many adults cannot solve; however, before they work those problems, they have to learn about number families, and the learning must be thorough.

The work with number families begins in Lesson 1. Students learn the basic procedure for going from number families to problems. If the big number is missing, you add. If a small number is missing, you subtract.

Here's part of the introduction from Lesson 1:

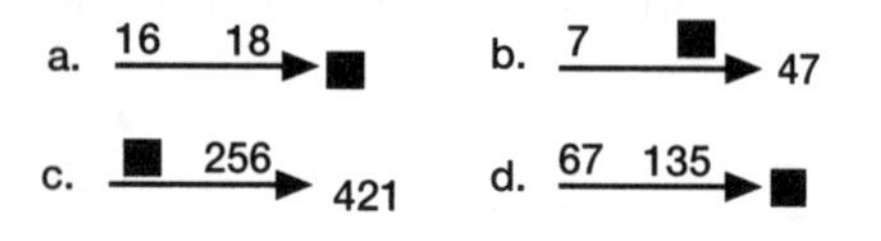

b. In some problems, one of the small numbers is missing. That's one of the numbers on top of the arrow. Remember the rules: To find the big number, **you add the small numbers.** To find a small number, **you start with the big number and subtract.**

c. Touch problem A.
Is a small number or the big number missing in that family? (Signal.) *The big number.*

- What do you do to find the missing big number? (Signal.) *Add.*
- Say the addition problem. (Signal.) *16 plus 18.*

d. Touch problem B.
Is a small number or the big number missing? (Signal) *A small number.*

- What do you do to find a missing small number? (Signal.) *Subtract.*
- Say the subtraction problem. (Signal.) *47 minus 7.*

e. Touch problem C.
Is a small number or the big number missing? (Signal.) *A small number.*

- What do you do to find a missing small number? (Signal.) *Subtract.*
- Say the subtraction problem. (Signal.) *421 minus 256.*

f. Touch problem D. Is a small number or the big number missing? (Signal.) *The big number.*

- Say the problem. (Signal.) *67 plus 135.*

g. Your turn: Write the number problem and the answer for family A. Write the problem in a column. Box your answer. Raise your hand when you're finished.
(Observe students and give feedback.)

- (Write on the board:)

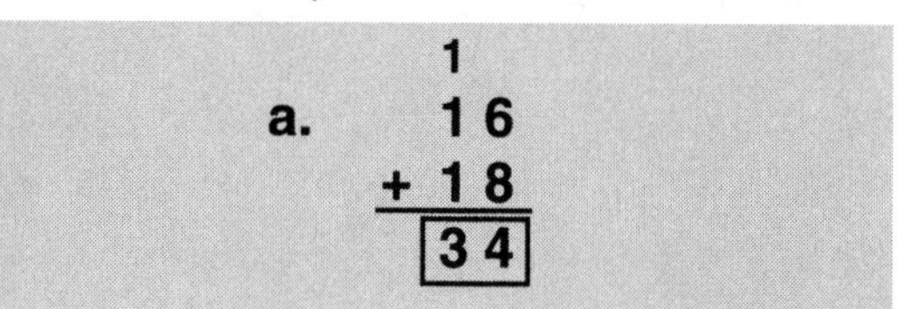

- You added: 16 plus 18. The answer is 34. That's the big number.

h. Your turn again: Write the number problem and the answer for family B. Raise your hand when you're finished.
(Observe students and give feedback.)

- (Write on the board:)

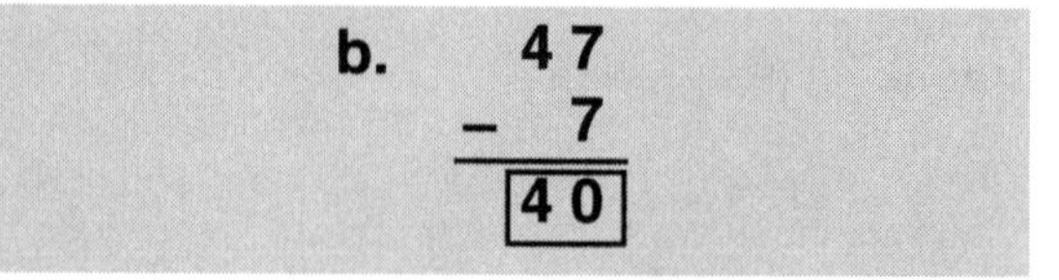

- The missing small number is 40.

Teaching note: In steps c through f, make sure that students are absolutely firm in saying the problem. A written problem must have three parts, each corresponding to a value shown in the number family. The problem must also have an operational sign.

Do not permit students to take short cuts or write problems that do not have the sign, the equals bar, or the box. The rules for writing problems are based solely on the information given in the number family. Be very precise about the rule for subtracting. **You start with the big number and subtract the small number that is shown.** Make sure that students understand this rule and apply it appropriately. It's not enough for them to know that you subtract to find the missing small number. They must know that you start with the big number and that the big number is always at the end of the arrow. The simplest test is for them to say the subtraction problem.

When correcting mistakes, refer to the other information that you gave students about the procedures. For example, for problem B:

if a student writes this problem:

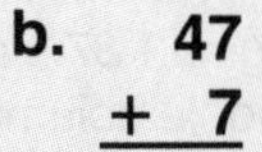

You would say: "Look at the family."

"Touch the missing number. Is the big number or a small number missing in that family?" *A small number.*

"What do you do to find the missing number?" *Subtract.*

"Say the subtraction problem you'll work." *47 minus 7.*

"Work it. And remember, you find missing small numbers by subtracting."

TABLES

Students use the logic of number families to complete 3-by-3 tables of this form:

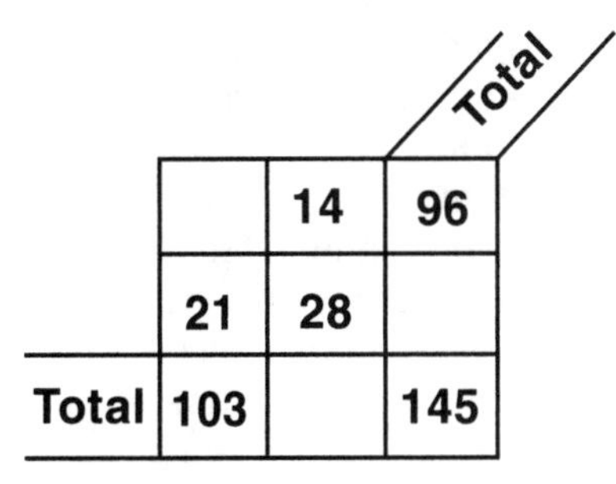

			Total
		14	96
	21	28	
Total	103		145

In Lesson 5, students figure out the missing numbers in **rows** of a table.

	14	96
21	28	
103		145

The arrows show that each row is a number family. If the big number is missing, you add to find that value. If a small number is missing, you subtract.

In Lesson 7, students work with vertical families shown in a table.

28	9	
17		51
	43	88

The arrows show that the big number is at the bottom of the column. The numbers above the big number are the small numbers.

Here's part of the introduction from Lesson 7:

Table A

		75	95
	29	12	
Total	49		136

b. Touch the first column of table A. Everybody, is the big number or a small number missing in that column? (Signal.) *A small number.*
- What do you do to find the missing number? (Signal.) *Subtract.*
- Say the problem. (Signal.) *49 minus 29.*

c. Touch the second column.
Everybody, is the big number or a small number missing in that column? (Signal.) *The big number.*

- What do you do to find the missing number? (Signal.) *Add.*
- Say the problem. (Signal.) *75 plus 12.*

d. Touch the third column.
Everybody, is the big number or a small number missing in that column? (Signal.) *A small number.*

- What do you do to find the missing number? (Signal.) *Subtract.*
- Say the problem. (Signal.) *136 minus 95.*

e. Your turn: Figure out the missing number for each column in the table. Write the column addition or subtraction problem and the answer. Then copy the missing numbers in the table. Raise your hand when you're finished.
(Observe students and give feedback.)

f. Check your work.

- Everybody, what's the missing number in the first column? (Signal.) *20.*
- What's the missing number in the second column? (Signal.) *87.*
- What's the missing number in the third column? (Signal.) *41.*

Teaching note: This exercise does not have a repeat-until-firm direction. However, make sure that the students are quite firm on steps b, c and d. If students are not sure whether a big number or a small number is missing, they'll have trouble working the problem that is appropriate for that column. If students seem to be confused, tell them, "Touch the missing number in the column . . . Is it the big number or a small number missing? . . . So what kind of problem will you work? . . . Say the problem." Practice this correction routine and use it when appropriate. It will help students understand the relationship between number families and problems they solve.

In Lesson 13, students apply what they know about number families to work a 3-by-3 table that does not have number family arrows:

	37	**95**
16		**35**
74		

Students first work all the rows that can be worked, then the columns. A row that can be worked has two values shown. A row with only one value cannot be worked.

Here's the introduction from Lesson 13:

- Open your workbook to lesson 13 and find part 1. √
- This is a table without number-family arrows. You're going to figure out all the missing numbers. Remember, first you work all the rows you can work. Then you work all the columns that have two numbers.

b. Your turn: Work the rows. Figure out the missing numbers for the rows you can work. Write the numbers in the table. Raise your hand when you've finished the rows.
(Observe students and give feedback.)

- (Write on the board:)

	37	**95**
16		**35**
74		

- Check your work. Read the problem and the answer for the top row. (Signal.) *95 minus 37 equals 58.*
- (Write **58** in the top row.)
- Read the problem and the answer for the middle row. (Signal.) *35 minus 16 equals 19.*
- (Write **19** in the middle row.)
- This is what your table should look like so far.

c. Now do the columns. Figure out the missing column numbers and write them in the table. When you're done, you should have all the numbers in the table. Raise your hand when you're finished.
(Observe students and give feedback.)

- Check your work. The first column already has three numbers. Read the problem and the answer for the middle column. (Signal.) *37 plus 19 equals 56.*
- (Write **56** in the middle column.)
- Read the problem and the answer for the last column. (Signal.) *95 plus 35 equals 130.*
- (Write **130** in the last column.)

d. Raise your hand if you figured out all the missing numbers in the table.

Teaching note: In step b, you observe and give feedback. If students have trouble, remind them that they can figure out the missing number in any row that has two numbers. If students try to figure out the value in the bottom row, ask them:
"How many numbers are shown in the bottom row?" *One.*
"How many numbers have to be shown before you can work the problem?" *Two.* "So you can't work the problem for the bottom row."

In Lesson 33, students are introduced to tables that cannot be solved by working all the rows with two numbers, then working all the columns. These tables require students to work rows first, then at least one column, then possibly more rows and columns.

Here's an example from Lesson 33:

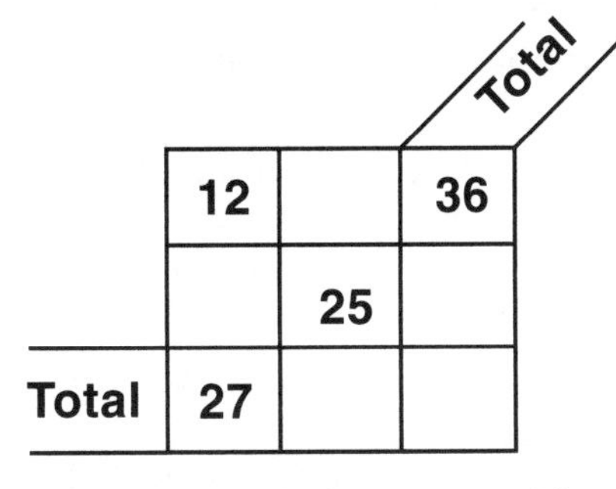

The students first work the row problem:

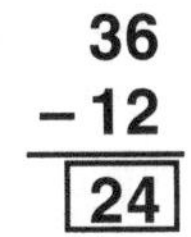

Then they are able to work two column problems:

$$\begin{array}{r} 27 \\ -\ 12 \\ \hline \boxed{15} \end{array} \qquad \begin{array}{r} 24 \\ +\ 25 \\ \hline \boxed{49} \end{array}$$

The table still has two missing numbers:

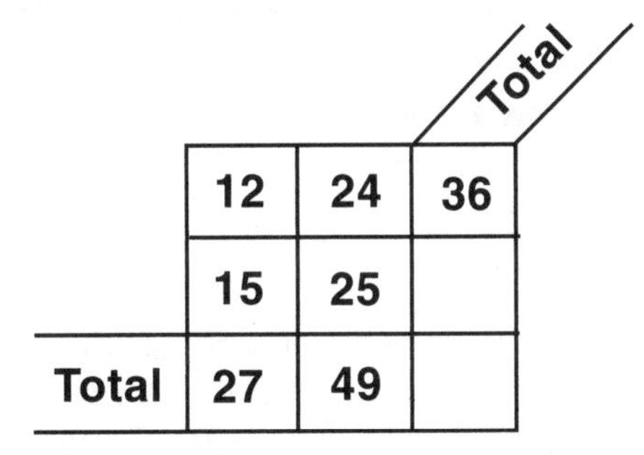

They are big numbers for the middle row and the bottom row. To complete the table, students work row problems:

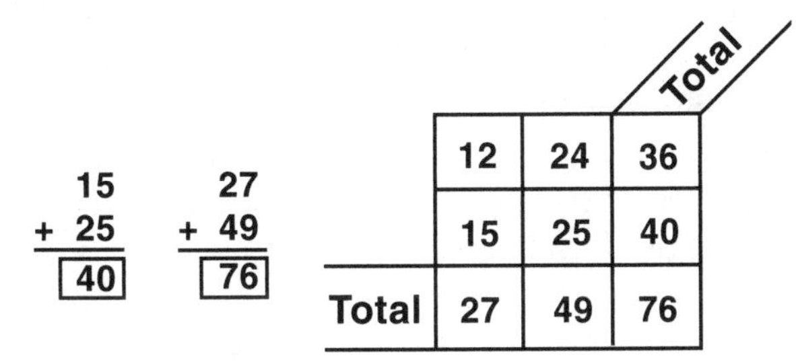

> ***Teaching note:*** If students apply the rule about finding a row or column with two numbers, they will not have difficulty with this variation of the table.

EQUATIONS

In Lesson 15, students make number families from equations that do not end with the unknown.

For example:

After making the number family, students work an addition or subtraction problem to figure out the unknown.

This exercise may be difficult for the following reasons:

1) This is the first time that students will have created number families.

2) This is the first time that students use information provided in equations to figure out where values go in a number family.

3) The equation that students start with does not necessarily imply the operation that is required to solve the problem. Students may start with a subtraction equation and solve it with an addition problem.

Here's an example of what students do:

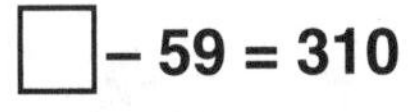

First, they identify the big number in the equation. The problem subtracts so the **first number is the big number.** Students circle the big number:

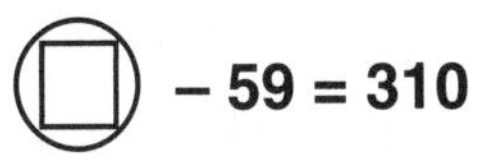

Then students make the number family with the three values shown in the equation:

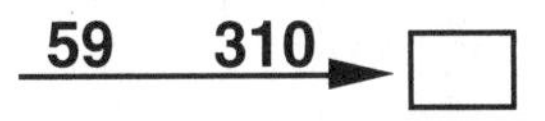

Then students write the problem for figuring out the missing value:

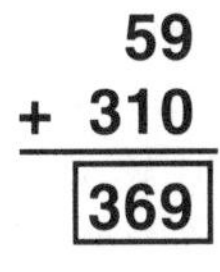

Here's part of the exercise that follows the introduction in Lesson 15:

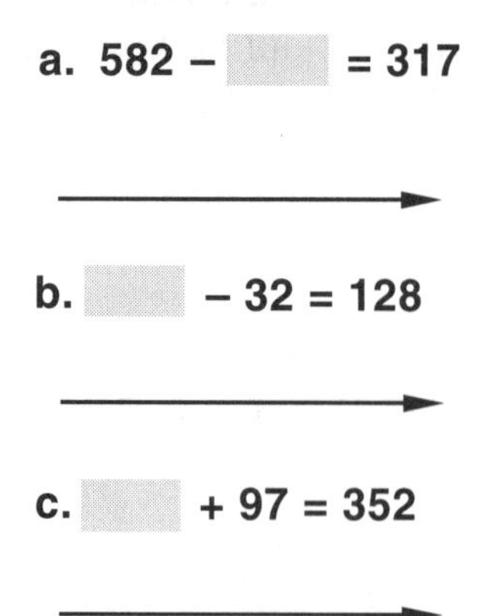

b. Circle the big number for problem A. Below, make the number family. Raise your hand when you're finished.
(Observe students and give feedback.)
- Everybody, which value is the big number? (Signal.) *582.*
- (Write on the board:)

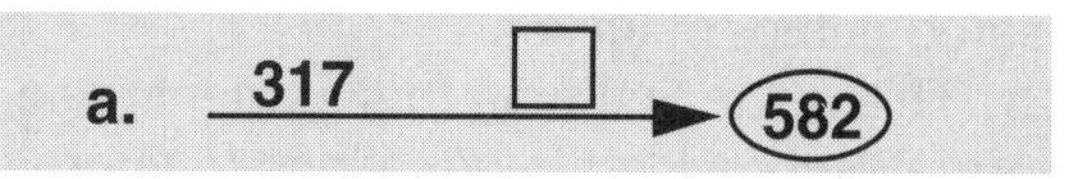

- Here's what you should have.

c. Circle the big number for problem B. Raise your hand when you are finished.
- Everybody, name the value that is the big number. (Signal.) *Box.*
- Make the number family for problem B. Raise your hand when you're finished.
- (Write on the board:)

- Here's what you should have.

Teaching note: When checking students' work, make sure that the number families are correct. They are incorrect if they have signs. This family is unacceptable:

Families are incorrect if the numbers are in the wrong places. This family is incorrect:

582 317 → ☐

Also check to make sure that students circle the big number in the equation. Even if a student shows the correct number family, require the student to show the big number circled in the equation. This is unacceptable:

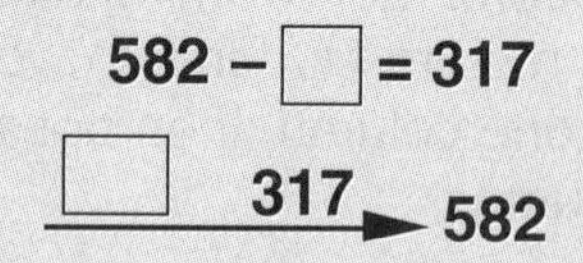

(Students are not required to circle the big number in the number family, only in the equation.)

When correcting student mistakes, present the tasks in order:

"Are you adding or subtracting in the equation?"

"So is the big number the starting value or the ending value?"

"Did you circle the right number?"

"Where does the big number go in the number family?" *At the end of the arrow.*

"Did you put it there?"

"Did you show the other values as small numbers?"

"Fix any mistakes."

If you present the tasks in this order, students will have less trouble understanding the relationships. They start with the sign that tells them to add or subtract. That implies where the big number is. Once they know the big number, they can put all values in the number family. Repeat the exercise in Lesson 15 if a lot of students have trouble.

OTHER EXTENSIONS

In Level E, students work with number families that are more elaborate than those presented in earlier levels of *Connecting Math Concepts.* Two additional number-family extensions are discussed in this section: fraction number families and complex number families. These families are an integral part of problem-solving strategies and are discussed as preskills to those strategies.

Fraction number families are the same as regular number families except that they have three related fractions, all with the same denominator:

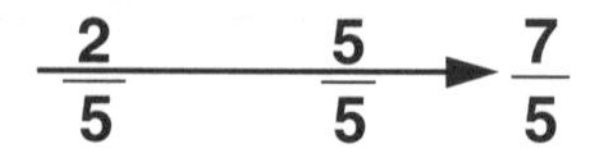

Fraction number families are used in complex ratio and proportion problems that involve tables (see p. 101).

Complex number families have a main number family and small vertical number families:

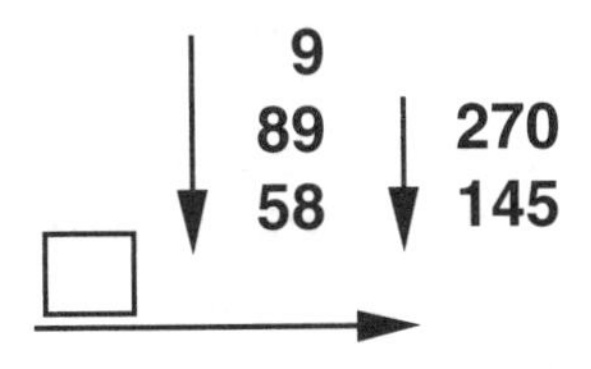

First, students must figure out two values on the main arrow. They work the small number families and write the big number for each on the main arrow:

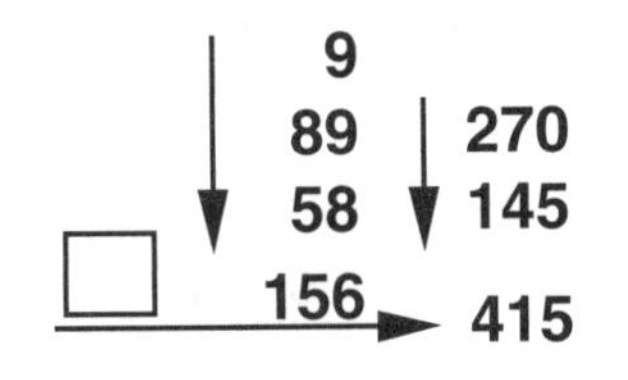

Now, students can figure out the missing number on the main arrow:

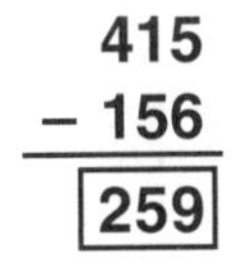

These number families are used to solve a variety of multi-step problems (see page 87).

Decimal Operations

In Level E, students add and subtract decimal values, multiply decimal values, and do limited work with division of decimal values. Early in the program (beginning in Lesson 31) students add and subtract dollar-and-cent values.

For example:

$$\begin{array}{r} \$\ 45.60 \\ +\ \ 13.90 \\ \hline \$\ 59.50 \end{array}$$

Beginning in Lesson 75, students review the procedures for multiplying a dollar-and-cent amount by a whole number:

$$\begin{array}{r} \$\ \ 3.60 \\ \times\ \ \ \ \ \ 4 \\ \hline \$\ 14.40 \end{array}$$

They do the multiplication the way they normally would, then place the decimal point in the answer so the answer shows hundredths. Then they make a dollar sign in the answer.

In Lesson 73, students review the steps for addition and subtraction of dollar-and-cent amounts. Students line up the decimal points, write the decimal point in the answer, do the addition or subtraction and write the dollar sign.

The first decimal problems that do not involve dollar-and-cent amounts are introduced in Lesson 85. The first exercises present row problems that show decimal values. Students write the values in columns and perform the addition operation.

Students follow this procedure:

1) Line up the decimal points.

2) Add zeros to any values that do not have as many places as the value with the greatest number of decimal places.

3) Perform the operation.

Problems include those that have a whole number minus a decimal value:

$$15 - 8.275$$

To work this problem, students add a decimal point and three zeros to the whole-number value:

$$\begin{array}{r} 15.000 \\ -\ 8.275 \\ \hline \end{array}$$

Beginning with Lesson 99, students work problems that multiply a whole number by a decimal value that is less than 1. Students initially work these problems by changing the values into a fraction, then multiplying, then writing the fractional answer as a decimal value.

For example:

$$23 \times .3$$

Students rewrite .3 as the fraction 3/10:

$$\frac{23}{1} \times \frac{3}{10} =$$

Students multiply and write the fraction answer:

$$\frac{23}{1} \times \frac{3}{10} = \frac{69}{10}$$

Now they express 69/10 as a decimal value: 6.9.

Fraction multiplication is used as the basis for confirming decimal multiplication because students have done extensive work with fraction multiplication. Working problems in this manner also verifies the rules about multiplying. In this example, 23 is multiplied by a value that is less than 1. The answer—expressed either as a fraction or as a decimal value—is less than 23.

In Lesson 102, students work similar problems that have two decimal values. Students rewrite both values as fractions, figure out the fractional answer and write the corresponding decimal answer.

In Lesson 103, students learn a general procedure that does not involve fractions:

1) Multiply and write the digits in the answer.
2) Count the total number of decimal places in the values that are multiplied together.
3) Show the same number of decimal places in the answer.

This procedure is often mysterious for students; however, those who have worked the decimal problems as fractions have seen that when there are more decimal places in the values that are multiplied together, there are more decimal places in the answer.

In Lesson 104, students work problems that require a zero in the answer.

Here's the first part of the introduction from Lesson 104:

a. You learned to work decimal problems the fast way. Remember, first you multiply the way you would if there were no decimal places. Then you count the decimal places in the values that are multiplied. You show the same number of decimal places in the answer.

b. (Write on the board:)

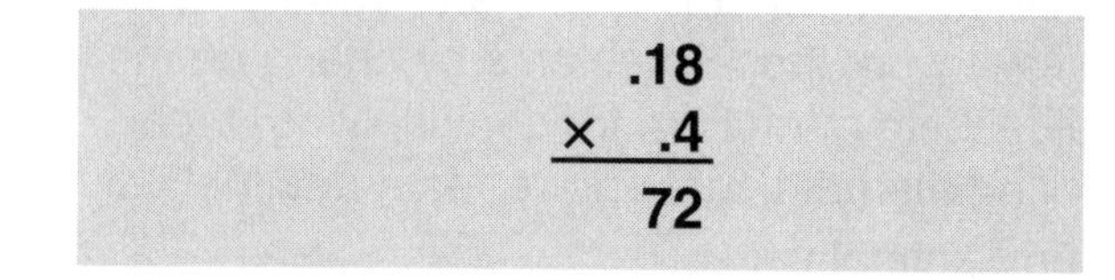

- For some multiplication problems, you don't get as many digits in the answer as you need. Here's that kind of problem. When I multiply, I get 72. Raise your hand when you know how many decimal places go in the answer.
- Everybody, how many? (Signal.) *3.*
- But I only have two digits. So I count off **three** places and make the decimal point. And I write a zero in front of the digits I've written. Watch.
- (Write to show:)

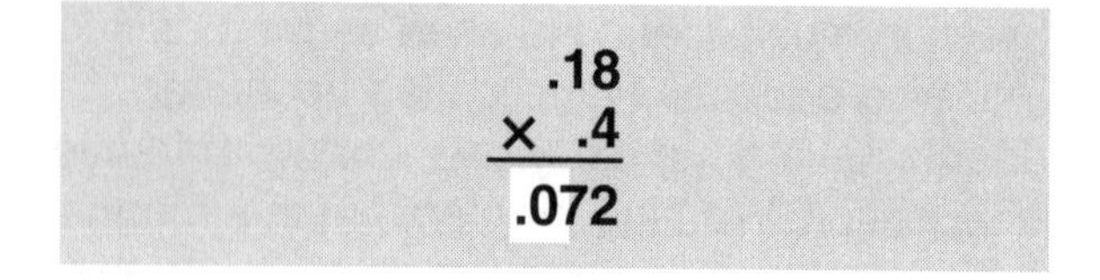

- Remember, the zero must go in **front** of the digits you've written.

In Lesson 123, decimal division is introduced. The problems that students work are limited to those that have a decimal value under the division sign, but not in the divisor.

Students follow this procedure:

1. Write the decimal point in the answer directly above the decimal point that is shown.
2. Divide and write the digits in the answer.
3. Make sure that there is a digit in the answer for every place after the decimal point.

For this problem:

7 |.4 5 5

a digit in the answer is needed immediately after the decimal point:

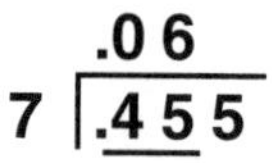

Here's the introduction from Lesson 123:

b. I'll work the sample problem.

- (Write on the board:)

5 |.3 0 5

- I make the decimal point above the other decimal point.
- (Write to show:)

- Now I divide. 3 divided by 5. I can't do that. So I write a zero above the 3.
- (Write **0.**)
- 30 divided by 5. What's the answer? (Signal.) *6.*
- (Write to show:)

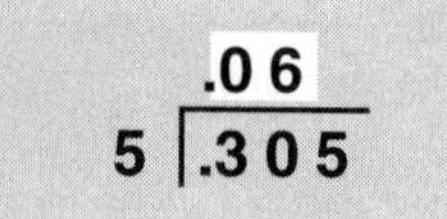

- 5 divided by 5. What's the answer? (Signal.) *1.*
- (Write to show:)

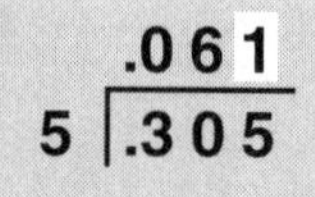

- The answer is 61-thousandths.

In Lesson 124, students use decimal division to work word problems that divide a dollar-and-cent amount.

For example:

If a person earns $10.60 in 4 hours, how much does the person earn in 1 hour?

Coordinate System

In Lesson 49, the coordinate system is introduced. Students write the X and Y values for points shown on the coordinate system. The X value is the distance of a point in this direction from zero:

→

The Y value is the distance of the point in this direction from zero:

↑

Here's part of the introduction from Lesson 49:

- Here are the x and y values for the point at A: $x = 5$, $y = 7$.
- To get to point A, you go 5 places in the x direction and then 7 places up for y.

a. Touch A on the coordinate system.
- Here are the values for that point. X equals 5, Y equals 7. That means: To get to point A, you go 5 places in the X direction, then 7 places up for Y.

b. (Write on the board:)

c. Your turn: Use lined paper. Write the X value and Y value for point B. Remember, write the number of places for X and the number of places for Y. Raise your hand when you've written what X equals and Y equals.
(Observe students and give feedback.)
- (Write to show:)

B $x = 7$, $y = 4$

- Here's what you should have for point B. X equals 7. Y equals 4.

d. Write the X and Y values for C. Write what X equals and what Y equals. Raise your hand when you're finished.
(Observe students and give feedback.)
- (Write on the board:)

C $x = 1$, $y = 6$

- Here's what you should have. X equals 1. Y equals 6.

Starting with Lesson 52, students make points on the coordinate system. They work from information about the X and Y values for the point.

For example:

Point A: $x = 5$, $y = 7$

Students go 5 places along the X axis and then 7 places up for Y. They make a point and write the letter A next to the point.

In Lesson 54, students work from a coordinate system that shows points that are lined up:

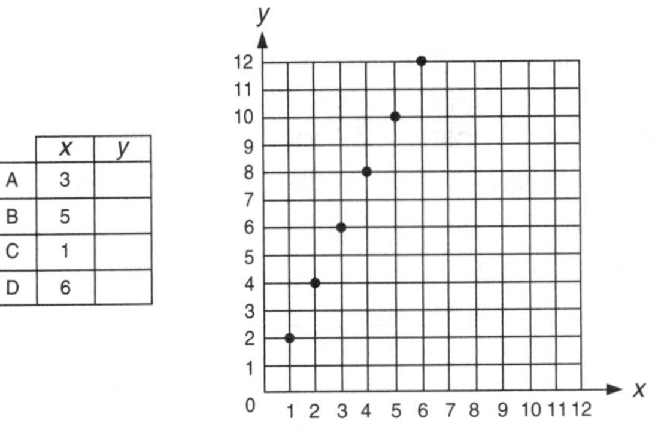

	x	y
A	3	
B	5	
C	1	
D	6	

Students first draw a line that connects the points. Then they complete a table to show the X and Y value for selected points on the line.

Here are the directions that you give the students before they draw their line:

a. Here's a coordinate system with lots of points lined up.

b. Use your ruler. Very carefully draw a line through all the points. The line you draw must go through the point for zero on your coordinate system. Raise your hand when you're finished. √

Teaching note: Students use a ruler to draw the line. Be extremely particular about whether a line is acceptable. If the line is not perfect, direct the student to redo it. A perfect line goes through all points including the point at zero. A line is unacceptable if it is too short on either end, if it misses any points, or if it is not straight. While an imprecise line for this exercise will make little difference in how the student completes the table, incorrect lines in later exercises will result in serious mistakes.

In Lesson 56, students plot two points, draw a line, then refer to the line to complete a table.

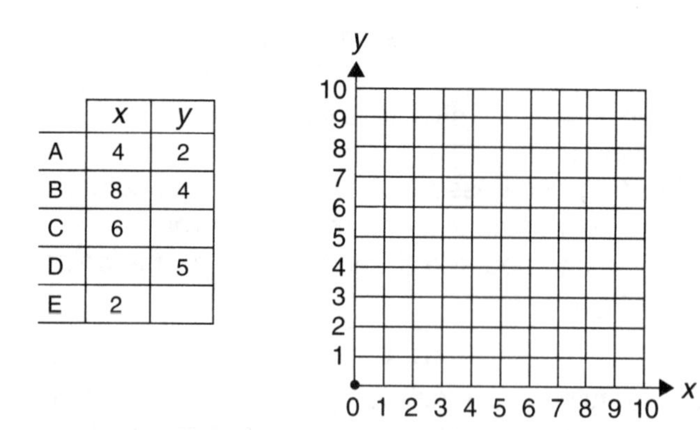

	x	y
A	4	2
B	8	4
C	6	
D		5
E	2	

Students will not be able to complete some of the rows in the table unless the line is drawn correctly—through the two points the students make and through zero.

Starting in Lesson 68, students use the coordinate system to confirm answers to proportion problems. Students first complete a series of equivalent fractions that are based on a proportion rule.

For example:

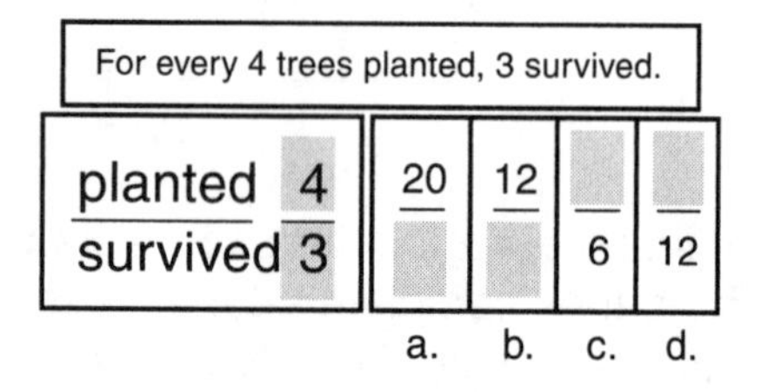

Students then use the numerator of each fraction as the Y value and the denominator as the X value. The letter under each fraction shows the letter that students write on the coordinate system to identify the point. Students draw a line that connects all the points. The line confirms that all the values in the table are correct. If a value is not correct, the point for that value will not fall on the line.

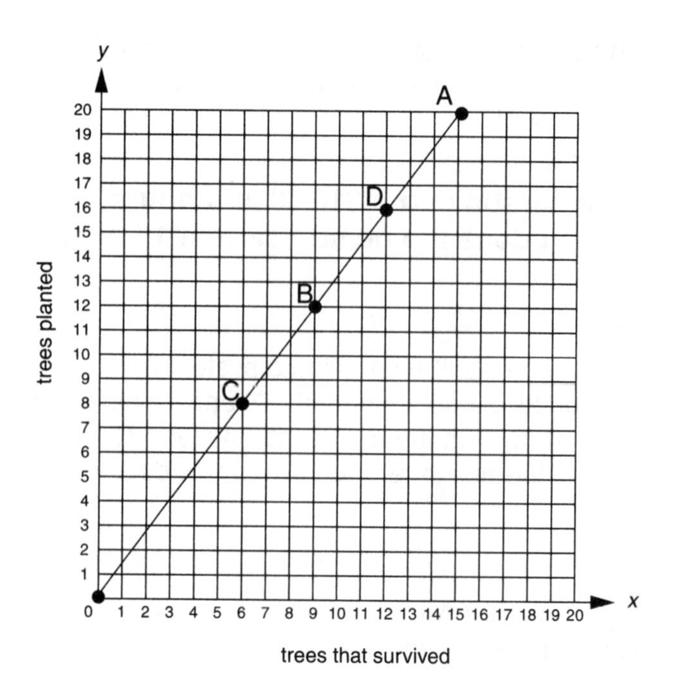

In Lesson 114, students are introduced to functions. A function is the rule for operating on X. If the function is X plus 3, you start with any X value and add 3 to obtain the corresponding Y value. If the function is X times 4, you start with any X value and multiply it by 4 to obtain the corresponding Y value. Students complete tables of the form:

x	Function X + 2	y

To complete each row of the table, students start with the X value, apply the function rule, and write the Y value. For the X value of 7, students write:

x	Function X + 2	y
7	7 + 2	9

After completing the table, students plot the points, and draw the line.

In Lesson 117, students formulate a function by testing the two functions that are shown.

For example:

x	Function $x + 5$ or $x \times 2$	y
5		10
7		14
3		
8		

The two possible functions for the first row are: X plus 5 and X times 2. The function X times 2 applies to the second row as well; therefore, that's the function for all the rows of the table.

x	Function ~~$x + 5$~~ or $x \times 2$	y
5	5×2	10
7	7×2	14
3	3×2	6
8	8×2	16

In Lesson 118, students figure out the two possible functions for the first row of a table and determine which of those functions also works for the second row. Students then apply that function to all the rows.

In Level E, the coordinate system is also used to validate the equations used to figure out the area of rectangles, triangles, and parallelograms. This work begins in Lesson 62 and continues through Lesson 96. (See **Geometry** track.)

APPLICATIONS

In Level E, applications encompass a range of problems that involve words, tables, the coordinate system, and geometric figures. Some problems require students to construct tables, graphs, or lines. Other problems require students to refer to tables or other sources of information to work problems. For problems that involve measurement units, students refer to the table of weights and measures at the back of their textbook:

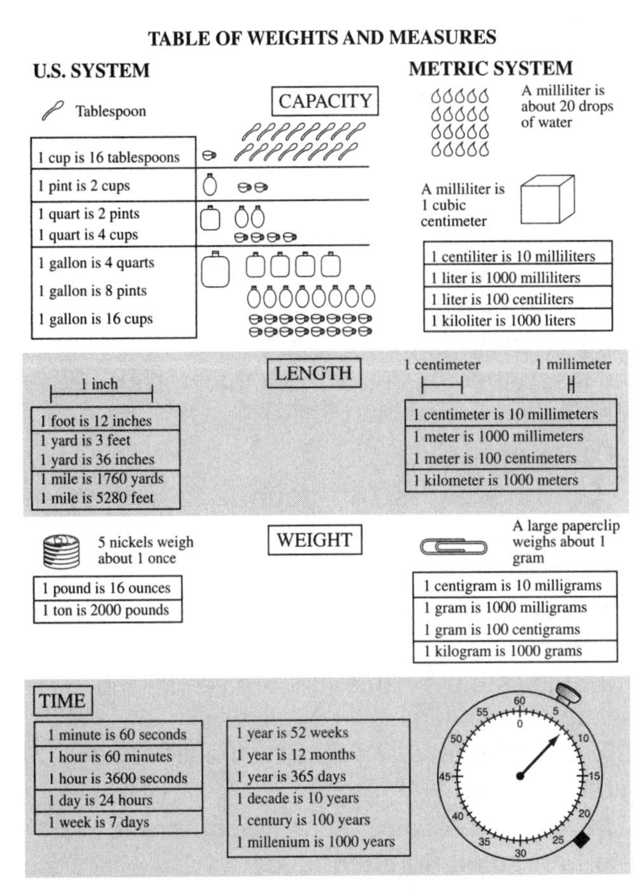
TABLE OF WEIGHTS AND MEASURES

U.S. SYSTEM

METRIC SYSTEM

CAPACITY

Tablespoon

1 cup is 16 tablespoons
1 pint is 2 cups
1 quart is 2 pints
1 quart is 4 cups
1 gallon is 4 quarts
1 gallon is 8 pints
1 gallon is 16 cups

A milliliter is about 20 drops of water

A milliliter is 1 cubic centimeter

1 centiliter is 10 milliliters
1 liter is 1000 milliliters
1 liter is 100 centiliters
1 kiloliter is 1000 liters

LENGTH

1 inch

1 foot is 12 inches
1 yard is 3 feet
1 yard is 36 inches
1 mile is 1760 yards
1 mile is 5280 feet

1 centimeter

1 millimeter

1 centimeter is 10 millimeters
1 meter is 1000 millimeters
1 meter is 100 centimeters
1 kilometer is 1000 meters

WEIGHT

5 nickels weigh about 1 once

1 pound is 16 ounces
1 ton is 2000 pounds

A large paperclip weighs about 1 gram

1 centigram is 10 milligrams
1 gram is 1000 milligrams
1 gram is 100 centigrams
1 kilogram is 1000 grams

TIME

1 minute is 60 seconds
1 hour is 60 minutes
1 hour is 3600 seconds
1 day is 24 hours
1 week is 7 days

1 year is 52 weeks
1 year is 12 months
1 year is 365 days
1 decade is 10 years
1 century is 100 years
1 millenium is 1000 years

As a general rule, for every tool skill that students learn in Level E, there are corresponding problem-solving applications. After students work with equivalent fractions, they solve ratio and proportion problems that apply the same steps. Similarly, after students learn about number families, they apply their knowledge to a variety of complex word problems that require addition and subtraction. After students learn about decimal values, they work money problems that require the operational steps they have learned.

This point is important for the students and also for you. Skills that students work on are not ends. These skills will be used in more complex applications. If students are not well practiced in component skills, they will lack the tools they need to be successful with the problem-solving extensions.

The major categories of applications that students work in Level E are problem solving, probability and geometry. Problem solving includes: number family extensions to addition and subtraction, including multi-step problems;

ratio and proportion problems; problems that involve multiplication and division; and inverse-operation problems. Probability develops relationships between sets and trials.

Geometry includes: perimeter; area and volume; circles; angles; and lines.

Problem Solving

NUMBER FAMILIES

The work with number-family word problems begins in Lesson 12. Students make number families from sentences that compare two values. (Students do not work the problem—they just make the number family.)

For example:

Donna weighs 149 pounds less than Fran.

Students follow this procedure:

1. Identify which value is more. That is the big number in the family.
2. Indicate the name that is given for the second small number in the family.
3. Indicate the difference as the first small number in the family.

Note: For all comparisons, the **difference is the first small number.**

Here's part of the introduction from Lesson 12:

e. Problem B: Earl has 6 and 1-half more than George. Write the letters and the difference number. Raise your hand when you're finished.
(Observe students and give feedback.)

- (Write on the board:)

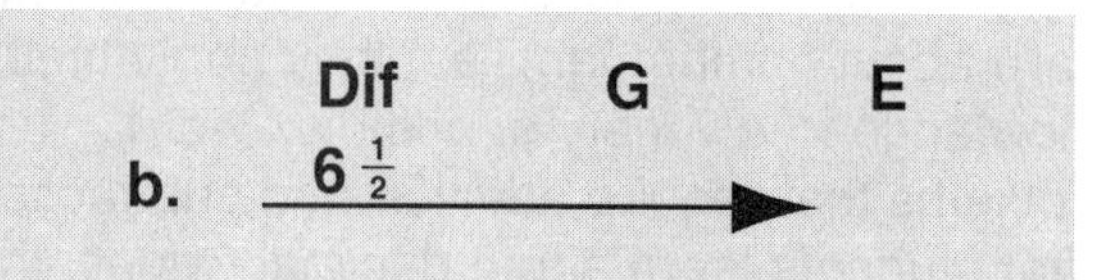

- Here's what you should have. **Earl** has more. His name is the big number. **George** has less. The difference number is 6 and 1-half.

f. Problem C. James has 14 fewer than Bonnie. Make the family. Raise your hand when you're finished.
(Observe students and give feedback.)

- (Write on the board:)

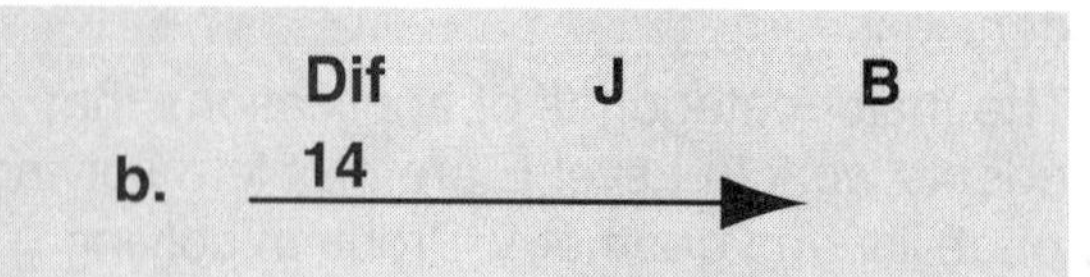

- Here's what you should have. The names are **James** and **Bonnie.** James has fewer. So James is a small number. Bonnie is the big number. The difference is **14.**

Teaching note: The part of the sentence that gives a number for more or less is the difference number: **14 more** tells about the difference number of 14; **36 fewer** tells about a difference number of 36. If students have trouble, direct them to write the difference number for the sentence first. Then tell them to read the sentence and put the letter of the person who has more as the big number and put the other letter as the second small number. Repeat any problems that give students difficulties.

In Lesson 14, students work entire problems. These problems give two values and the names.

For example:

Pile A weighs 75 pounds more than pile B. Pile A weighs 128 pounds. How many pounds does pile B weigh?

Students make the number family based on the first sentence. The family has the names and the difference number:

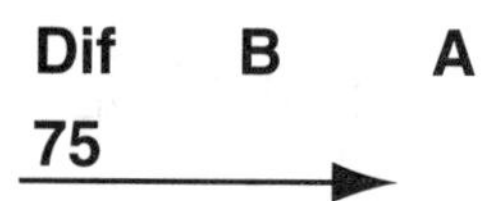

Students put in the value for Pile A:

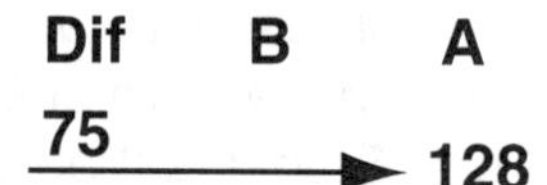

Students work the subtraction problem to figure out the missing number.

For these problems, students answer the question by writing the number only. (Later, students will be required to write the number and the unit name for answering the question to any word problem.)

Here's part of the work from Lesson 14:

f. Problem B: A truck went 231 miles farther than a car went. If the car went 490 miles, how many miles did the truck go? Make the number family for the first sentence. Then write the number for one of the letters. Raise your hand when you have two numbers in your number family.

- (Write on the board:)

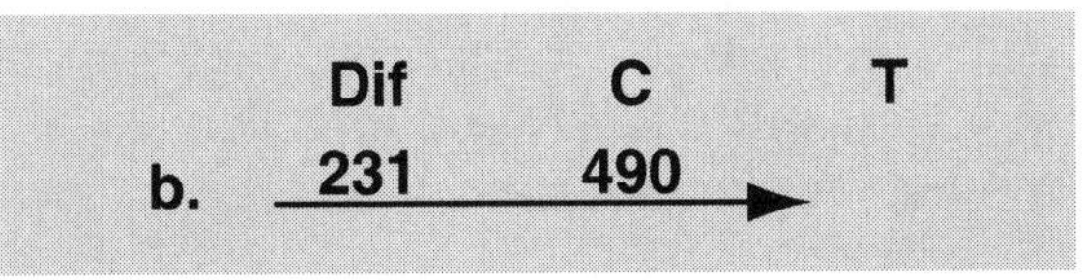

- The truck went farther than the car. So **truck** is the big number. **Car** and **231** are small numbers. You wrote **490** for the car. Figure out the miles for the truck. Box your answer. Raise your hand when you're finished.
- Check your work. To find the miles for the truck, you add. The answer is **721.** Raise your hand if you got it right.

Teaching note: Be very particular about the number families that students make.

1) They must have a family with an arrow. This family is unacceptable:

Dif C T
231 490

2) The letters must be shown above the family and in the right places. These families are unacceptable:

Dif C T
231 490 →

231 490 →

Even if students have no difficulties with the calculation, require them to make the number families. Students who are not practiced in making families will have serious problems when the problems become more difficult.

NUMBER-FAMILY TABLES

In Lesson 1, students begin working with the information conveyed in 3-by-3 tables of this form:

	Cars	Trucks	Total
Lot A	17	23	40
Lot B	38	19	57
Total	55	42	97

The questions presented in Lesson 1 are literal: **How many trucks are on lot B? What's the total number of cars on both lots?** In later lessons, students answer inferential questions, such as: **On which lot were there more trucks?**

Starting with Lesson 17, students work with incomplete tables.

For example:

	Boys	Girls	Total Students
Rock School	210		655
Knox School		117	
Total	528		

Students apply what they know about number families to fill in the missing numbers. Then students answer questions.

In Lesson 26, students use sentences that provide comparative information to figure out the missing value in a table.

Here's part of the exercise from Lesson 26:

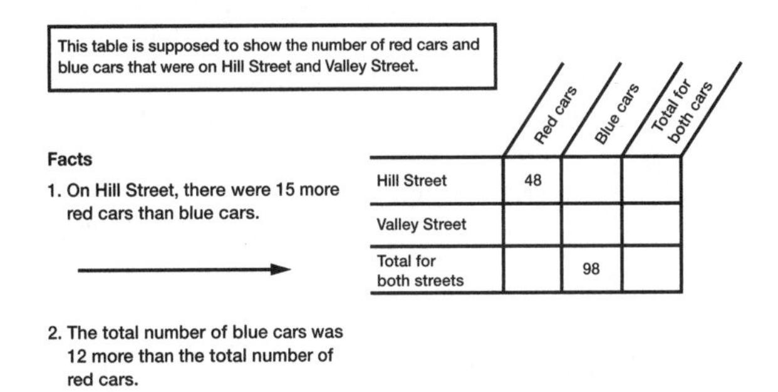
This table is supposed to show the number of red cars and blue cars that were on Hill Street and Valley Street.

Facts

1. On Hill Street, there were 15 more red cars than blue cars.

2. The total number of blue cars was 12 more than the total number of red cars.

	Red cars	Blue cars	Total for both cars
Hill Street	48		
Valley Street			
Total for both streets		98	

a. This table is supposed to show the number of red cars and blue cars that were on two different streets. Hill Street and Valley Street. The table has lots of numbers missing. The facts next to the table give you information about two of the missing numbers.

b. Fact 1 tells about Hill Street. It says: On Hill Street, there were 15 more red cars than blue cars. Make the number family for red cars and blue cars below fact 1. Your family should have two letters and a difference number. Raise your hand when you're finished.

- (Write on the board:)

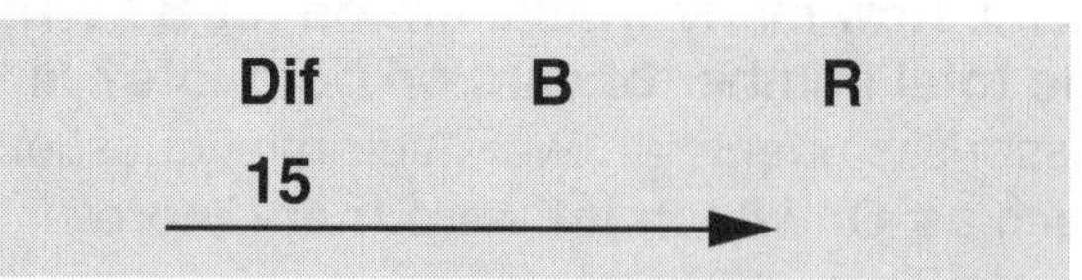

- Here's what you should have. The fact for your number family tells about two of the cells in your table.

c. Listen: On Hill Street, there were 15 more red cars than blue cars.
- The fact tells about red cars on Hill Street and blue cars on Hill Street. Put a small check mark in the two cells the fact tells about. Raise your hand when you're finished.
  (Observe students and give feedback.)
- You should have made your check marks in the top row. Make sure you have check marks in the **first cell** and the **middle cell** of the top row. √
- One of the cells with a check mark already has a number in it. Is that the cell for red cars or blue cars? (Signal.) *Red cars.*
- Write that number where it belongs **in your number family.** Then figure out the number of blue cars. Raise your hand when you're finished.
  (Observe students and give feedback.)
- (Write to show:)

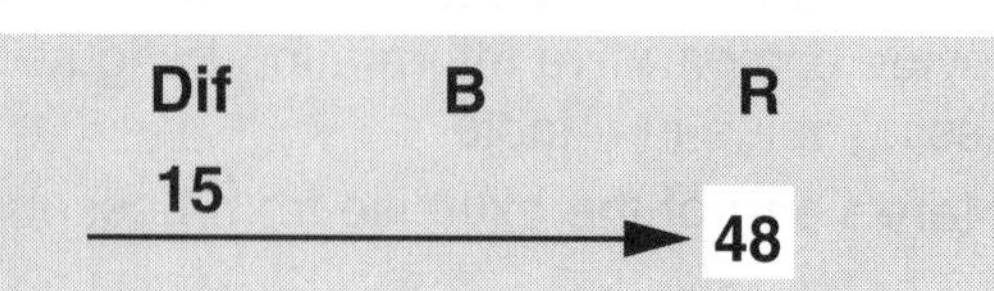

- Your number family should have a big number of 48 and a difference number of 15. Everybody, what's the number for blue cars? (Signal.) *33.*
- You figured out the number of blue cars on Hill Street. Write it where it belongs in the table. Raise your hand when you're finished.

Teaching note: Step c is the critical step in this exercise. Students first identify the two cells that are compared. The first part of the sentence tells them about the row that is involved: On Hill Street. . . . The rest of the sentence tells which two cells are involved: . . . more red cars than blue cars. Students put a check in each of these cells:

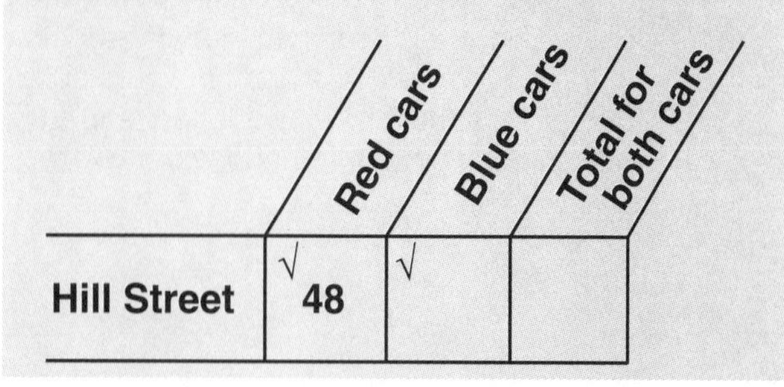

	Red cars	Blue cars	Total for both cars
Hill Street	√ 48	√	

One of the cells has a number. That's the cell for red cars. Students copy that number in their number family and then figure out the number for blue cars:

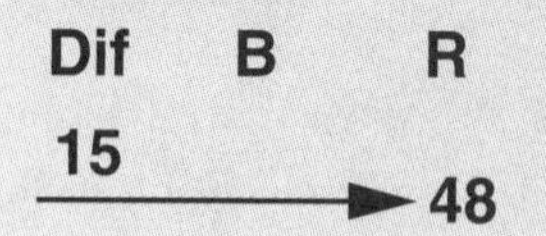

The missing number is a small number; students work the problem, 48 minus 15, to figure out the number for blue cars. After finding the missing number, students write it in their tables:

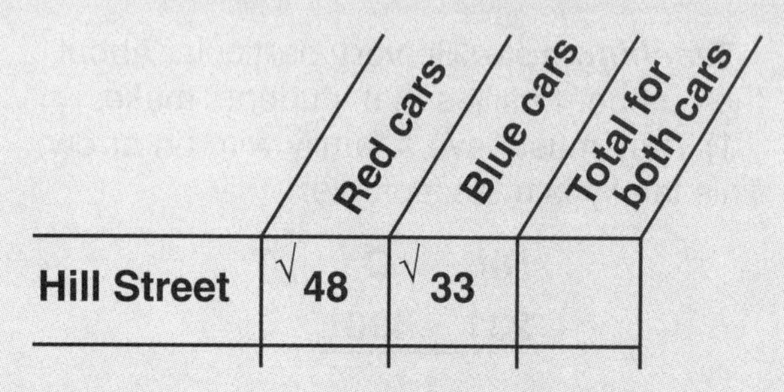

	Red cars	Blue cars	Total for both cars
Hill Street	√ 48	√ 33	

The steps in the procedure that are the most difficult for students are:

1) Putting check marks in the appropriate cells; and

2) Putting the missing number from the number family in the appropriate cell of the table.

To correct mistakes associated with making check marks, take students through the steps:

"Listen: **On Hill Street** . . . Touch the row or column you're working with.

Listen: **On Hill Street, there were 15 more red cars than blue cars.**

That sentence names two of the cells in the row for Hill Street. Touch those cells . . .

You should be touching red cars and blue cars in the Hill Street row.

Make checks in those cells."

To correct mistakes associated with the missing number in the number family:

"You figured out a number. That number goes in the table. You have a mark to show where it goes. What's the name for the missing number? . . . Write it where it belongs."

If students tend to have a lot of trouble with the problems presented in Lesson 26, repeat the problems. Direct students to erase what they have written in their workbooks. Start over and present the exercise. Once students have successfully completed the sequence of activities for one of these problems, they'll tend to work quickly on subsequent table problems of this type.

In Lesson 33, students make a complete table from a word problem. Here are the procedures that students follow to construct the table:

1) Identify the first names in the problem and write them as column headings. If the word problem says, **There were blue cars and red cars on two lots,** students write column headings for blue cars, red cars, and total. If the word problem says, **At two camps there were boys and girls,** the column headings are boys, girls, and total. If the word problem says, **In 1978 and 1979 babies were born in two countries,** the column headings are 1978, 1979, and total.

2) Identify the next names in the problem and write them as row headings.

3) Write the numbers the problem gives in the appropriate cells.

4) Figure out the missing numbers.

5) Answer the questions.

Here's part of the introduction from Lesson 33, after students have worked a sample problem:

<u>Game wardens put trout and bass in two different lakes. The lakes were Blue Lake and Ross Lake.</u> The Wardens put 125 trout in Blue Lake. They put 74 bass in Blue Lake and 128 bass in Ross Lake. They put a total of 231 fish in Ross Lake.

a. How many trout were put in Ross Lake?

b. How many total fish were put in Blue Lake?

c. How many bass were put in both lakes?

g. The first sentence says: Game wardens put trout and bass in two different lakes. What are the column headings? (Signal.) *Trout and bass.*

- The next sentence tells about the row headings. Your turn: Make the table with headings for the columns and the rows. Remember the totals. Raise your hand when you've done that much.
- (Write on the board:)

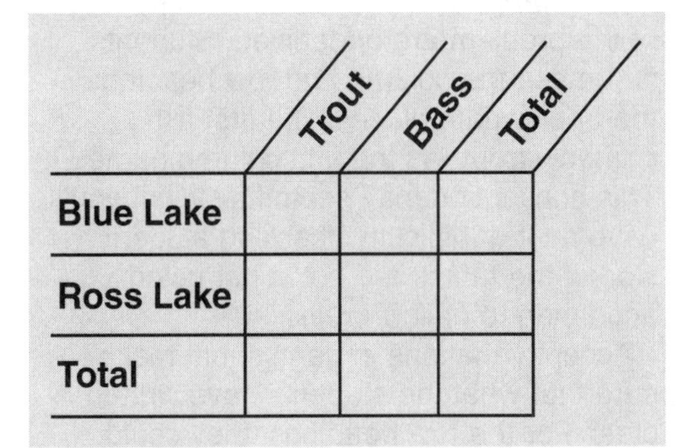

	Trout	Bass	Total
Blue Lake			
Ross Lake			
Total			

- Here's what you should have. Now put in all the numbers the facts tell about. Raise your hand when you have four numbers in your table. (Observe students and give feedback.)
- (Write to show:)

	Trout	Bass	Total
Blue Lake	**125**	**74**	
Ross Lake		**128**	**231**
Total			

- Here's what you should have.

h. Now figure out the missing numbers for the table and answer the questions. Raise your hand when you're finished.

- (Write to show:)

	Trout	Bass	Total
Blue Lake	**125**	**74**	**199**
Ross Lake	**103**	**128**	**231**
Total	**228**	**202**	**430**

- Here's what you should have. Raise your hand if you got everything right.

i. Everybody, how many trout were put in Ross Lake? (Signal.) *103.*

- How many total fish were put in Blue Lake? (Signal.) *199.*
- How many bass were put in both lakes? (Signal.) *202.*
- That was a hard problem.

Teaching note: The first two sentences of the problem are underlined. Students first make the column and row headings in the appropriate places. The first fish named—trout—is the first column name. This convention may seem fussy, but you'll have a lot of difficulty checking student work if the tables are not constructed according to uniform rules.

Accept variations in names, but make sure that what the students have written is clear. For the row headings, they could write: **Blue** and **Ross.** You may accept initials, such as **BL** and **RL**; however, you should not permit such abbreviations unless you're sure that the student understands what they mean and that they are clear. For instance, in Lesson 33 you wouldn't accept the abbreviation **B** for **Blue Lake,** because the students may become very confused about whether the **B** refers to **Blue Lake** or to **Bass.** The *Answer Key* shows the names written out fully.

If students have trouble putting numbers in the appropriate place, ask about the two names in the statement. For the statement: **They put 74 bass in Blue Lake,** ask, "What kind of fish does that statement tell about?

Which lake does it tell about?

Touch the cell for that fish and that lake.

Write the number that goes in that cell."

In Lesson 36, students work a problem that presents a comparative statement.

Baseball cards and football cards were collected by two people. The people were Milly and George. Milly had 27 baseball cards in her collection. George had 52 football cards. George had a total of 75 cards.

a. How many Baseball cards did George have?
b. How many football cards did both people have?
c. Which person had fewer total cards?

Milly had 25 more football cards than George had.

The information presented above the questions gives students information about the headings and three numbers that go in the table. One more number is needed before students can figure out the missing numbers. The fact at the bottom of the problem provides comparative information. After students have the three numbers in their table, they read the comparative sentence: **Milly had 25 more football cards than George had.** Students make a number family based on this sentence:

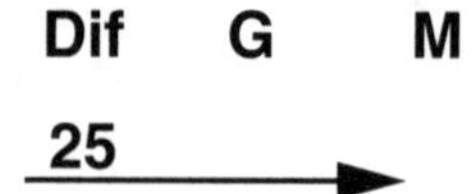

They put check marks in the two cells that are compared;

	Baseball	Football	Total
Milly	27	√	
George		√52	75
Total			

copy the number from the cell for George's football cards;

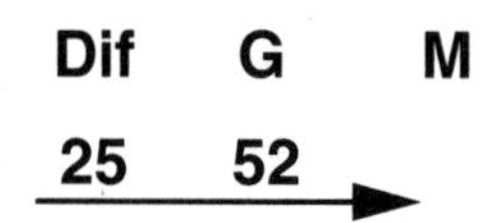

figure out the missing number in the family;

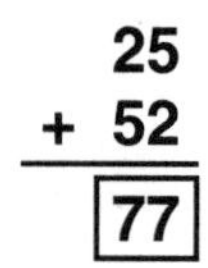

and copy that number in the table.

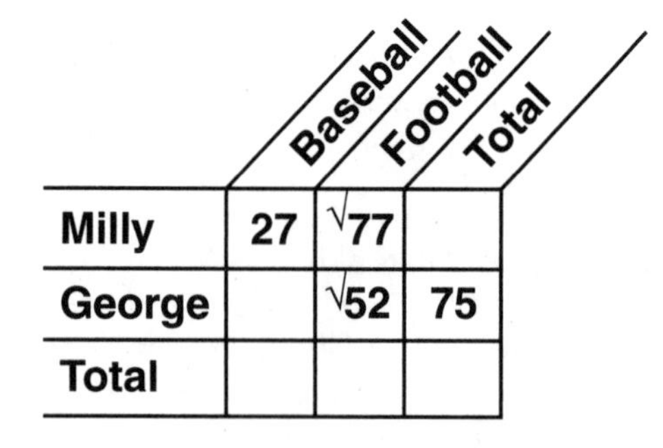

	Baseball	Football	Total
Milly	27	√77	
George		√52	75
Total			

Then students complete the table and answer the questions:

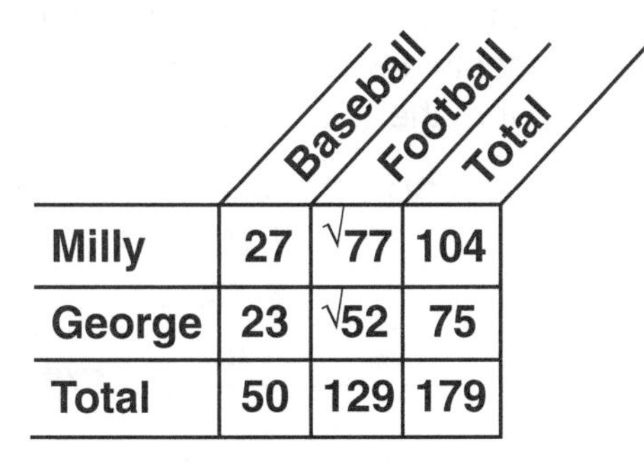

	Baseball	Football	Total
Milly	27	√77	104
George	23	√52	75
Total	50	129	179

a. **How many baseball cards did George have? 23**

b. **How many football cards did both people have? 129**

c. **Which person had fewer total cards? George**

The final problem type that requires a 3-by-3 table has the comparative sentence embedded in the problem—not in a box apart from the other information used to construct the table.

Here's an example from Lesson 38:

Workers planted fir trees and maples in two parks—Rock Park and Wilson Park. They planted 128 fir trees in Rock Park. The total number of maples planted in both parks was 543. In Rock Park, they planted 17 more maples than firs. A total of 400 trees were planted in Wilson Park.

a. What's the total number of trees that were planted?

b. Were there more maples planted in Rock Park or Wilson Park?

c. How many firs were planted in Wilson Park?

d. In which park were more trees planted?

> ***Teaching note:*** The sentence: **In Rock Park, they planted 17 more maples than firs,** is not highlighted or promoted in the problem. Students identify that sentence. They use the information from that sentence after they have used the information from all the other sentences. (This order is necessary in some problems because students may not be able to construct the number family before all the other numbers given are in the table.) Point out to students that these are very difficult problems and that they are very smart if they can work them with no mistakes.

MULTI-STEP PROBLEMS

Starting in Lesson 34, students work with number family problems that have the headings, **in, out,** and **end up.** Before students work multi-step problems, they work simpler problems to establish important conventions. For these families, **in** is the big number. **End up** is the first small number. Students write these names and then work problems that give information about quantities that go in and out. The conventions are:

1) If a sentence tells the amount that somebody has, that's a number for **in.** The sentence **Tim had 17 dollars** gives a number for **in.**

Also, if a sentence tells about a gain, it tells about a value for **in.** The sentence **Molly collected 226 shells** tells the gain in shells that Molly achieved. 226 is a number for **in.**

The sentence The water in the tank increased by 56 gallons tells about a gain. 56 is a number for **in.**

2) Values for **out** tell about losses or reductions. **13 gallons leaked out of the tank,** tells about **out. She gave away some shells** tells about **out.**

3) The value for **end up** is the residual amount that is left—the **difference** between the amount in and the amount out. In most of the problems, the amount for **end up** is the amount the person has after the final loss or gain the problem describes.

Initially, students work simple problems that refer to only three values. A value referred to as "some" or that has no assigned number is represented with a box. This is the missing value in the problem. The question in the problem confirms the missing value. For instance: **She started out with some money.** The value for **in** is the missing value. **A lot of water drained out of the tank.** The value for **out** is the missing value. **How much money did she end up with?** The value for **end up** is the missing value. **How much water was in the tank to begin with?** The value for **in** is the missing value.

Here are the problems from Lesson 34, and their solutions:

a. **Molly collected 228 shells. She gave away some shells. She ended up with 49 shells. How many did she give away?**

The first sentence gives the number for **in**: 228. The second sentence indicates that the missing value is for **out.** The third sentence tells the number she **ended up** with:

end up out in

49 → 228

$$\begin{array}{r} 228 \\ -\ 49 \\ \hline \boxed{179\text{ shells}} \end{array}$$

b. A bank account had some money in it. Then $45.60 was taken out of the account. There was still $13.90 in the account. How much was in the account to begin with?

Both the first and the last sentence indicate that the missing value is the value for **in.** The second sentence gives a value for **out,** and the next sentence gives the value for **end up.**

end up out in

13.90 45.60 →

$$\begin{array}{r} 13.90 \\ +\ 45.60 \\ \hline \boxed{\$\ 59.50} \end{array}$$

c. At the end of the day, there were 95 cartons of milk in the store. Earlier that day, the store sold 118 cartons. How many cartons did the store have at the beginning of the day?

The first sentence tells about the last event, which is the amount for **end up.** The next sentence tells the number for **out**—118. Students add 95 and 118 to find the number for **in.**

end up out in

95 118 →

$$\begin{array}{r} 95 \\ +\ 118 \\ \hline \boxed{213\text{ cartons}} \end{array}$$

Notice that by this lesson of the program, students write the answer to any word problem as a number and a unit name and box it.

Beginning with Lesson 37, students work number-family problems that have more than one value for **in** and/or **out.**

For example:

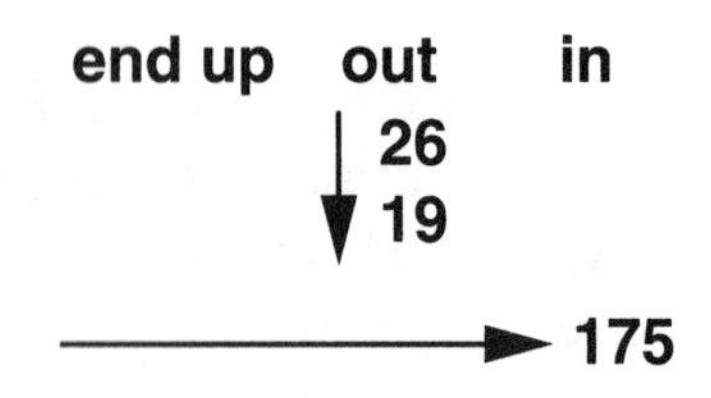

The strategy for working these problems is to obtain **two numbers on the main arrow,** then figure out the missing number. In the example just given, students add the amounts for **out:** 26 and 19. They write the total for **out** on the main arrow:

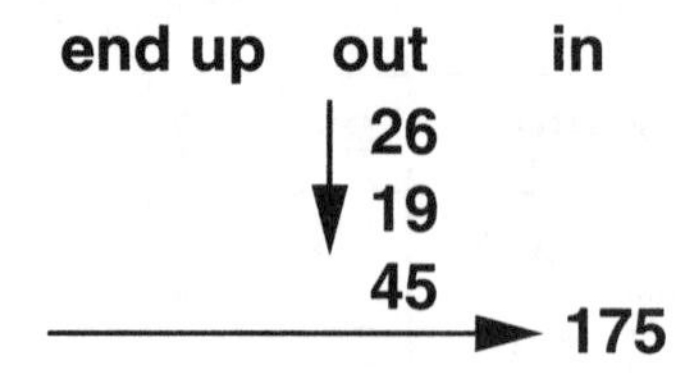

Now, students compute the number for **end up** by subtracting 45 from 175:

$$\begin{array}{r} 175 \\ -\ 45 \\ \hline \boxed{130} \end{array}$$

Here's part of the introduction from Lesson 37:

c. Problem A. Is the little number family shown for **in** or for **out?** (Signal.) *Out.*

- Copy problem A. Figure out the total for **out.** Raise you hand when you've done that much. (Observe students and give feedback.)
- (Write on the board:)

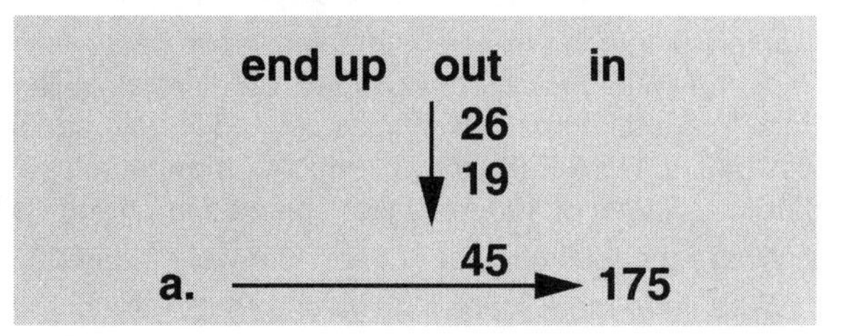

- Here's what you should have. The total for **out** is 45. Now you have two numbers on the main arrow. So you can figure out the number for **end up.** Do it. Remember to box the answer. Raise your hand when you're finished. √
- Everybody, what's the number for **end up?** (Signal.) *130.*

d. Problem B. Is the little number family shown for **in** or for **out?** (Signal.) *In.*

- Your turn: Copy problem B and work it. Remember, first figure out the total for the little number family. Then work the problem for the main number-family arrow. Raise your hand when you're finished. (Observe students and give feedback.)
- (Write on the board:)

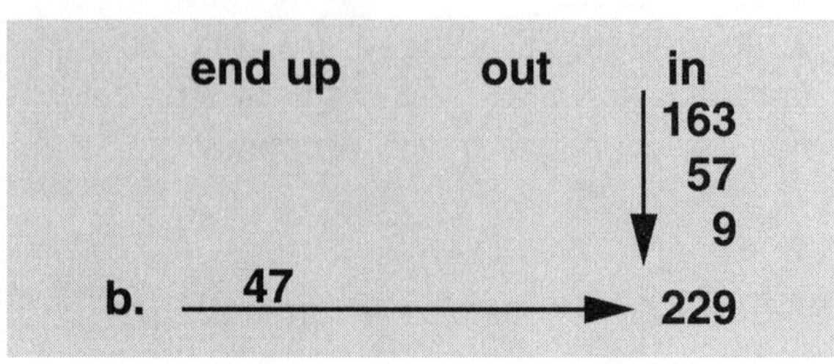

- Here's what you should have. The total for **in** is 229. The value for **end up** is 47. Everybody, what's the value for **out?** (Signal.) *182.*
- Raise your hand if you got it right.

Teaching note: Students are not to write a plus sign or an equals bar on the vertical number family. However, they may do the calculations without writing a separate addition problem.

In Lesson 39, students construct these complex number families from word problems. The problems are of the same basic form that students have represented with number families that have only one value for **in** and for **out.** However, the new problems give more than one value for either **in** or **out.**

Here's part of the introduction from Lesson 39:

a. At the end of the day, a tank has 140 gallons of water in it. The tank started out with 112 gallons in it. Later in the day another 336 gallons were added. Then some water was removed from the tank. How many gallons of water were removed?

e. Problem A: At the end of the day, a tank has 140 gallons of water in it. The tank started out with 112 gallons in it. Later in the day another 336 gallons were added. Then some water was removed from the tank.

- The problem gives more than one value for either **in** or **out.** Make the number family with the names and the little family where it belongs. Show the numbers for that family. Raise your hand when you've put in the numbers the problem gives.
- (Write on the board:)

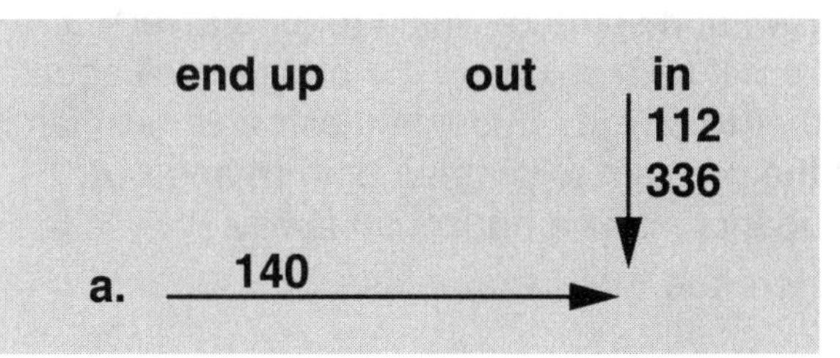

- Here's what you should have. The little family is for **in.** The values are 112 and 336. The number for **end up** is 140.
- Figure out the total for **in** and the number for **out.** Raise your hand when you've worked the problem and boxed the answer to the question.
(Observe students and give feedback.)
- Check your work. Everybody, what's the total for **in?** (Signal.) *448.*
- How many gallons were removed from the tank? (Signal.) *308.*
- Raise your hand if you got it right.

Teaching note: The basic wording conventions are the same as they are for the earlier problem type. The amount that something has to begin with and any amounts that are added are values for **in.** Any amounts that are removed are values for **out.** Since students have had practice in working similar problems, they shouldn't have difficulty in classifying the information given in the new problems.

Here are some of the difficulties students may have in setting up the problems appropriately:

1) They may write their values too close to the main arrow:

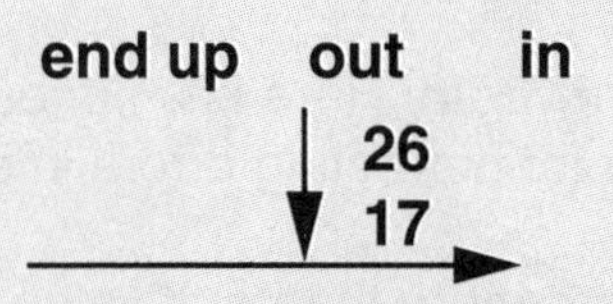

Remind students: "Leave room so that you can write a total on the main arrow. "

2) They may make a vertical arrow that is not necessary:

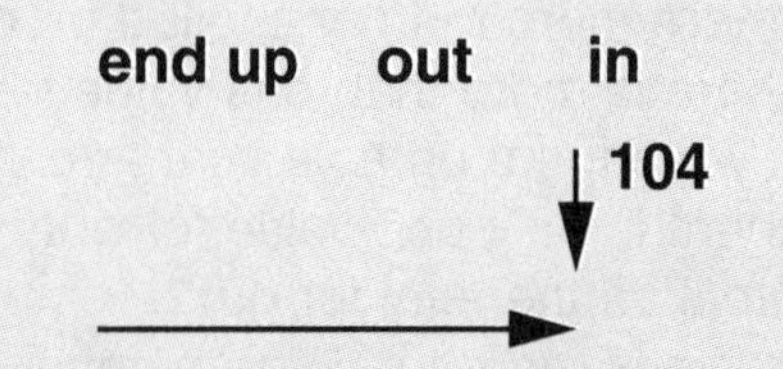

Remind students: "Don't make any arrows that you don't need. You don't need an arrow for **in** if there's only one value in the problem for **in.**"

3) They may not understand that the problem they will ultimately solve is on the main arrow and that the purpose of the little arrows is to provide a number that is needed on the main arrow.

If students have difficulty understanding the process, point out to them that they do not have enough numbers **on the main arrow** when the problem is written like this:

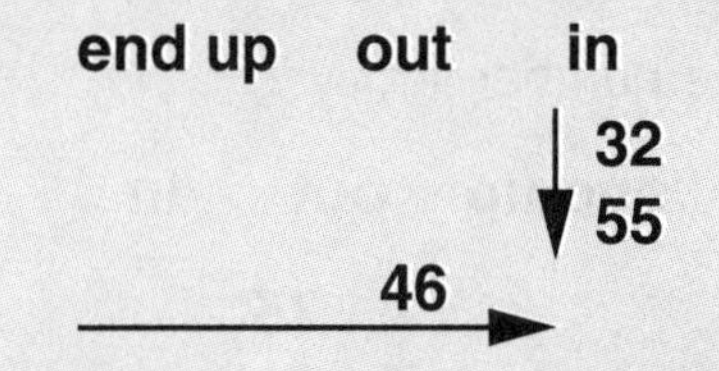

After students write the second number on the main arrow, require them to say the problem they'll work (87 minus 46).

In Lesson 45, students are introduced to problems that have more than one value for **in** and more than one value for **out.**

Here's an example:

a. A plane had 131 people in it. Then 81 more people got in the plane. Then 46 people got off the plane. Then 51 people got in the plane. Then 76 people got off the plane. How many people were still in the plane?

Students make this number family:

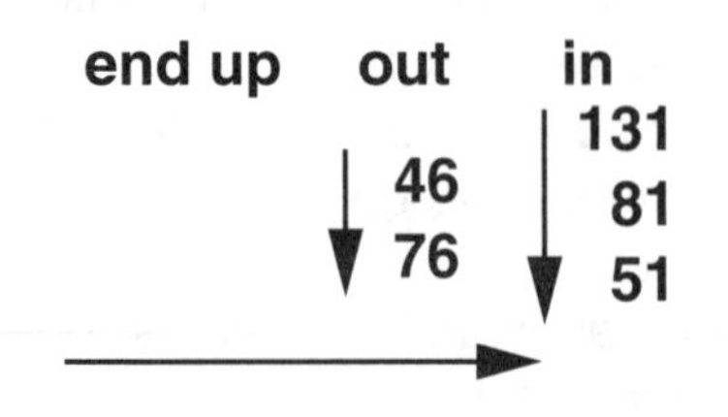

> ***Teaching note:*** Here is a series of questions for correcting errors in student strategies:
>
> 1) Is there more than one value for **in?**
> 2) If there is more than one value for **in,** did you write them on the vertical arrow?
> 3) If there is only one value for **in,** did you write it as the total for **in?**
> 4) Is there more than one value for **out?**
> 5) If there is more than one value for **out,** did you write them on a vertical arrow?
> 6) If there is only one value for **out,** did you write it as the total for **out?**
> 7) If there is more than one number missing on the main arrow, what do you do first?
> 8) What number answers the question?

In Lesson 81, students work a variation of this number-family problem type that involves purchasing and receiving change. All items have more than one amount for **out.**

For example:

Jan purchased a notebook for $1.75 and a clock for $4.60. She gave the clerk $10.00. How much change did she receive?

Here's the number family:

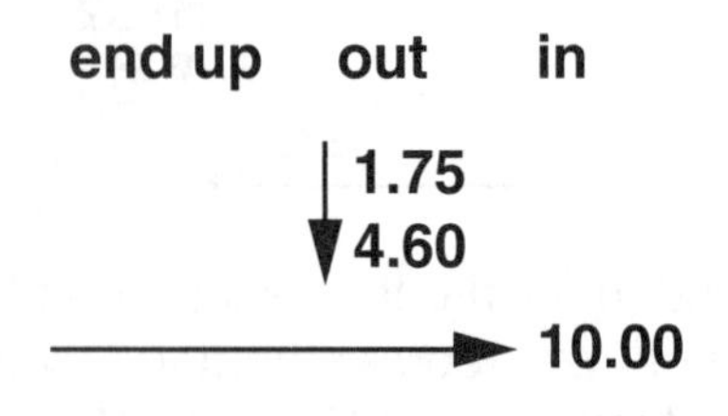

Beginning with Lesson 93, students discriminate between problems that require a main arrow and those that are simply represented with a vertical number family.

Here's part of the work from Lesson 93:

b. These problems tell about only **in** or only **out.** You don't make a family for **in, out** and **end up.** You just make a vertical family for **in** or a vertical family for **out.**

c. Look at the sample problem: John lost some weight in March. Then he lost another 14 pounds in April. The total mount of weight he lost during both months was 23 pounds. How much weight did he lose in March?

- All these values are values for **out.** So you make a vertical number family for **out.**
- (Write on the board:)

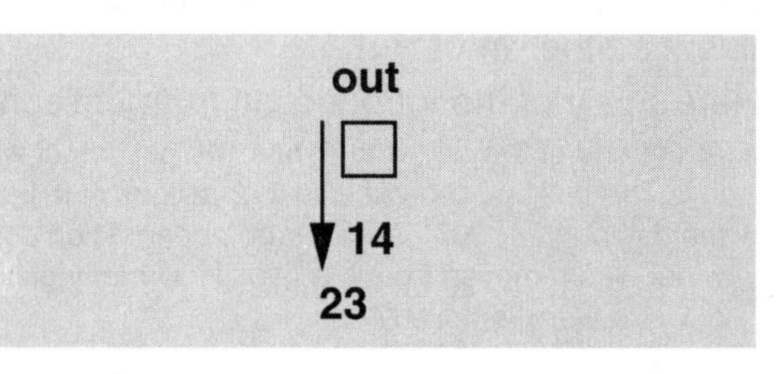

- Here's the family—a box for March, 14 for April and 23 for the total. You have to figure out a small number.
- Say the problem for figuring out that number. (Signal.) *23 minus 14.*
- What's the answer? (Signal.) *9.*
- That's the amount he lost in April—9 pounds.

After working simple vertical problems for several lessons, students work a mixed set of problems, some of which require a horizontal arrow, and some of which require a vertical arrow. If both values in the problem tell about either **in** or **out,** students make a vertical family. If the problem tells about both **in** and **out,** students make a horizontal family.

Here are three examples:

a. There were 91 people in a train. At the first stop, more people got in the train. The train ended up with 133 people in it. How many people got in the train at the first stop?

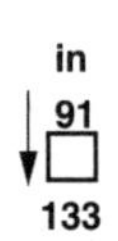

b. There were some people in a train. 91 people got off the train. The train ended up with 133 people in it. How many people were in the train to begin with?

end up out in
133 91

c. In the morning, the temperature dropped 12°. Then the temperature dropped another 41°. How much did the temperature dop in all?

out
12
41

In Lesson 87, students are introduced to the final number-family problem type. It describes goals. The names for the family are: **Goal, now,** and **difference.** The **goal** may be the big number or a small number. If the **goal** is to have an amount that is less than the current amount, the **goal** is a small number:

Dif G N

→

If the **goal** is to have an amount that is more than the current amount, the **goal** is the big number:

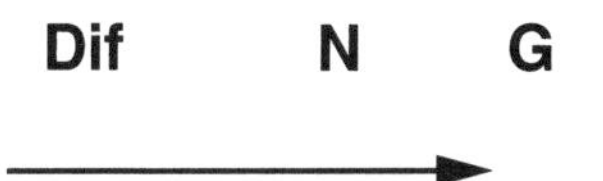

Here's part of the exercise from Lesson 96, where students first work with vertical number-families for this type of problem.

f. Problem B: Ginger's goal is to buy soap, eggs, and chips at the store. Soap costs $1.20; eggs cost 90 cents; chips cost 90 cents. Ginger has $2.70. How much more money does she need to reach her goal?

- First figure out the total amount that Ginger needs. That's her **goal.** Then show the amount she has **now** and figure out the amount she still needs. Raise your hand when you're finished.
  (Observe students and give feedback.)
- (Write on the board:)

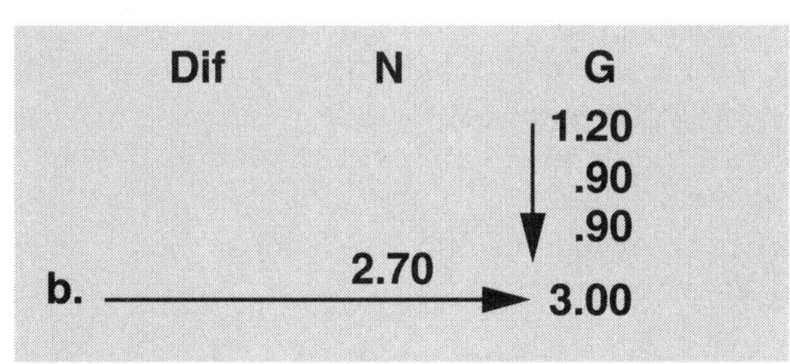

- Here's what you should have. For the goal, you added $1.20, 90 cents and 90 cents. That's $3. She has $2.70. So she still needs 30 cents. Raise your hand if you got that right.

g. Work problem C. It gives more than one number for **goal** and more than one number for **now.** Show the number families. Raise your hand when you're finished.
(Observe students and give feedback.)

- (Write on the board:)

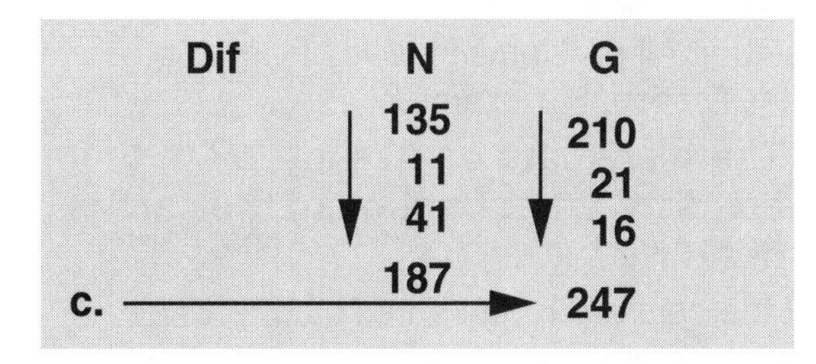

- Here's what you should have—a vertical number family for goal and for now. The total amount for Andy's **goal** is $247. The total amount he has **now** is $187. He needs $60 more. Raise your hand if you got it right.

Teaching note: Here are the steps students take to work the problem:

1) They determine whether the **goal** is the big number or a small number.
2) They make the family with the names (showing **goal** in the appropriate place). When they make the family, they should leave enough room under the headings to write more than one number.
3) They put in the values the problem gives. The values for **now** include any current amount and any past amount. For example: **If Ginger mowed 20 square feet and then 450 square feet,** the values for **now** are 20 and 450. The **goal** is what the person originally set out to do. The **difference** is what remains to be done in order to reach the **goal.** The problems may give more than one number for **goal** and more than one number for **now.** There is always only one **difference** number.
4) They figure out the total for any values written on a vertical number family.
5) They work the problem for the main arrow and write the answer as a number and unit name.

FRACTION NUMBER FAMILIES

In preparation for work with ratio tables and problems involving proportions, students are introduced to fraction number families. The work begins in Lesson 46. Fraction number families are like whole number families except that all the values are fractions with the same denominator, and one of the fractions equals one whole.

The word problems introduced in Lesson 47 have the fraction that equals 1 as the big number. All problems involve binary classification. For example:

There are cars on Al's lot. 2/7 of them are dirty. What fraction of the cars is not dirty?

All the cars are represented as one whole: 7/7. The denominator of the fraction is determined by the other fraction in the problem—2/7 The missing fraction is the value that is combined with 2/7 to give 7/7.

Beginning with Lesson 74, students work comparison fraction problems. The problem compares some value to 1 or to a letter that is represented by 1.

Example:

M is 7/5 of 1.

M is more than 1. Here's the family:

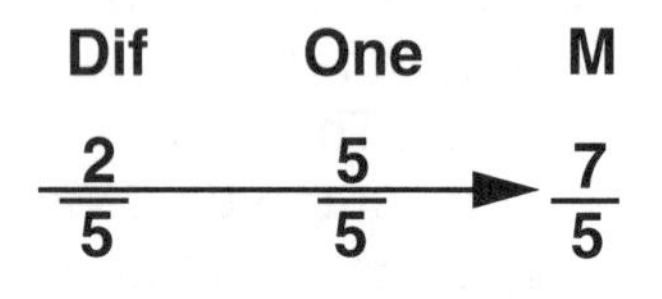

Example:

J is 3/4 of B.

The sentence compares J to B. B is 1. Here's the family:

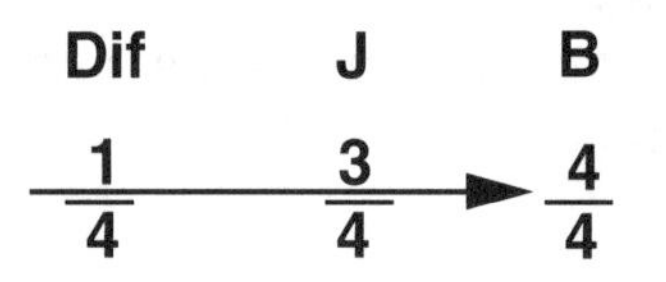

Example:

R is 8/5 of T.

The sentence compares R to T. T is 1. R is more than 1. Here's the family:

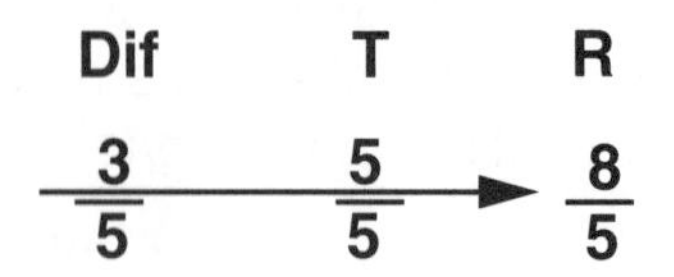

Here's part of the introduction from Lesson 76:

c. Sample sentence: J is 1/4 of T. That's just like: J is 1/4 of 1. T is 1.
- Listen: J is 1/4 of T. So is J more than T or less than T? (Signal.) *Less than T.*
- So **J** is a small number. **T** is the big number. And T is 1.
- (Write on the board:)

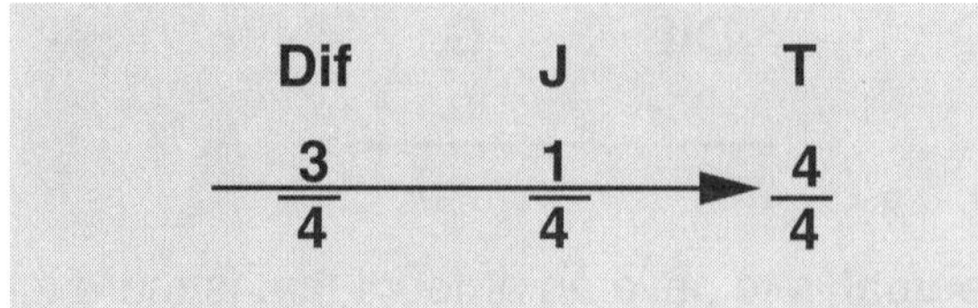

- Here's the number family for: J is 1/4 of T.

d. Problem A: M is 7/3 of B. That's just like: M is 7/3 of 1. B is 1.
- Listen: M is 7/3 of B. Is M more than B or less than B? (Signal.) *More than B.*
- So **M** is the big number. **B** is a small number. And B is 1. Make the number family. Raise your hand when you are finished. √
- (Write on the board:)

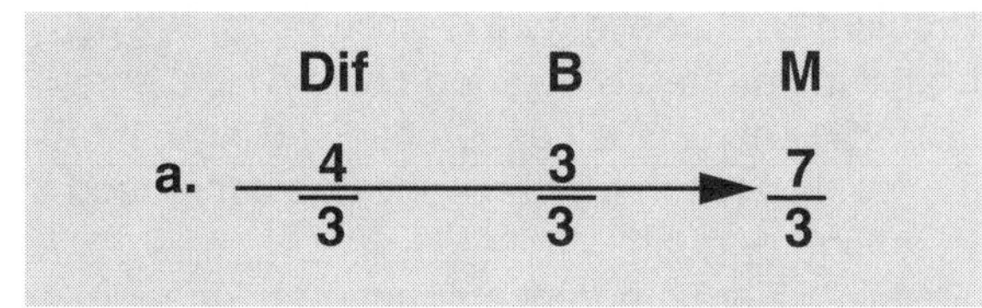

- Here's what you should have. M is 7/3 of B. **M** is the big number. **B** is a small number. It equals 1 whole—3/3. The difference is 4/3. Raise your hand if you got it right.

e. Problem B: R is 5/8 of B. Which letter equals 1? (Signal.) *B.*
- Listen: R is 5/8 of B. Is R more than B or less than B? (Signal.) *Less than B.*
- Make the number family. Raise your hand when you're finished.
  (Observe students and give feedback.)
- (Write on the board:)

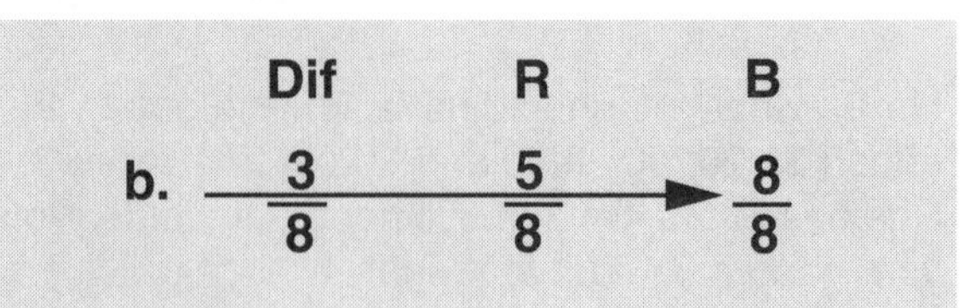

- Here's what you should have. R is 5/8 of B. **R** is a small number. **B** is the big number. B is 1. It's 8/8.

f. Work problem C. Raise your hand when you're finished.

(Observe students and give feedback.)

- (Write on the board:)

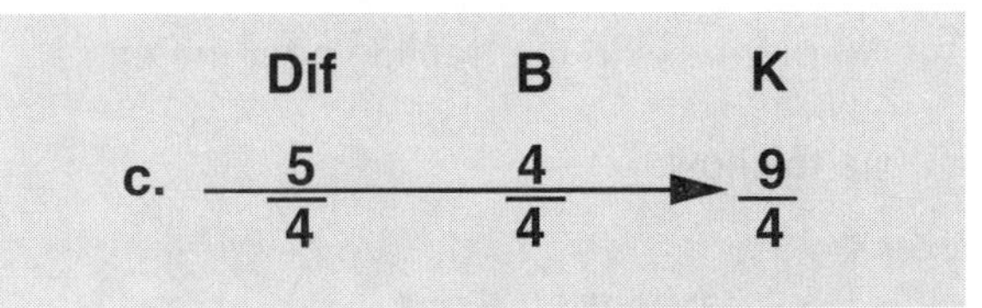

- Here's what you should have. K is 9/4 of B. K is more than B. **K** is the big number. **B** is a small number. It's 4/4. The difference is 5/4.

> ***Teaching note:*** Students have worked problems of the type that compares a value to 1. (T is 5/6 of 1.) If students have trouble with sentences such as **R is 5/8 of B,** ask these questions:
>
> "Which letter equals 1?" *B.* (That's the letter at the end of the sentence.)
>
> "What's the fraction for the other letter?" *5-eighths.*
>
> "Which is more, 5/8 or 1?" *One.*
>
> "So which is the big number, R or B?" *B.* (The bigger value is the big number.)

In Lesson 78, students make number families from sentences that compare two names. For example:

Donald runs 7/8 as far as Ginger; Fran is 5/4 the height of Ann; Today we collected 8/5 the amount we collected yesterday.

The procedure is the same as for previous lessons. The name something is compared to is 1. It's the name at the end of the sentence. The other name is either more than 1 or less than 1, depending on the value of the fraction.

Here's part of the introduction from Lesson 78:

c. Sentence A: The train was 3/4 as long as the station.
- Everybody, which name equals 1? (Signal.) *The station.*
- The first thing named is the train. Is it more than the station or less than the station? (Signal.) *Less than the station.*
- Make the number family with three names and three fractions. Raise your hand when you're finished.
  (Observe students and give feedback.)
- (Write on the board:)

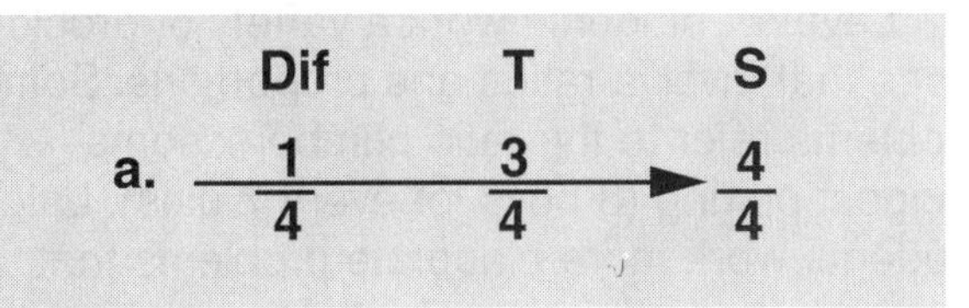

- Here's what you should have. The train is a small number. The station is the big number. It's 4/4. The difference is 1/4.

d. Sentence B: The cost of the book was 5/3 of the cost of the radio.
- Everybody, which name equals 1? (Signal.) *The radio.*
- Does the book cost more or less than the radio? (Signal.) *More.*
- Make the number family. Raise your hand when you're finished.
  (Observe students and give feedback.)
- (Write on the board:)

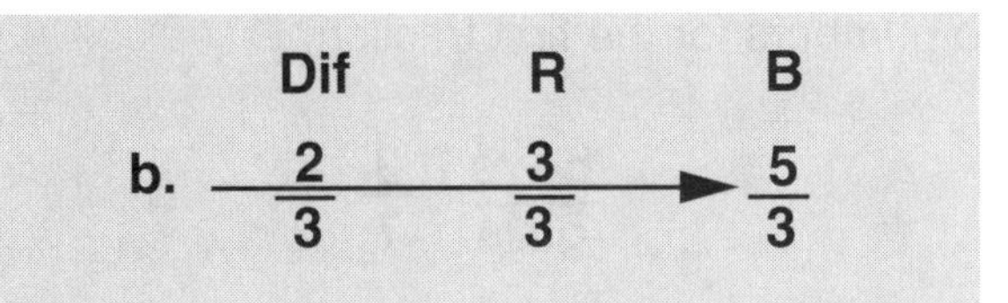

- Check your work. Here's the family you should have. The book is the big number. The radio is a small number. It's 3/3. The difference is 2/3.

With the knowledge of how comparative statements translate into fraction number families, students are prepared to work problems that involve percents.

For example, here's a sentence:

The regular price of shoes is 120% of the sale price.

Here's the family:

Dif	SP	RP
20/100	100/100	120/100

The regular price is more than 1. It's the big number. The sale price is 1. The difference is 20-hundredths or 20 percent.

The work with fraction number families prepares students for later work with complex proportion problems involving fractions, probability, and percents.

In Level E, students work a variety of problem types that involve ratios and proportions. Some problems refer to the ratio numbers; some suggest pairing (3 boys for every 7 girls). Later, students work more elaborate problems that require the combination of ratio equations with addition or subtraction. These problems are processed through ratio tables.

The initial work with ratios begins in Lesson 27. At this point, students are practiced at working with equivalent fractions. Ratios are presented as problems that are solved by working equivalent-fraction problems. For example:

There are 3 boys for every 7 girls. If there are 28 girls, how many boys are there?

The first sentence tells the names and gives the numbers for the first fraction:

The second sentence gives the number for girls. The number for girls goes in the denominator:

Students figure out the fraction that equals 1 then figure out the number for boys:

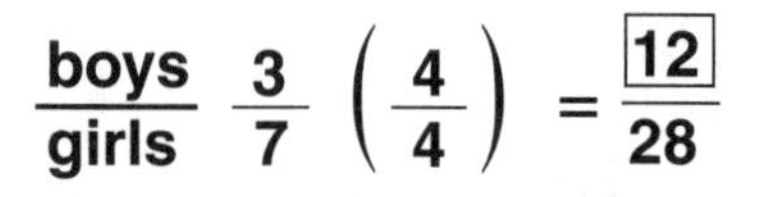

Here's part of the introduction from Lesson 27:

d. Here's the first sentence: There are 5 perch for every 8 bass. Those are fish.
- Your turn: Write the names and the fraction for the first sentence. Write the number for perch on top and the number for bass on the bottom. Raise your hand when you're finished with the names and the first fraction.
- (Write on the board:)

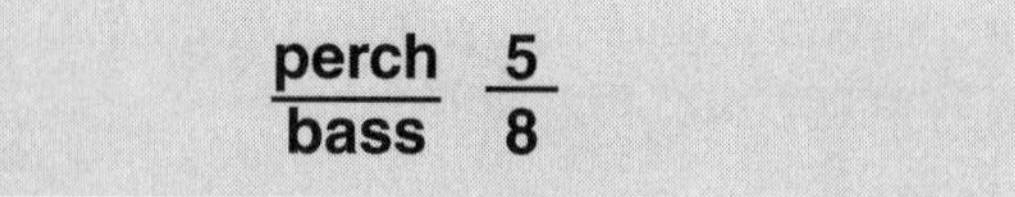

- Here's what you should have.
- Listen to the next sentence: If there are 24 bass, how many perch are there? Write parentheses for your times sign, then write the equal sign and the number for bass in the fraction after the equal sign. √
- (Write to show:)

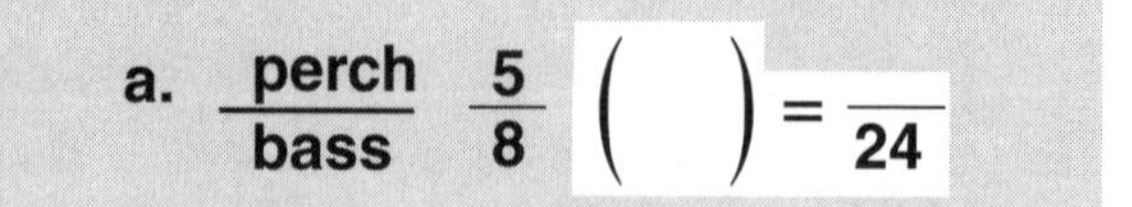

- The number for bass goes on the bottom. Now figure out the fraction that equals 1 and then multiply to find the number of perch. Make sure you box the answer. That's the number of perch. Raise your hand when you're finished. (Observe students and give feedback.)
- Everybody, what's the fraction that equals 1? (Signal.) *3-thirds.*
- And how many perch are there? (Signal.) *15.*
- (Write to show:)

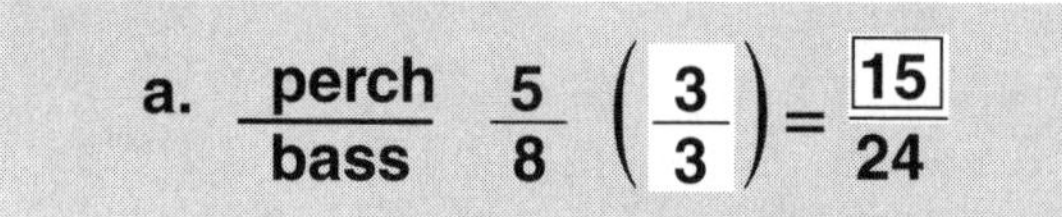

- If there are 24 bass, there are 15 perch. Write the answer in the space after the question. √

Teaching note: The convention for writing the names is that the first-mentioned name goes on top and the second-mentioned name goes on the bottom. The numbers go next to the corresponding names; if the name **boys** is on top, the numbers for boys go on top.

Anticipate these students difficulties:

1) Students don't follow the convention for writing the names or don't put the numbers in the appropriate place. Correct by guiding students through the steps. "What's the name mentioned first in the problem? . . . Where does that name go? . . . What's the first number for that name? . . . Is there another number for that name?"

2) Students don't leave enough room to show the fraction that equals 1 or omit the fraction that equals 1.

3) Students omit the equals sign.

4) Students do not realize that the answer to the problem is the missing number in the last fraction. Students will catch on quickly if they box the answer and rewrite that number after the question. Writing the

correct number after the question shows that they have correctly solved the problem.

Be very particular about how students work the problems. If students do not box the answer or are not required to write the number that answers the questions in the problem, students may not fully understand what they are doing and why.

Beginning in Lesson 29, students work problems that are presented in their textbook. To work these problems, students write the complete equation with names and three numbers. They figure out the fraction that equals 1, compute the missing number in the last fraction, and box the number that answers the question the problem asks.

Here's part of the exercise from Lesson 29:

b. Problem A: There are 5 birds for every 3 cats. How many cats are there if there are 25 birds?

- The names are **birds** and **cats.**
- (Write to show:)

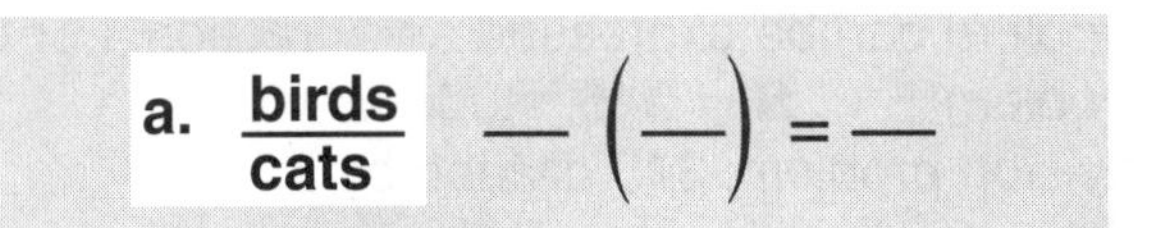

- Your turn: Write the names and the whole equation. Be careful. Put in all the numbers that the problem tells about. Then work the problem. Remember to box the answer to the question. Raise your hand when you're finished. (Observe students and give feedback.)
- (Write on the board:)

- Here's what you should have. The names are **birds** and **cats.** The values for **birds** are on top. The values for **cats** are on the bottom. Listen: How many cats are there if there are 25 birds? (Signal.) *15.*
- Yes, there are 15 cats. Raise your hand if you got all the names, the signs, and the numbers correct.

Teaching note: Make sure students can respond confidently to the question: **How many cats are there if there are 25 birds?**

In Lesson 30, students are introduced to wording that is more difficult. The text does not juxtapose each name with its number (4 boys for every 5 girls); instead, the names and numbers are separated: **The ratio of bats to players is 2 to 11. There are 16 bats. How many players are there?** In the first sentence, the first number goes with the first name; the second number with the second name:

$$\frac{\textbf{bats}}{\textbf{players}} \quad \frac{2}{11}$$

Students should have no trouble with these problems if they have been successful with the earlier problems.

From Lesson 40 on, students are required to write the complete answer to ratio problems. The answer consists of the number and a unit name.

In Lesson 43, students prepare for more difficult ratio problems by working equivalent fraction problems that have large numbers:

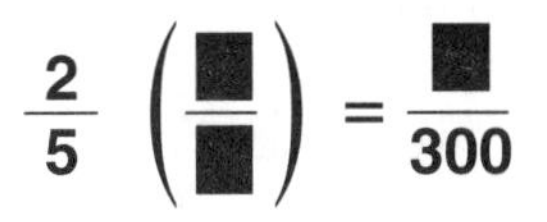

Students apply the knowledge that problems of the form 5 × ■ = 300 can be worked as division problems. For example: 300 ÷ 5. In this lesson, students are presented with pairs of equivalent fractions.

Example:

$$\frac{8}{3}\left(\blacksquare\right) = \frac{408}{153}$$

Students construct the fraction that equals 1. They do this using their calculator to work the problem for the top numbers: 408 ÷ 8 and the problem for the bottom numbers: 153 ÷ 3 The results confirm that 8/3 is multiplied by 1:

$$\frac{8}{3}\left(\frac{51}{51}\right) = \frac{408}{153}$$

So the fractions 8/3 and 408/153 are equivalent.

In Lesson 49, students work ratio problems that have large numbers.

Here's part of the introduction:

b. I'll read problem A: The ratio of boys to girls is 5 to 4. There are 300 boys. How many girls are there?

- Your turn: Write the equation with names and the three numbers the problem tells about. Raise your hand when you've done that much.
  (Observe students and give feedback.)
- (Write on the board:)

$$\text{a. } \frac{\text{boys}}{\text{girls}} \quad \frac{5}{4} = \frac{300}{}$$

- Here's what you should have. The names are **boys** and **girls.** The first fraction is 5/4. The numerator of the other fraction is 300. That's a number for boys.
- Say the division problem for the top numbers. (Signal.) *300 divided by 5.*
- Figure out the fraction that equals 1. Then figure out the answer to the question the problem asks and box the answer. Write the whole answer as a number and a unit name. Raise your hand when you're finished.
  (Observe students and give feedback.)
- (Write to show:)

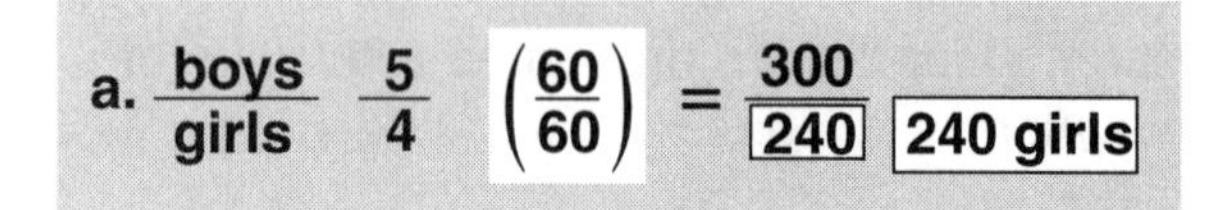

- Here's what you should have. If there are 300 boys, there are 240 girls. Raise your hand if you got everything right.

Teaching note: Make sure that students write the complete answer to the question as the number and a unit name.

The next ratio word problems that students work involve whole number answers. For instance:

There are 3 pounds of sand for every 11 pounds of gravel. There are 35 pounds of sand. How many pounds of gravel are there?

Here's the ratio equation:

The problem for the top numbers is: 3 times some value equals 35. The answer is not a whole number. The missing value is the answer to the division problem: 35 divided by 3. This value can be expressed as a fraction 35/3. Therefore, the fraction that equals 1 can be expressed as the fraction over itself:

$$\frac{\text{sand}}{\text{gravel}} \quad \frac{3}{11}\left(\frac{\frac{35}{3}}{\frac{35}{3}}\right) = \frac{35}{\square}$$

By working the problem in this manner, students can obtain the fractional answer (385/3 pounds of gravel) very quickly. Furthermore, the work is a simple extension of what they have done earlier with simpler problems. The only difference is that the fraction that equals 1 is expressed as a fraction over a fraction.

In Lesson 45, students take the first step to prepare for these difficult ratio problems. In this lesson, they verify the fact that a division problem can be expressed as a fraction. For this problem: $5 \times \blacksquare = 345$, students work the division problem: 345 divided by 5. They can also write the division problem as the fraction: 345/5. They complete the equation showing the fraction.

$$5\left(\frac{345}{5}\right) = 345$$

Then they use their calculator to work the division problem implied by the fraction ($345 \div 5$). Finally, they rewrite the equation with a whole number in place of the fraction: $5\ (69) = 345$.

In Lesson 48, students work problems with a missing value that does not equal a whole number: $5\ (\ \ ) = 3$. Students express the missing value as a fraction. The missing fraction is composed of the numbers 5 and 3. The number after the equals sign goes on top:

$$5\left(\frac{3}{5}\right) = 3$$

In Lesson 49, students confirm that the missing fraction is correct by working the multiplication problem: $5 \times 3/5$. Students use their calculator. They first work the problem: 3 divided by 5. Then they multiply that value by 5. The answer is 3.

In Lesson 52, students work orally presented problems of the form: 4 times some fraction equals 7. Students write the missing fraction (7/4).

Here's the exercise from Lesson 52:

a. You're going to do some mental math.
b. I'll do the first problem: 5 times some fraction equals 3. What's the fraction? 3/5.
c. Your turn: 5 times some fraction equals 4. What's the fraction? (Signal.) *4-fifths.*
- 5 times some fraction equals 9. What's the fraction? (Signal.) *9-fifths.*
- 8 times some fraction equals 9. What's the fraction? (Signal.) *9-eighths.*
  (Repeat step c until firm.)

d. Write part O on your paper. Then write A through D. √
- I'll say some more problems. For each problem, you're going to write the missing fraction. Remember, don't write the whole equation, just the missing fraction. Everybody ready?

e. Problem A: 7 times some fraction equals 9. Write the fraction. (Tap your foot 3 times.)
- Problem B: 3 times some fraction equals 4. Write the fraction. (Tap your foot 3 times.)
- Problem C: 8 times some fraction equals 1. Write the fraction. (Tap your foot 3 times.)
- Problem D: 6 times some fraction equals 1. Write the fraction. (Tap your foot 3 times.)

f. Check your work.
- Problem A: What do you multiply 7 by to get 9? (Signal.) *9-sevenths.*
- Problem B: What do you multiply 3 by to get 4? (Signal.) *4-thirds.*
- Problem C: What do you multiply 8 by to get 11? (Signal.) *11-eighths.*
- Problem D: What do you multiply 6 by to get 1? (Signal.) *1-sixth.*

Teaching note: When presenting the problems in step e, tap your foot three times to give the students time to write the fraction. You should take about three seconds before you move on. Don't wait for students. If many of them are having trouble, you may try slowing your presentation a little, but don't slow it to five or more seconds. If students can't write the answer within three seconds, they don't understand the number relationships adequately.

Make sure that students are very firm on these problems. Make sure you give them correct answers. Then repeat the exercise (presenting the problems in a different order or presenting different problems of the same type). Don't proceed in the program until students are very automatic at this task. Students will need the skill later when working ratio problems.

In Lesson 55, students work equivalent fraction problems that have a complex fraction that equals 1.

Example:

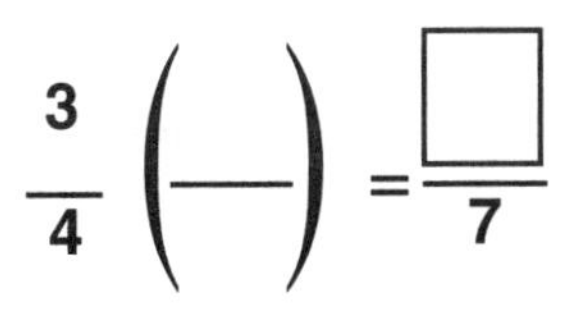

Students say the problem for the bottom numbers: 4 times some fraction equals 7. They write the missing fraction:

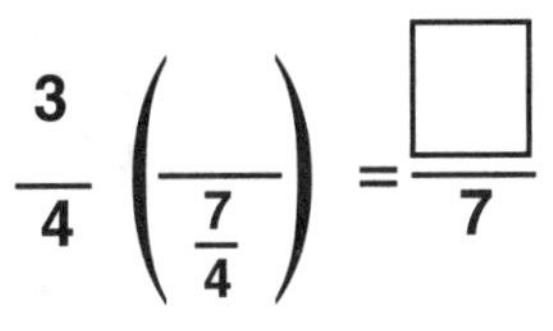

They complete the fraction that equals 1:

$$\frac{3}{4}\left(\frac{\frac{7}{4}}{\frac{7}{4}}\right) = \frac{\square}{7}$$

Then they multiply and figure out the missing value:

$$\frac{\frac{3}{1}}{4}\left(\frac{\frac{7}{4}}{\frac{7}{4}}\right) = \frac{\boxed{\frac{21}{4}}}{7}$$

Here's part of the introduction from Lesson 55:

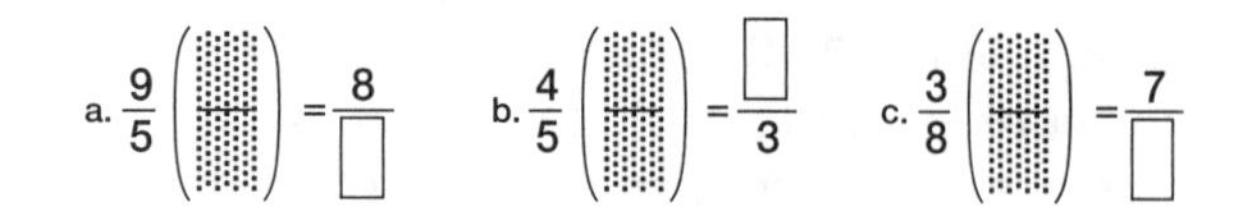

b. Problem A. Can you work the problem on top or on the bottom? (Signal.) *On top.*
- Here's the problem for the top numbers: 9 times some fraction equals 8.
- What's the answer? (Signal.) *8-ninths.*
- Write that answer on top. √
- (Write on the board:)

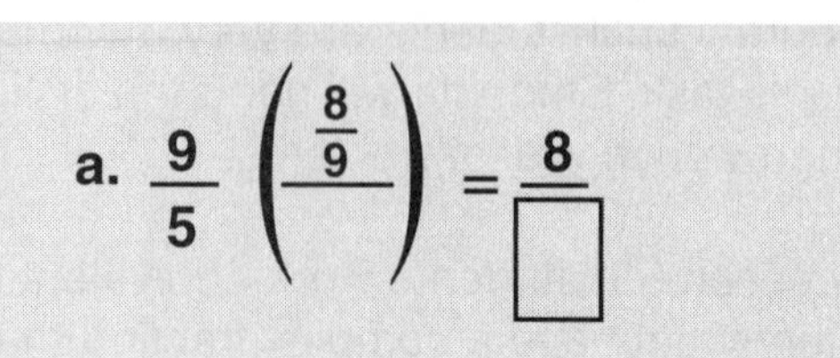

- Here's what you should have so far. The top part of the fraction that equals 1 is 8/9. So what's the whole fraction that equals 1? (Signal.) *8 ninths over 8 ninths.*
- Complete the fraction that equals 1. Then multiply on the bottom and write the answer in the box. Write it as a fraction. Raise you hand when you're finished.
  (Observe students and give feedback.)
- (Write to show:)

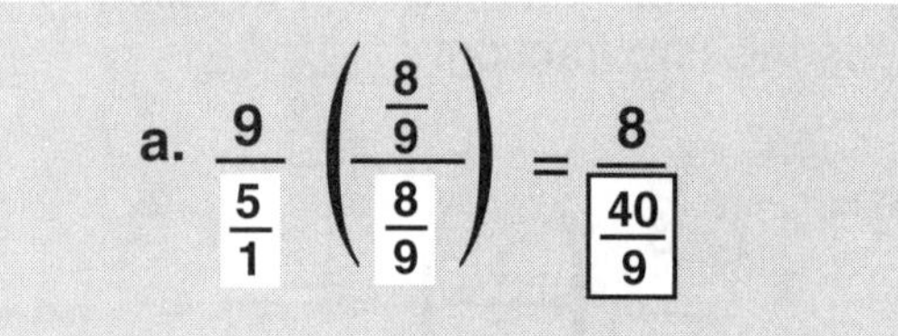

- Here's what you should have. On the bottom, you multiplied 5 over 1 by 8/9. The answer is 40/9. Raise your hand if you got it right.

Teaching note: Make sure that students are very firm when answering all questions. They must understand that the fraction that equals 1 is 8/9 over 8/9. If students sound weak when answering the questions, repeat the part of the presentation where you ask the questions. Also make sure that the students approach the problems correctly. First they say the problem for the top or the bottom (depending on where the two numbers are). They express the missing value as a fraction. They use that fraction as either the top or the bottom of a fraction that equals 1. Then they multiply to find the missing value. If students are firm on this procedure, they will proceed smoothly through the subsequent work with complicated ratio and proportion problems.

In Lesson 61, students apply what they have learned about fractions that equal 1 to work a set of problems, some of which have a complex fraction that equals 1 and some of which have a simple fraction that equals 1.

Here's part of the work:

a. These were ratio problems. To work some of them, you can use a simple fraction that equals 1. For other problems, you'll use a fraction over the same fraction.

b. Problem A: There are 9 bees for every 2 flowers. There were 20 flowers. How many bees were there?
- Write the names, the equation, and figure out the answer. Remember, you say the problem on top or on the bottom. If the answer is a whole number, you write the whole number. If the answer is not a whole number, write the fraction. Raise your hand when you've worked the problem and boxed the answer. (Observe students and give feedback).
- (Write on the board:)

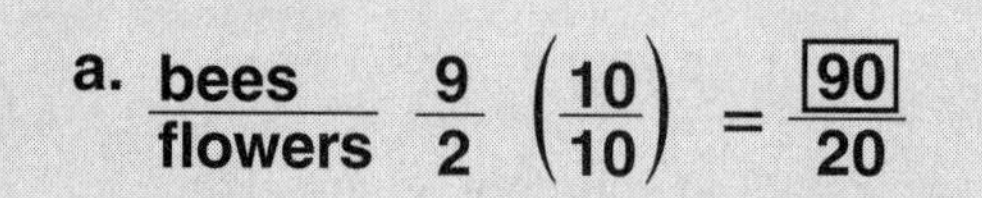

- Here's what you should have. The fraction that equals 1 is 10/10. Listen: After problem A, write the whole answer—90 bees—and box it.
- (Write to show:)

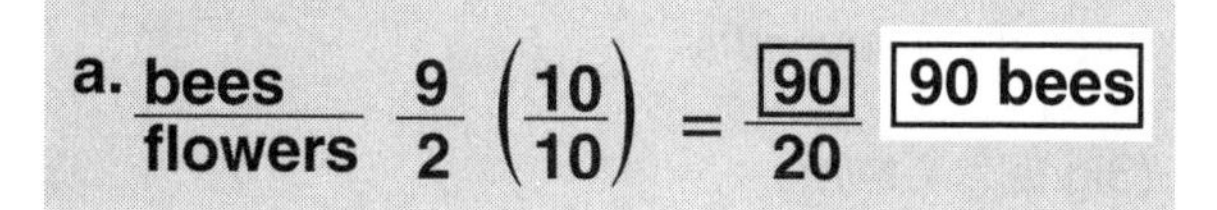

c. Problem B: There are 2 wasps for every 14 flowers. There were 9 wasps. How many flowers were there?
- Write the names, the equation, and figure out the answer. Remember, say the problem on top or on the bottom. If the answer is not a whole number, write the fraction. Raise your hand when you've worked the problem and boxed the answer. (Observe students and give feedback.)
- (Write on the board:)

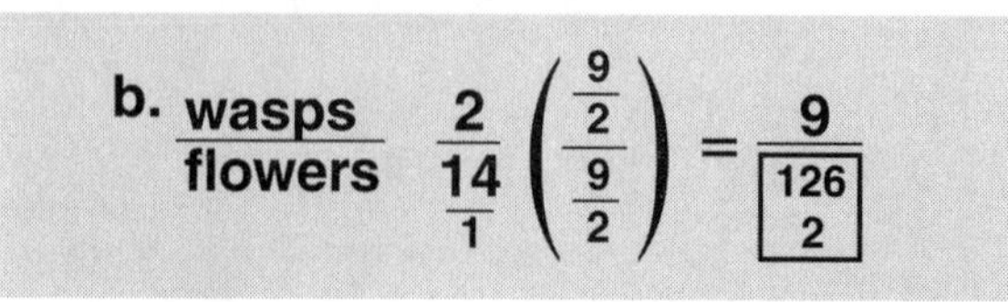

- Here's what you should have. The problem for the top numbers is 2 times some value equals 9. The answer is not a whole number. It's 9/2. So the fraction that equals 1 is 9/2 over 9/2. When you multiply on the bottom, you get 126/2. That's the answer. You should have boxed 126/2 in your ratio equation. Now you'll write the answer to the question in the word problem as **a number and a unit name.**
- Your turn: Work the division problem for the fraction:126/2. Write a mixed number or a whole number and the unit name just after the boxed fraction. Raise your hand when you're finished. (Observe students and five feedback.)
- (Write to show:)

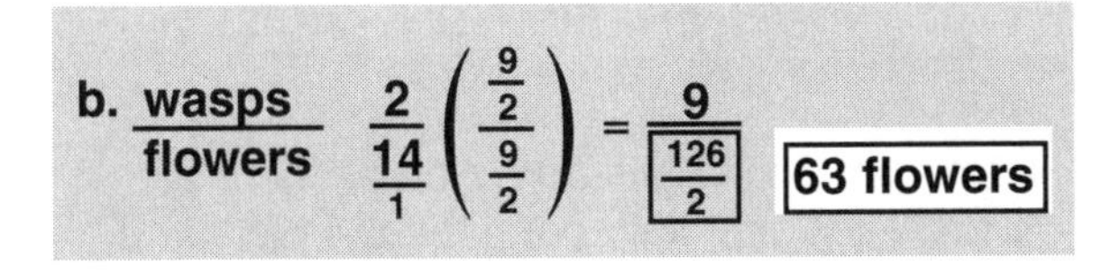

- Here's what you should have. The answer to the question is 63 flowers.

Teaching note: If you made sure that students were firm on the earlier taught skills, they should not have serious difficulties with this exercise even though the work is complicated.

If they have trouble, take them through the steps:

1) Write the equation with the numbers the problem gives.
2) Say the problem for either the top numbers or the bottom numbers.
3) Say whether the answer is a whole number or a fraction.
4) Use the answer as either the top half or bottom half of the fraction that equals 1.
5) Complete the fraction that equals 1.
6) Work the problem for obtaining the missing value in the fraction after the equal sign.
7) Box the answer.
8) If the answer is a fraction, work the division problem.
9) Write the answer to the question the problem asks as a number and a unit name.

Do not permit students to take shortcuts. The later work that they do with complex ratio and proportion problems requires facility with these steps. Also, the steps provide you with good information about whether the students understand what they are doing.

While students are working with complex fractions that equal 1, they begin work with ratio tables (starting with Lesson 52). Here's an example of a completed table:

men	**3**	**90**
women	**2**	**60**
adults	**5**	**150**

The numbers in each column are like those in a vertical-number family. The bottom number is the big number. The other two are small numbers. Each **row** involves the same multiplier. 3 is multiplied by 30. 2 is multiplied by 30. And 5 is multiplied by 30. Therefore, any two rows can be combined to make a ratio equation:

$$\frac{\text{men}}{\text{women}} \quad \frac{3}{2}\left(\frac{30}{30}\right) = \frac{90}{60}$$

$$\frac{\text{women}}{\text{adults}} \quad \frac{2}{5}\left(\frac{30}{30}\right) = \frac{60}{150}$$

$$\frac{\text{men}}{\text{adults}} \quad \frac{3}{5}\left(\frac{30}{30}\right) = \frac{90}{150}$$

Because of its structure, a ratio table provides a powerful way to represent the information provided by complicated problems involving three names. For example:

> **The ratio of sand to gravel in a mixture is 4 to 9. If there are 260 pounds in the total mixture, how many pounds of sand are there? How many pounds of gravel are there?**

First, students make a table and put in the three numbers the problem gives. The ratio numbers go in the first column of the table:

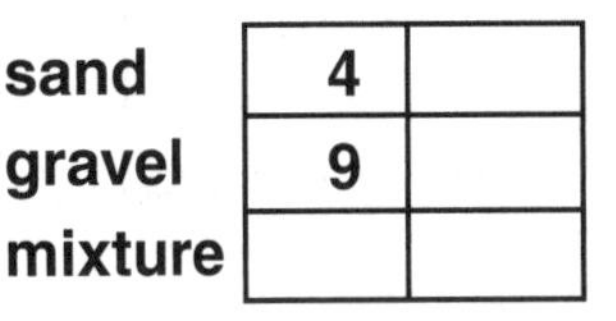

sand	**4**	
gravel	**9**	
mixture		

The number of pounds for total mixture goes in the second column:

sand	4	
gravel	9	
mixture		260

Students add to figure out the total for the ratio numbers in the first column:

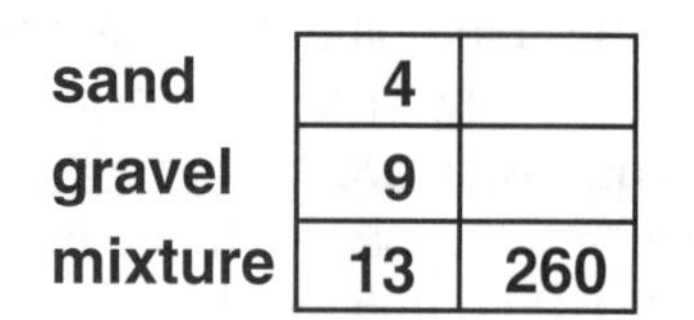

sand	4	
gravel	9	
mixture	13	260

The ratio equation for a table includes a row that has two numbers and either of the other rows. Here are the two equations that are based on the table above:

$\frac{\text{sand}}{\text{mixture}}\ \frac{4}{13}\left(\ \right) = \frac{\square}{260}$ $\frac{\text{gravel}}{\text{mixture}}\ \frac{9}{13}\left(\ \right) = \frac{\square}{260}$

Solving either equation provides a number for the second column. For instance:

$\frac{\text{sand}}{\text{mixture}}\ \frac{4}{13}\left(\frac{20}{20}\right) = \frac{\boxed{80}}{260}$

sand	4	80
gravel	9	
mixture	13	260

Now the final number in that column can be computed by subtraction (260−80). The completed table provides answers to the questions the problem asks: There are 80 pounds of sand and 180 pounds of gravel.

In Lesson 52, students are introduced to the basic properties of the table. Students figure out the missing numbers in both columns.

Here's part of the introduction:

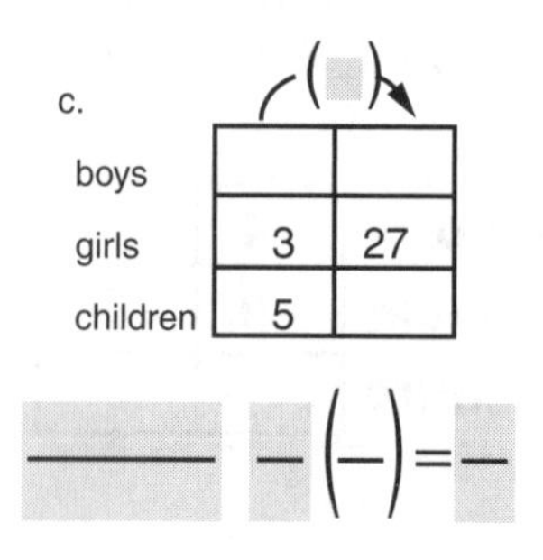

g. Table C. Write the number for boys in the first column. Raise your hand when you've done that much. √

- Everybody, what's the number for boys in the first column? (Signal.) *2.*
- Yes, 2. What's the name of the **row** that has two numbers? (Signal.) *Girls.*
- Write the equation for the ratio of **girls** to **children.** Show girls on top. Figure out the number of children in the second column. Then figure out the other missing number in the second column. Raise your hand when you've written all the numbers in your table.
  (Observe students and give feedback.)
- (Write on the board:)

c. $\frac{\text{girls}}{\text{children}}\ \frac{3}{5}\left(\frac{9}{9}\right) = \frac{27}{\boxed{45}}$

- Here's the ratio of girls to children. There are 45 children. You put that number in the table and figured out the number of boys in the second column. Everybody, what number? (Signal.) *18.*
- Yes, there are 27 girls and 18 boys. That's 45 children. Raise your hand if you got everything right.

Teaching note: The work involves a relatively simple extension of what the students have done earlier in the program. From their work with 3-by-3 tables, students know that if there are two numbers in a column, the third number can be found by addition or subtraction. That's what they do when working with ratio tables. They know that a ratio equation must have two numbers for one of the names. When students construct an equation, the missing value answers the question the problem asks and refers to a particular name. Students put the answer to the ratio equation into the second column of the table. Then they figure out the final missing number by either adding or subtracting.

In Lesson 56, students work from a word problem that is solved with a ratio table. Students put names and numbers in the table, figure out the missing numbers, and answer the questions the problem asks.

Here's part of the work from Lesson 56:

b. There were perch and bass in a pond. The ratio of perch to bass was 8 to 5. There was a total of 260 fish in the pond.

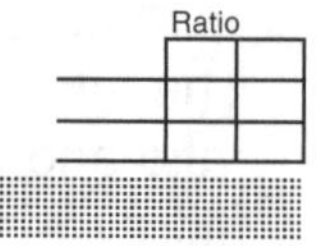

1. How many bass were in the pond?
2. How many perch were in the pond?

c. Problem B: There were perch and bass in a pond. The ratio of perch to bass was 8 to 5. There was a total of 260 fish in the pond.

- Put the names and numbers in the ratio table. Figure out the missing number in the first column. Raise your hand when your table has four numbers.
  (Observe students and give feedback.)
- (Write on the board:)

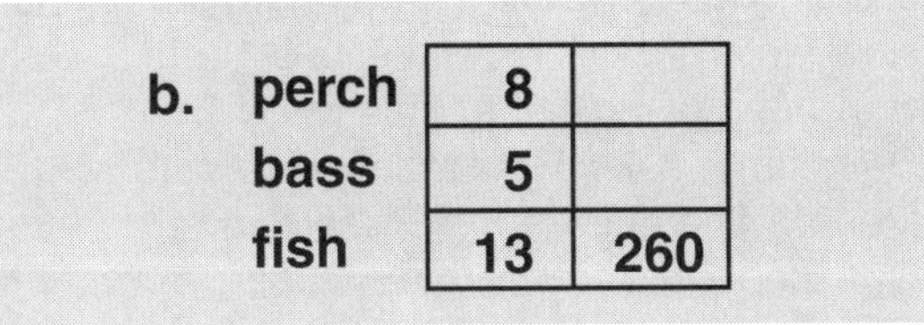

b.			
	perch	8	
	bass	5	
	fish	13	260

- Here's what you should have. Now write the ratio equation for **bass** to total **fish.** Then complete the table and write the answers to the questions. Raise your hand when you're finished.
  (Observe students and give feedback.)
- (Write to show:)

b.			
	perch	8	160
	bass	5	100
	fish	13	260

- The answer to question 1 is: **100 bass.** The answer to question 2 is: **160 perch.**

Teaching note: Students should be able to work quickly. The only new skill is writing the names and numbers where they go in the table. One mistake that students may make is to put the number that belongs in the second column in the first column. For the problem above, students may put the number 260 in the first column. To correct this mistake, say: "The numbers in each column are like a number family. What are the small numbers in the first column?" *8 and 5.*

"What's the big number for 8 and 5?" *13.*

"You have 260 in the wrong column. It's the big number for the **second** column."

Beginning in Lesson 57, students work with ratio-table problems that involve larger numbers. These problems are presented in the textbook. Students construct the table, put in the values the problem gives, and use their calculators to figure out the fraction that equals 1. All the problems that they work during this lesson span have whole-number answers.

Here are the problems from Lesson 57:

a. There are boys and girls in a school. There are 3 girls for every 5 children. There are 402 boys in the school.
   1. How many children are in the school?
   2. How many girls are in the school?

b. For every 7 students, 4 wear glasses. The rest do not wear glasses. There are 64 students who wear glasses.
   1. How many students do not wear glasses?
   2. What is the total number of students?

c. There are blue balloons and red balloons at a party. The ratio of blue balloons to red balloons is 3 to 5. There is a total of 240 balloons.
   1. How many blue balloons are there?
   2. How many red balloons are there?

Teaching notes: Remind students that the numbers for the first column of the table must "add up." The top two numbers are small numbers in a number family. The bottom number is the total.

For problem c above, students may want to put the number 240 in the first column. Point out that the other numbers—3 and 5—don't add up to 240. The big number in the first column must be 8.

In Lesson 64, students work ratio table problems that involve fractions. To work these problems, students first make a number family based on the fraction the problem gives. Then, they use the numerators of the fractions as ratio numbers for the first column of their table.

Example:

In a factory, 3/5 of the employees were women. The rest were men. There were 890 employees. How many employees were men? How many employees were women?

The first sentence implies the number family: 3/5 of the employees were women.

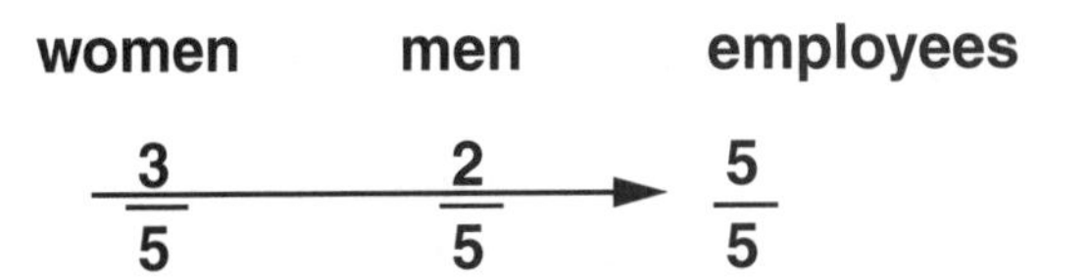

The names and numerators are used in the table:

women	**3**	
men	**2**	
employees	**5**	

The problem gives a number for the second column:

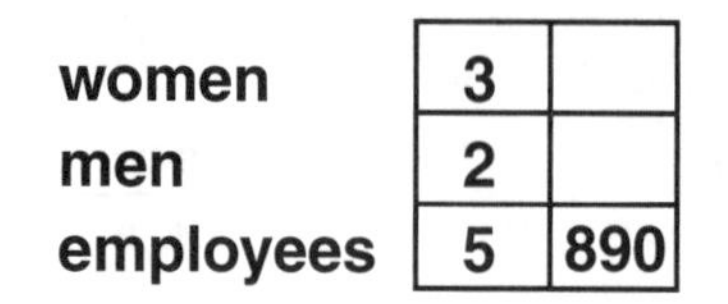

women	**3**	
men	**2**	
employees	**5**	**890**

With this number, the students can figure out the missing numbers in the table and answer the questions.

The problems that students work in Lesson 64 have an underlined part that gives information needed for the number family.

Here's part of the introduction from Lesson 64:

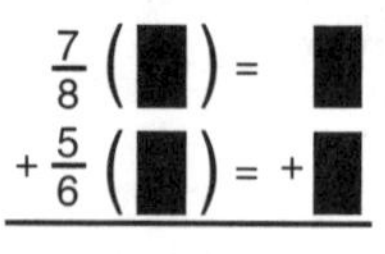

e. Problem A. The underlined part says: There were used cars and new cars on a lot. 3/7 of the cars were used.

- Make the number family with the names and all the fractions. Raise your hand when you've done that much.
  (Observe students and give feedback.)
- (Write on the board:)

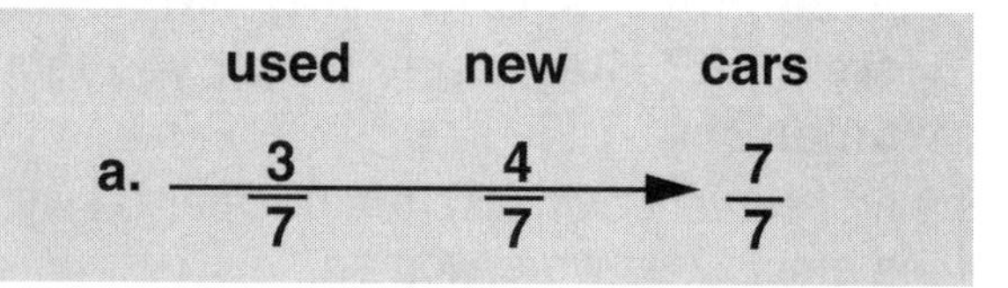

- Here's what you should have. The names are **used, new** and **cars.** 3/7 of the cars were used. So the fractions are 3/7, 4/7 and 7/7.
- Everybody, what are the **ratio** numbers for these fractions? (Signal.) *3, 4 and 7.*
- Write the names and ratio numbers in a ratio table. Write **3, 4** and **7** in the first column. Put in the other number the problem tells about in the second column. Write a ratio equation to figure out the other numbers in the second column. Then complete the table. You can use your calculator. Raise your hand when you've completed the table.
  (Observe students and give feedback.)
- (Write on the board:)

used	**3**	**48**
new	**4**	**64**
cars	**7**	**112**

- Check your work. Here's what you should have. Now write answers to questions 1 and 2. Raise your hand when you're finished. √
- Question 1 asks: How many used cars were on the lot? The answer is **48 used cars.**
- Question 2 asks: How many total cars were on the lot? The answer is **112 cars.**

Teaching note: In some ways, this problem is easier than ones worked earlier because the underlined part gives students good information about the names and the ratio numbers involved in the table.

Expect some students to want to take shortcuts and not show the number family. Don't permit shortcuts at this point in the program. In later lessons, students will work problems that compare. For these problems, the big number is not always 1. Unless students are practiced with making number families from statements in the problem, they will have trouble with the later problem type and also with the discrimination between the comparative type and the type that involves two subcategories that equal a whole (moving cars, cars that are not moving, all cars).

In Lesson 82, students work ratio table problems that compare. The problem contains a sentence that indicates the basis for the comparison: **The weight of the sand was 5/3 the weight of the cement.** The sand is compared to the cement. Therefore, the cement is 1 whole. This number family is implied:

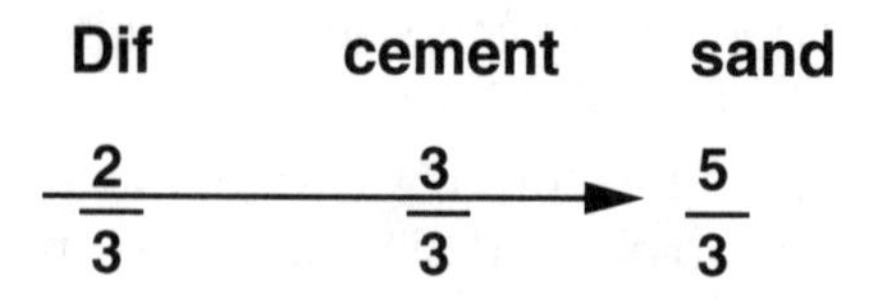

The rest of the problem gives information for making the ratio table: **If the sand weighs 720 pounds, how much does the cement weigh?**

How much less does the cement weigh than the sand weighs? Students put the numerators in the first column and 720 for sand in the second column:

Dif	2	
cement	3	
sand	5	720

Here's the part of the exercise from Lesson 82:

d. Problem B: Abbey Hill is 3/8 as high as Howard Hill. Abbey Hill is 240 feet high. How high is Howard Hill? How much higher is Howard Hill than Abbey Hill?

- Your turn: Make the family. Raise your hand when you've done that much.
  (Observe students and give feedback.)
- (Write on the board:)

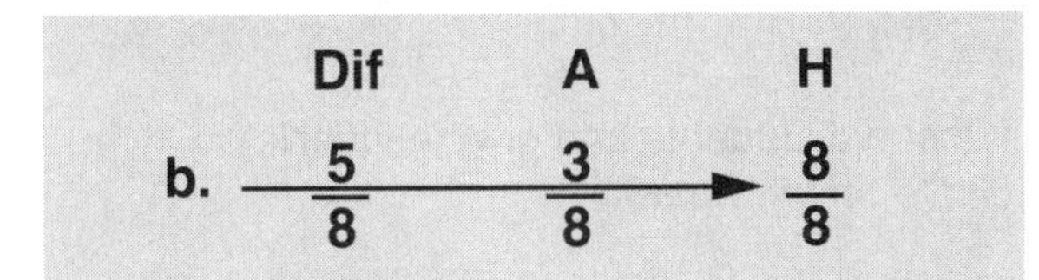

- Here's the family. Now make the ratio table. You can use abbreviations for **difference, Abbey Hill** and **Howard Hill.** Figure out all the numbers and answer the questions. You can use your calculator. Raise your hand when you're finished.
  (Observe students and give feedback.)
- (Write on the board:)

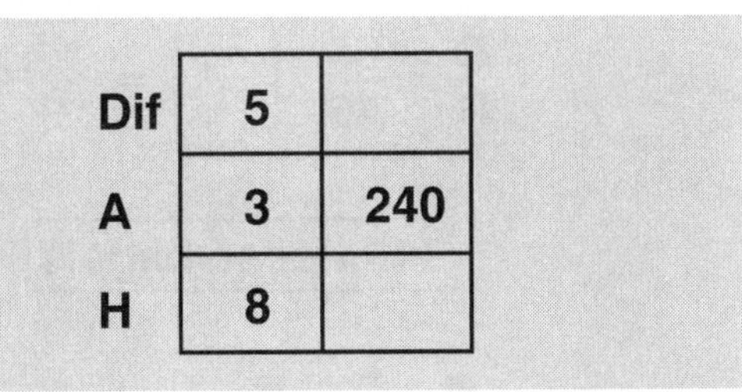

Dif	5	
A	3	240
H	8	

- Here's the table with the numbers the problem gives. Everybody, how high is Howard Hill? (Signal.) *640 feet.*
- How much higher is Howard Hill than Abbey Hill? (Signal.) *400 feet.*

Teaching note: If students are firm on the component skills that have been taught through Lesson 81, they should have no difficulties working these problems quickly and accurately.

Note that you permit students to use abbreviations. Abbreviations are acceptable earlier, but it should be clear what the abbreviations refer to. If students write the names in full, the chances of serious confusion are reduced. Now that students are practiced in working with both ratio tables and number families, the potential for confusion is reduced.

In Lesson 88, students begin preparation for table problems that have mixed numbers in the second column.

Here are the problems from Lesson 88:

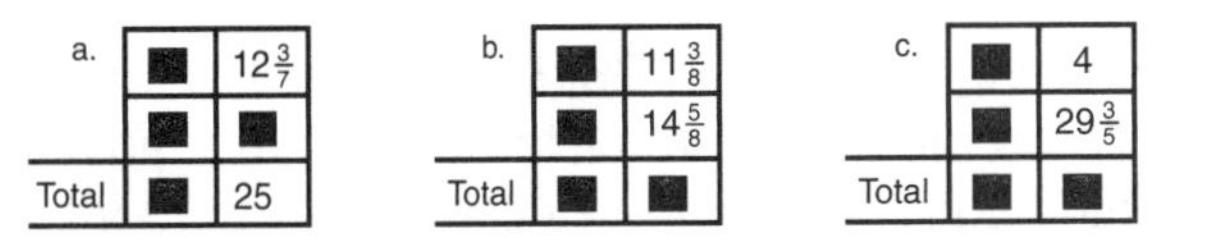

a.

	■	$12\frac{3}{7}$
	■	■
Total	■	25

b.

	■	$11\frac{3}{8}$
	■	$14\frac{5}{8}$
Total	■	■

c.

	■	4
	■	$29\frac{3}{5}$
Total	■	■

Students compute the missing number in the second column of each table. For table a, they work the problem:

$$\begin{array}{r} 25 \\ -\ 12\frac{3}{7} \\ \hline \end{array}$$

Working this problem requires borrowing from the ones column of 25:

$$\begin{array}{r} 4\frac{7}{7} \\ 2\not{5} \\ -\ 12\frac{3}{7} \\ \hline \end{array}$$

For table b, students work this problem:

$$\begin{array}{r} 11\frac{3}{8} \\ +\ 14\frac{5}{8} \\ \hline \end{array}$$

The answer is 25 8/8, which students rewrite as 26.

In the following lessons, students work similar problems involving partially completed tables.

In Lesson 91, students work from word problems that result in ratio tables with mixed numbers in the second column. For these problems, the numbers in the second column are not always multiples of the corresponding numbers in the first column. To solve these problems, students work a ratio equation in which the fraction that equals 1 is a fraction over a fraction. They rewrite the fractional answer as a mixed number, then figure out the final missing number by addition or subtraction.

Example:

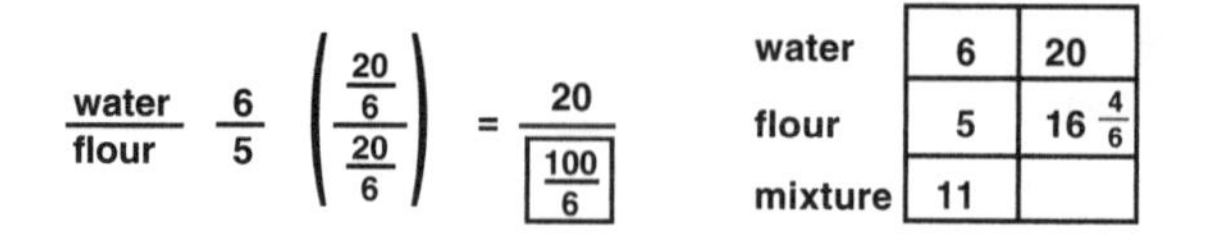

Starting in Lesson 106, students solve ratio table problems that refer to percent. In many settings, students find the concept of percent difficult to understand because it seems to be a "unit name" like dollars or pounds. However, percent is different because it is a proportion. 40 percent of something is 40/100 of that thing. This relationship is clearly articulated by the use of the number family. The family shows that the percent notation is expressed as a fraction and that percent numbers function just like ratio numbers in the first column of a ratio table.

Example:

Train A is 40% longer than train B. If train B is 400 meters long, how long is train A? How much longer is train A than train B?

The fraction number family shows the percents as fractions:

$$\overset{\text{Dif}}{\frac{40}{100}} \quad \overset{\text{B}}{\frac{100}{100}} \longrightarrow \overset{\text{A}}{\frac{140}{100}}$$

The numerators are ratio numbers for the table. The number 400 goes in the second column:

Dif	40	
B	100	400
A	140	

Here's part of the exercise from Lesson 106:

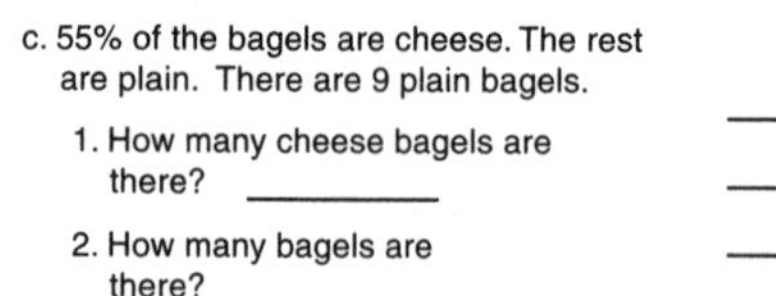

c. 55% of the bagels are cheese. The rest are plain. There are 9 plain bagels.

1. How many cheese bagels are there? ________
2. How many bagels are there? ________

%

d. Your turn: Make the number family for problem C. Raise your hand when you're finished.
(Observe the students and give feedback.)

- (Write on the board:)

$$\text{c.} \quad \overset{\text{C}}{\frac{55}{100}} \quad \overset{\text{P}}{\frac{45}{100}} \longrightarrow \overset{\text{B}}{\frac{100}{100}}$$

- Here's what you should have. Put the ratio numbers in the table. Figure out the number of cheese bagels. Raise your hand when you've written answers to both questions.
(Observe students and give feedback.)
- (Write on the board:)

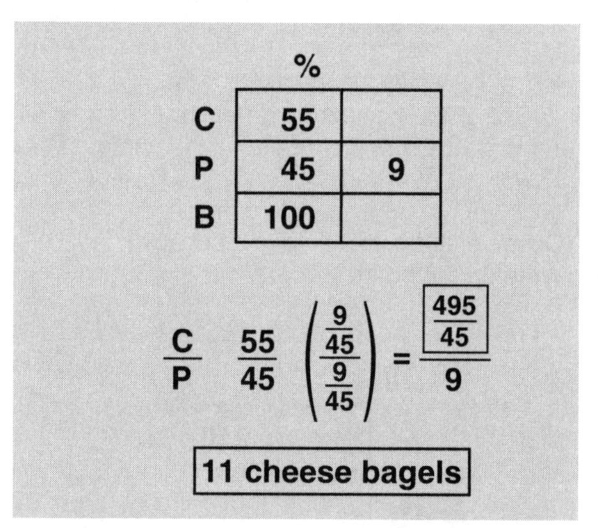

- Check your work. Here's the ratio table and the ratio equation. Everybody, how many cheese bagels are there? (Signal.) *11.*
- How many total bagels are there? (Signal) *20.*
- (Write **11** and **20.**)

Teaching note: This problem, like many percent problems, has smaller numbers in the second column than in the first column. The sentence: **55% of the bagels are cheese,** gives information for the fraction number family.

Students should not have trouble figuring out where to place the numbers in the table because the number family shows the numbers for the first column. The ratio problem that students work involves a complex fraction that equals 1:

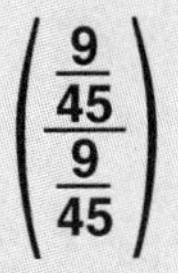

Students first get a fractional answer:

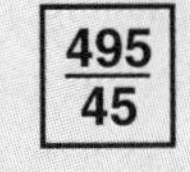

Then they work the division problem:

$$45 \overline{)495}$$

and write the whole number answer:

11 cheese bagels

MULTIPLICATION/DIVISION

Starting with Lesson 71 and continuing through the end of the program, students work a variety of problems that require multiplication or division. The general rules that students work from are:

1) If the problem tells about 1 and asks about more than 1 of the same category, you multiply.
2) If the problem tells about more than 1 and asks about 1 of the same category, you divide.

Division also is implied by problems that tell about more than 1 and ask about the number of equal-sized divisions or groups.

The strategy that students use is to find the name for 1 object. Then they see if the problem gives another number for that name.

If so, the problem is a multiplication problem or a division problem.

For instance:

Each basket costs $6. Maria buys 21 baskets. How much does she pay?

Each basket is 1 basket. The problem asks about more than 1 basket, so it's a multiplication problem.

Here's another example:

Maria spends $56 on notebooks. She buys 8 notebooks. How much does each cost?

The problem tells about more than 1 and asks about 1. So it's a division problem.

If the problem is neither a multiplication problem nor a division problem, it's a ratio problem.

For example:

Each sheet of paper costs 3¢. Maria spends 72¢ on paper. How many sheets of paper does she buy?

Here's the ratio equation:

$$\frac{\text{paper}}{¢} \quad \frac{1}{3}\left(\quad\right) = \frac{\square}{72}$$

INVERSE OPERATIONS

In Level E, students learn that addition is the inverse of subtraction and multiplication is the inverse of division. An understanding of inverse operations enables students to work difficult word problems.

For example:

There was some gas in a gas tank. The amount of gas was doubled when the tank was filled at the gas station. Then 22 gallons were used up on a trip. Another 15 gallons were added to the tank. There were now 39 gallons in the tank. How much gas was in the tank to begin with?

The procedure for solving the problem that is presented in Level E involves expressing the problem with equations, some of which have four numbers.

Here are the equations for the problem and the part of the problem that generates each equation:

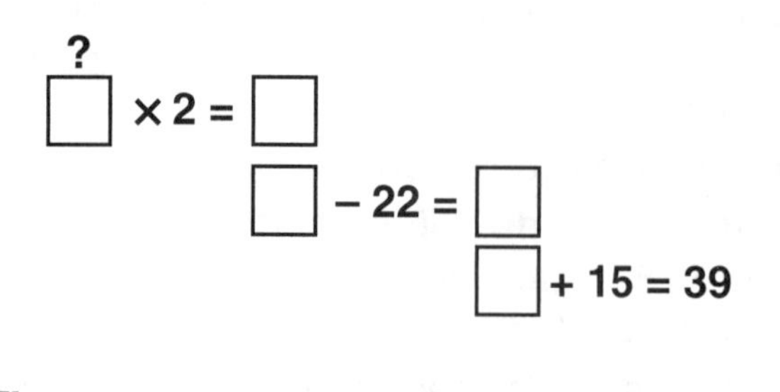

There was some gas in a gas tank. The amount of gas was doubled when the tank was filled at the gas station.

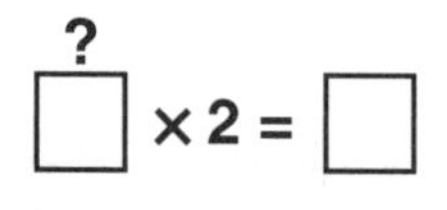

Then 22 gallons were used up on a trip.

$\square - 22 = \square$

Another 15 gallons were added to the tank. There were now 39 gallons in the tank.

$\square + 15 = 39$

To solve the problem, students work backward and use information about inverse operations to figure out the missing values. For the last equation, **15 was added** to reach 39. Therefore, the first value in the last equation can be calculated by starting with 39 and **subtracting 15**:

$\boxed{24} + 15 = 39$

The middle equation is now:

$\square - 22 = \boxed{24}$

The missing value is determined by starting with 24 and adding 22. The missing value is 46:

$\boxed{46} - 22 = \boxed{24}$

The starting number in the first equation is obtained by starting with 46 and dividing by 2. The starting number is 23:

$\overset{?}{\boxed{23}} \times 2 = \boxed{46}$

Inverse operations are first made explicit in Lesson 11, where students use their calculators to check addition problems by working corresponding subtraction problems. After working the problem $235 + 49 = 284$, students work the subtraction problem that starts with 284: $284 - 49$. If the problem is worked correctly, the answer is 235, the starting number in the addition problem.

In Lesson 13, the inverse relationships are further extended. Students check subtraction problems by working corresponding addition problems.

In Level E, students work problems that are solved by using inverse operations. Students are taught the operations as a way of "undoing." You undo addition by subtracting: you undo subtraction by adding. You undo multiplication by dividing: you undo division by multiplying.

Before students are introduced to "undoing" problems, they work problems that tell about two different operations (Lesson 104). Problems are of the form:

You start with 14 and multiply by 3. Then you add 5. What number do you end up with?

The first sentence translates into an equation that has one box:

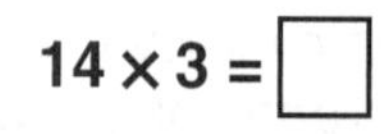

The second sentence translates into an equation that has two boxes. The answer to the first equation is the starting number for the second equation:

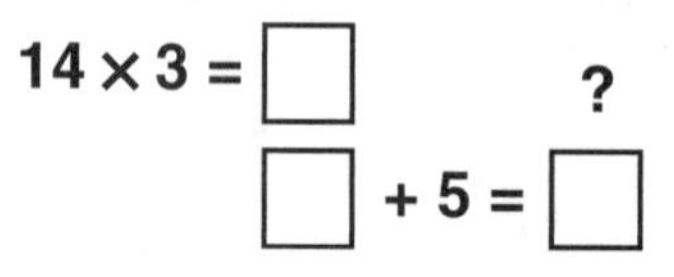

In Lesson 105, students work problems that have the same basic structure in that the ending value of the first equation is the starting value of the second equation. The difference is that the starting number is missing:

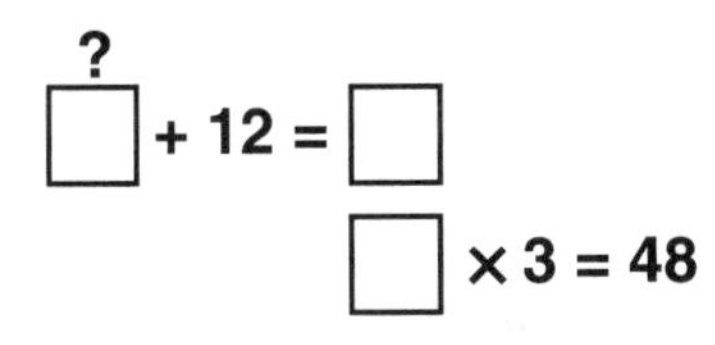

Students work the problem by undoing each part. The ending number is 48. What did students do just before they ended up with 48? They multiplied by 3. To undo multiplying by 3, you divide by 3:

$$3\overline{)48} = 16$$

The answer is the first number in the second equation:

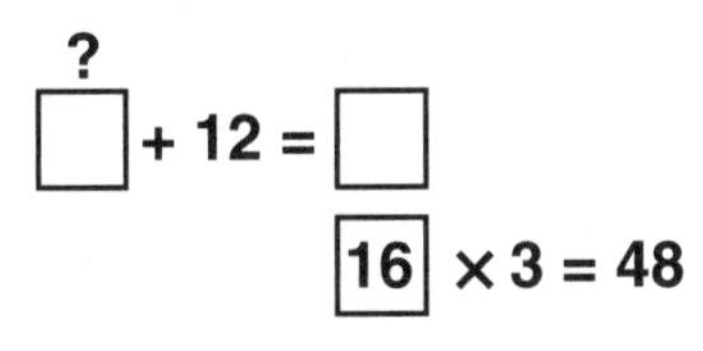

That number is also the ending number of the first equation:

$$\underset{?}{\square} + 12 = \boxed{16}$$
$$\boxed{16} \times 3 = 48$$

Now students figure out the missing number in the first equation. To reach 16 in the first equation, students added 12. To undo adding 12, you subtract 12. The first number in the equation is 4:

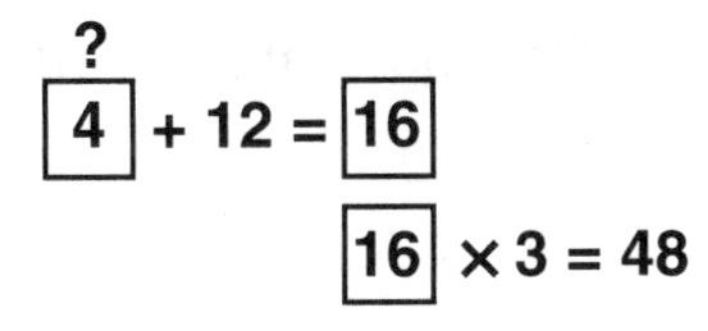

Here's part of the introduction of undoing from Lesson 105:

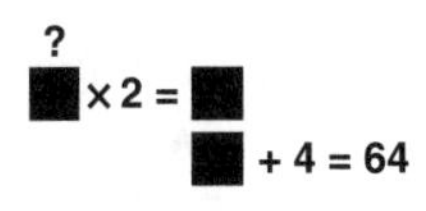

a. To work problems of this type, you start at the **end** of the second equation and work **backward.** You **undo** each step that was done.
- Here are the rules for undoing: If you **added,** you undo it by **subtracting** the same number.
- If you **subtracted,** you undo it by **adding** the same number.
- If you **multiplied,** you undo it by **dividing by** the same number.
- Those rules are important.

b. Everybody, how do you **undo** multiplying by 3? (Signal.) *Divide by 3.*
- How do you undo adding 6? (Signal.) *Subtract 6.*
- How do you undo subtracting 11? (Signal.) *Add 11.*

(Repeat step b until firm.)

c. We'll work the problem in the box a step at a time. We'll start at the end of the second equation and work backward.
- What's the last number in the second equation? (Signal.) *64.*
- What did we do in the second equation to get 64? (Signal.) *Added 4.*
- We added 4. How do you undo adding 4? (Signal.) *Subtract 4.*
- So you work the problem 64 minus 4. You can see the problem in a cloud below the rules.
- The answer is 60. You can see the bottom equation completed, and the 60 is also written at the end of the first equation.
- Now we'll work backward from 60 to figure out the mystery number. Everybody, what did we do in the first equation to get from the mystery number to 60? (Signal.) *Multiplied by 2.*
- We multiplied by 2. How do we undo multiplying by 2? (Signal.) *Divide by 2.*
- When we work the problem 60 divided by 2, we'll know the mystery number. Raise your hand when you've figured out the answer. √
- Everybody, what's the mystery number? (Signal.) *30.*
- Remember, start at the end. Work backward and undo each step.

Teaching note: If students have trouble, take them through each problem starting with the last value in the second equation:

"What number do you end up with?" *64.*

"Touch the part of the equation that

shows what you did to get to 64." (Student touches + **4**.) "Tell me what you did." *Added 4.*

"How do you undo adding 4?" *Subtract 4.*

"Say the problem." *64 minus 4.*

"Work it and write the answer as the first number in the second equation and the last number in the top equation."

"Touch the ending number in the top equation. What number?" *60.*

"Touch the part of the equation that shows what you did to get to 60." (Student touches × **2**.) "What did you do?" *Multiplied by 2.*

"How do you undo multiplying by 2?" *Divide by 2.*

"Say the problem." *60 divided by 2.*

"Work the problem. The answer is the mystery number."

In Lesson 109, students translate word problems into equations. For example:

You start with some number and multiply by 9. Then you add 15. You end up with 69. What's the mystery number?

Students write an equation for each operation that is mentioned (one equation for **multiply by 9;** another equation for **add 15**):

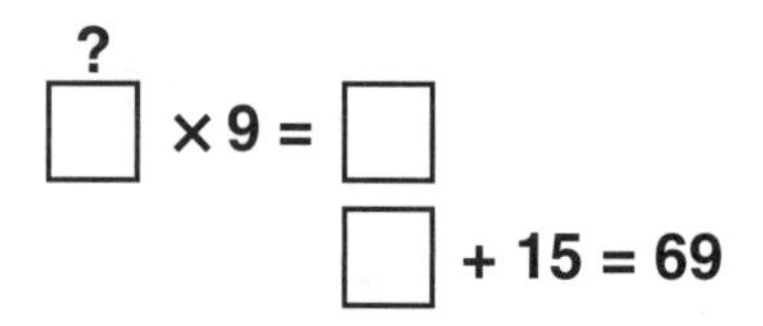

Here's part of the work from Lesson 109:

c. Problem B. The first sentence tells about the first equation: You start with some number and multiply by 9.

- Write the first equation. Raise your hand when you've done that much.
- (Write on the board:)

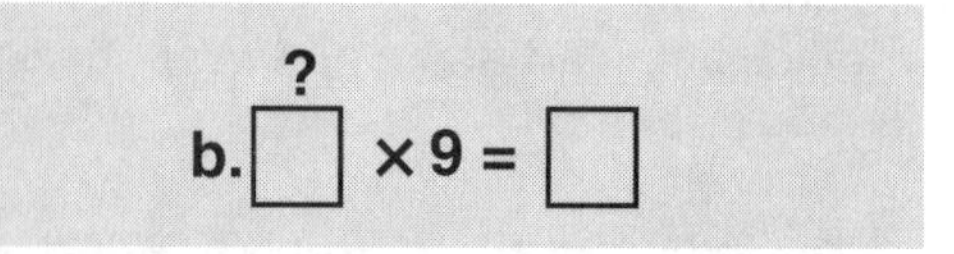

- Here's what you should have.
- The rest of the problem says: Then you add 15. You end up with 69. Write the second equation. Remember, it begins with a box. Raise your hand when you're finished.
- (Write to show:)

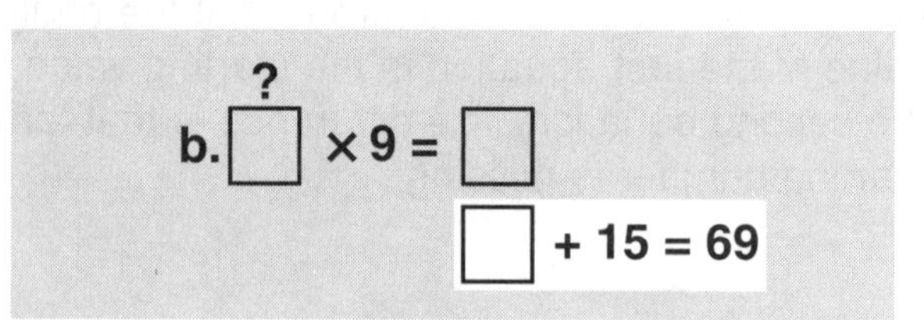

- Here's what you should have.

In Lesson 112, students work problems with more than two steps. For example:

You start with some number. Then you multiply by 5. Then you subtract 16. Then you add 11. Then you divide by 3. You end up with 30. What's the mystery number?

Students write an equation for each operation. All equations except the last one have two boxes.

Students write:

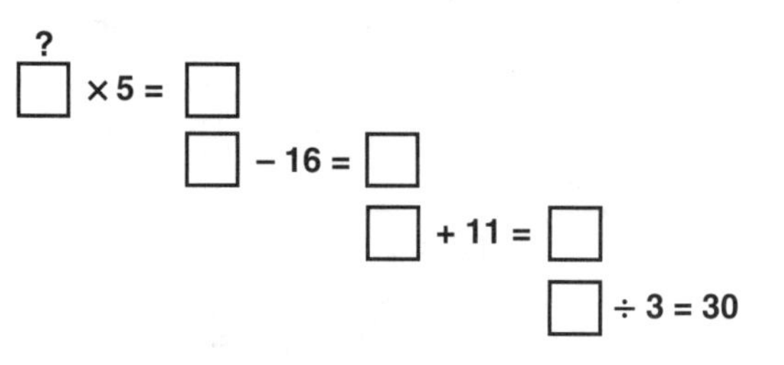

They solve the problem using the same steps required for two-equation problems. They start with the ending number of an equation, identify what they did to get that number, and work the problem to undo that operation.

In Lesson 124, students work more sophisticated problems that refer to doubling or tripling and that require translating actions into operations.

For example:

Jan had some money. She spent $41 on Christmas presents. She received $15 from her parents. She doubled the amount of money she had by selling her stereo. She ended up with $200. How much did she start out with?

Students write an equation for each operation mentioned in the problem:

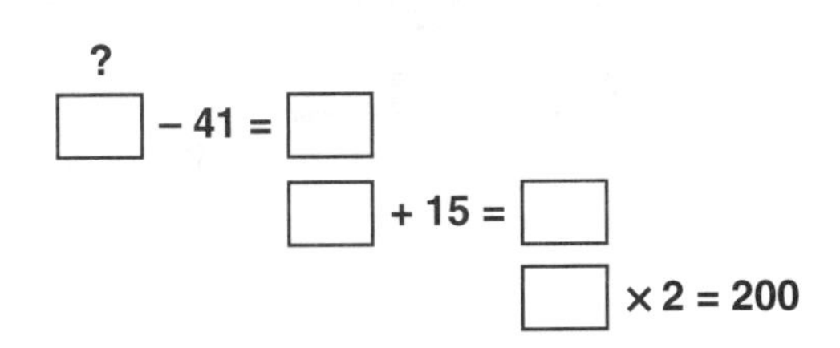

Then they work the problem through undoing:

?

$\boxed{126} - 41 = \boxed{85}$

$\boxed{85} + 15 = \boxed{100}$

$\boxed{100} \times 2 = 200$

The answer is $126.

Probability

Work on probability develops the relationship between sets and trials. It is an extension of earlier work with fractions and ratio tables. Students first learn that the composition of a set of objects determines the probability or chances of randomly selecting any one object from the set. Students also learn that probability is like an estimate. The outcome obtained experimentally will not necessarily be the mathematically determined number, but it will be close to that number. After students work ratio table problems that involve probability, they conduct probability experiments in which they make predictions and confirm their predictions.

In Lesson 112, students learn about expressing probability as a fraction. They work with bags that show Xs and circles.

Example:

The fraction tells the chances of pulling an X from the bag. The denominator of the fraction they write is the total number of things in the bag. The numerator is the number of targeted objects. For this bag, the fraction for the Xs is 2/5. There are 5 objects in the bag. Two of them are Xs. If the chances of pulling any object from the bag are the same, 2/5 of the trials would result in drawing an X. Stated differently, there are 5 things in the bag. The chances of drawing any one of them on a trial is the same. If you took enough trials so that every object in the bag would have one turn, you'd take 5 trials. In 2 of those trials, you'd expect to pull out an X. In 3 of those trials, you'd expect to pull out an object that is not an X.

In Lesson 112, students learn the rule that the bag with the fraction closest to 1 is the bag that gives the best chance of pulling out an X.

Here's the student work from Lesson 112:

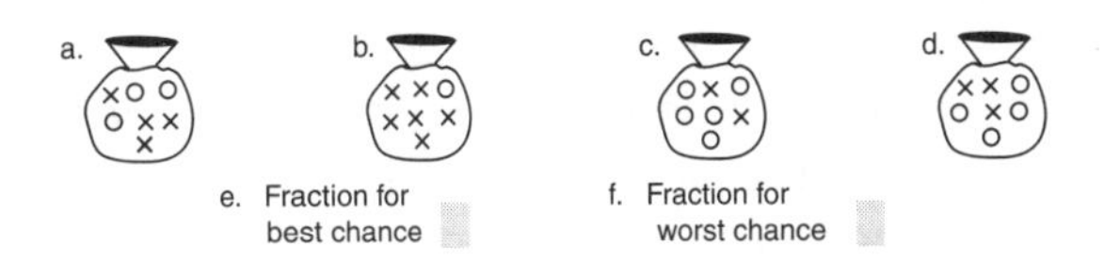

Students first write the fractions that give the chances of pulling an X from each bag:

a. $\frac{4}{7}$ **b.** $\frac{6}{7}$ **c.** $\frac{2}{7}$ **d.** $\frac{3}{7}$

Then they rank the bags to show the bag with the best chance (bag b) and the worst chance (bag c).

In Lesson 114, students learn about the relationship between the trials one takes at pulling an object from the bag and the probability of the thing being an X. The fraction that tells about the **bag** also tells about **trials.** If there are 5 things in the bag, the fraction tells that you would take 5 trials to give each thing in the bag one chance to be pulled out.

Students translate the number of things in a bag into predictions based on the number of trials they would take to give each thing in the bag one chance of being selected.

Here's one of the items from Lesson 114:

c.

1. How many trials would you take to give each thing in the bag one chance of being pulled out?
2. On how many of those trials would you expect to pull out an X?
3. On how many of those trials would you expect to pull out something that is not an X?

> ***Teaching note:*** In earlier lessons, students have responded to the bags by constructing fractions. In Lesson 114, however, they express the same information to answer questions about the number of trials to take and about the expected outcomes. The work in Lesson 114, therefore, forms a link between what students have done and the upcoming work with ratios.

In Lesson 115, the relationship between the fractions and ratios is fully developed. If the number of things in the bag tells about 1 trial for each thing, it is possible to make ratio equations that involve any number of trials. The problem gives information about the composition of a set and the number of trials a person takes. Students use the information to construct a fraction number family and a ratio table.

Here are the rules for the fraction number family:

1) The names for the fraction number family are: **X, Not X,** and **Total.**

2) The fraction for **X** has the number of Xs in the numerator and the total number of objects in the denominator.

3) The fraction for the big number is 1. It has the same denominator as the fraction for **X.**

4) The remaining small number is the fraction for **Not X.**

The ratio table has the numerators as ratio numbers. The name for the big number, however, is **trials.** The first column shows the number or trials needed to give each object one chance of being pulled out. The second column has a different number for total trials.

The steps involved in working the problems are familiar to the students. They have already constructed fractions for sets. They have also worked simple word problems that require the construction of fraction number families (2/5 of the workers in a factory wear gloves. What's the fraction of workers that do not wear gloves?)

Here's part of the work from Lesson 115:

c. You're going to work ratio-table problems.

d. Make the fraction number family for problem A. Show the fractions for **Xs, not Xs** and **total.** Then stop. Raise your hand when you've done that much. (Observe students and give feedback.)

- (Write on the board:)

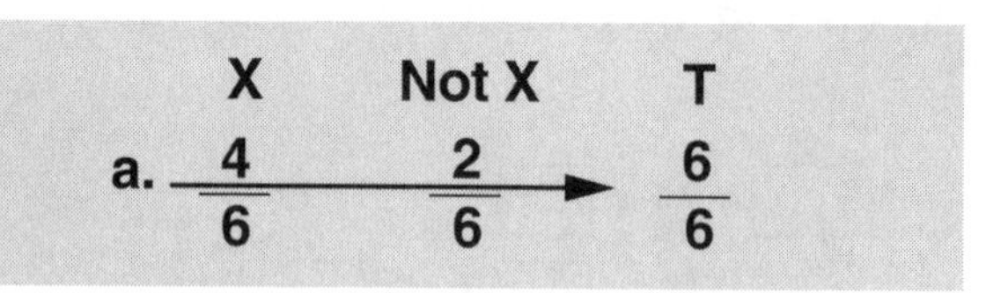

- Here's what you should have. The problem says: If you took trials until you pulled out 40 Xs, about how many trials would you take?
- That question asks about the **total** number of trials. Make the ratio table. Put the ratio numbers in the first column and 40 for Xs in the second column. Then figure out the number of trials you'd take to get 40 Xs. Raise your hand when you're finished. (Observe students and give feedback.)
- (Write on the board:)

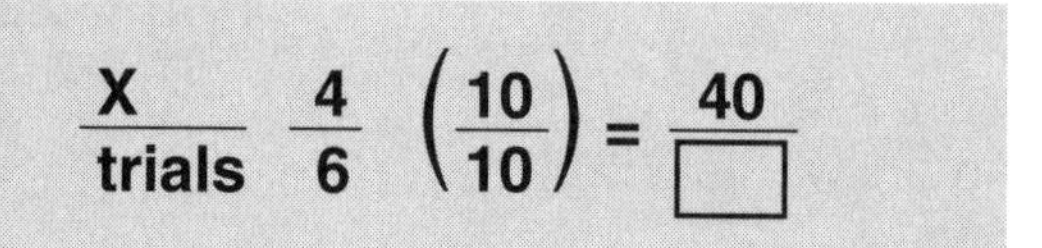

- Here's the ratio equation. Everybody, about how many trials would you take? (Signal.) *60.*

> ***Teaching note:*** The only tricky part in the exercise is the question about total trials: **If you took trials until you pulled out 40 Xs, about how many trials would you take?** The question does not ask about the trials for Xs, but about the total trials. If students have trouble understanding this sentence, tell them: "The question gives the number of trials in which you pulled out Xs. If you pulled out 40 Xs, you had 40 trials in which you pulled out Xs. The question asks, How many total trials did you need to pull out these 40 Xs?"

Beginning with Lesson 118, students work on a broader range of problems and probability contexts, such as the predicted number of rainy days, the number of ripe versus not ripe tomatoes, etc. The procedure is the same for these problems as it is for the bag problems. Students construct a fraction-number family and a ratio table that shows how the probability problem is like familiar ratio problems.

In Lesson 124, students compare the probability for sets that have different numbers of objects.

For example:

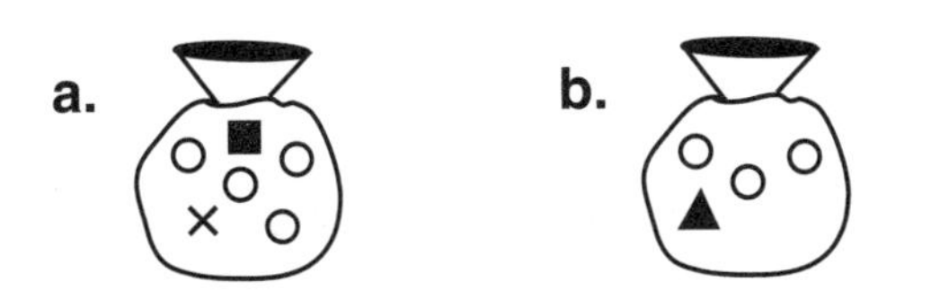

Which of these two bags gives you the better chance of pulling out a circle?

Students write a fraction for each bag:

$$\text{a. } \frac{4}{6} \quad \text{b. } \frac{3}{4}$$

To compare the fractions, they rewrite the fractions with a common denominator. The fraction that is closer to 1 is the fraction that gives the better chance.

$$\text{a. } \frac{4}{6}\left(\frac{2}{2}\right) = \frac{8}{12}$$

$$\text{b. } \frac{3}{4}\left(\frac{3}{3}\right) = \frac{9}{12}$$

Bag b gives the better chance.

After completing the sequence on probability, students do a series of products that involve applying what they have learned. (See **Projects.**)

Geometry

The two main geometry topics presented in Level E are two- and three-dimensional figures, and angles and lines. For the work with two- and three-dimensional figures, students compute the perimeter and area of rectangles, triangles, and parallelograms and the circumference and area of circles. They also compute the surface area of rectangular boxes and pyramids, and the volume of rectangular and triangular boxes. For the work with angles and lines, students learn about parallel lines, intersecting lines, and angles.

PERIMETER AND AREA

The work with perimeter begins in Lesson 58. Students apply the basic procedure for finding the perimeter: **Add the length of each side.**

The figures have three or four sides. For some of the four-sided figures, the length of only two sides is shown. These figures have opposite sides that are parallel; therefore, students are able to determine the length of all the sides.

Here's part of the exercise for Lesson 58:

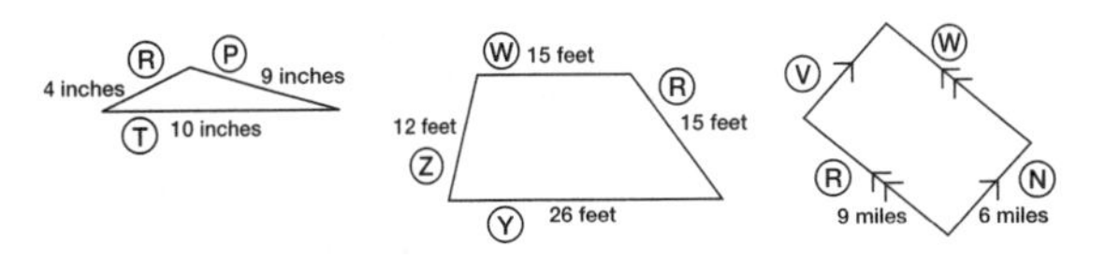

c. Work the addition problem to find the perimeter for figure A. Write the answer as a number and a unit name and box it. Raise your hand when you're finished.
(Observe students and give feedback.)

- (Write on the board:)

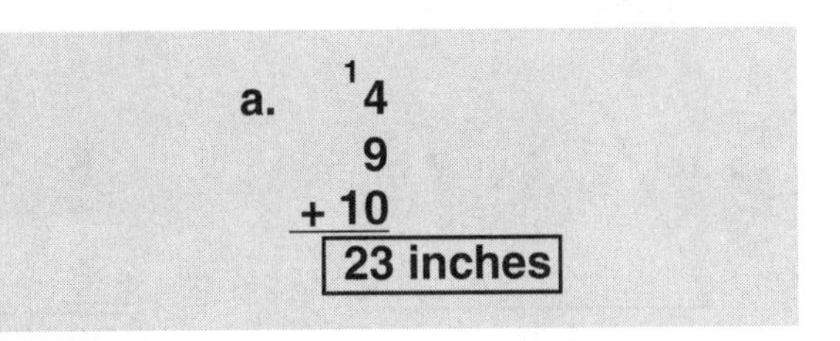

- Here's what you should have. You can have these numbers in any order, but you add these three values to get the total distance around the figure. The perimeter is 23 inches.

d. Your turn: Find the perimeter for figure B. Write the answer as a number and a unit name. Raise your hand when you're finished.
(Observe students and give feedback.)

- (Write on the board:)

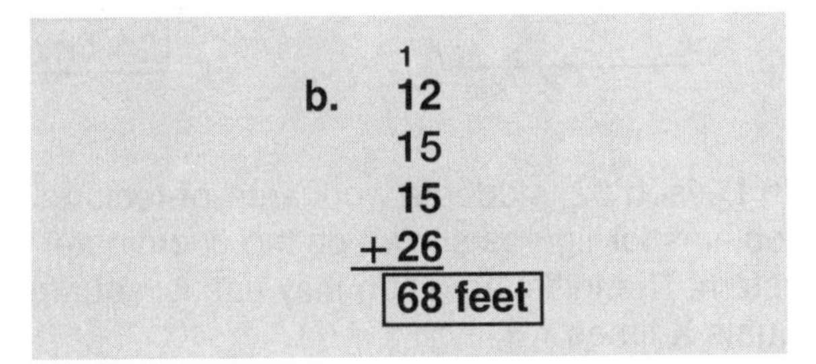

- Here's what you should have. You can have these numbers in any order, but you add these four values to get the total distance around the figure. The perimeter is 68 feet.

e. Find the perimeter for figure C. Raise your hand when you're finished.
(Observe students and give feedback.)

- Check your work. Both pairs of opposite sides are parallel. So you know that sides V and N are each 6 miles long. Sides R and W are each 9 miles long. The perimeter is 30 miles.

Teaching note: In Lesson 56, students learned the convention indicating parallel sides:

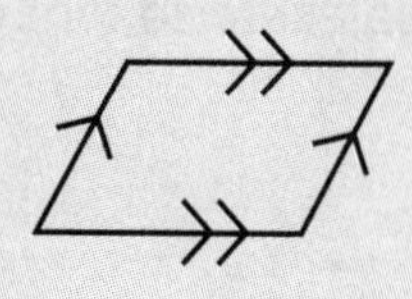

In this figure, sides with corresponding arrow markers are parallel. Students also learned that opposite sides of a parallelogram are equal in length.

Students may write the length of the sides in any order. The order that is shown in the workcheck starts with the left side and goes in a clockwise direction:

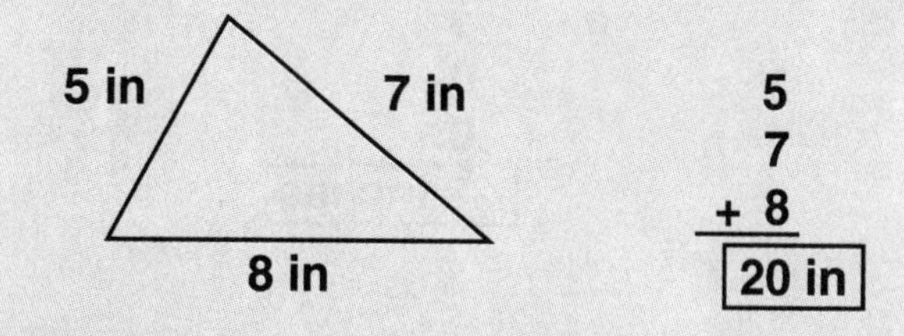

If the sides are paired, the numbers are ordered like this:

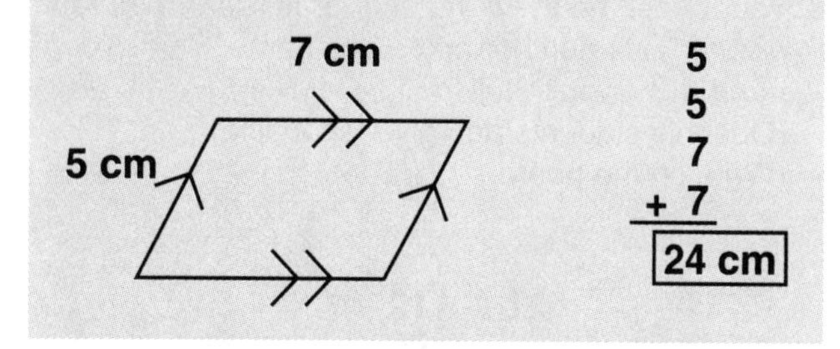

In Lesson 62, students work area-of-rectangle problems for figures shown on the coordinate system. The initial equation they use is: squares equals X times Y.

Here's part of the work from Lesson 62:

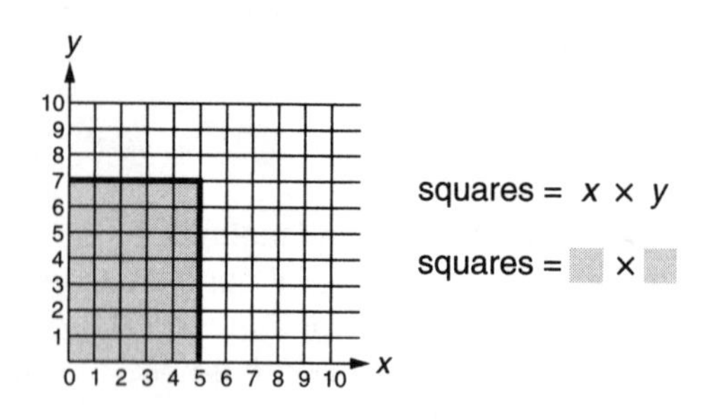

c. We'll work the sample problem together. Everybody, first write the equation: Squares equal X times Y. √

- (Write on the board:)

squares = $x \times y$

- Below, we'll write the equation with numbers. What's the number for X? (Signal.) *5.*
- What's the number for Y? (Signal.) *7.*
- (Write to show:)

squares = $x \times y$

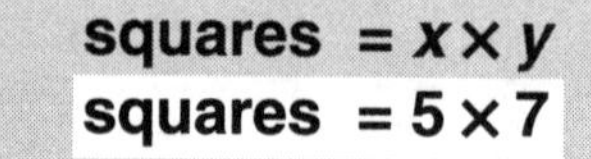

- Here's the equation with numbers. Write it below your first equation. Figure out the answer, write it below your number equation and box it. Raise your hand when you're finished.

  (Observe students and give feedback.)
- (Write to show:)

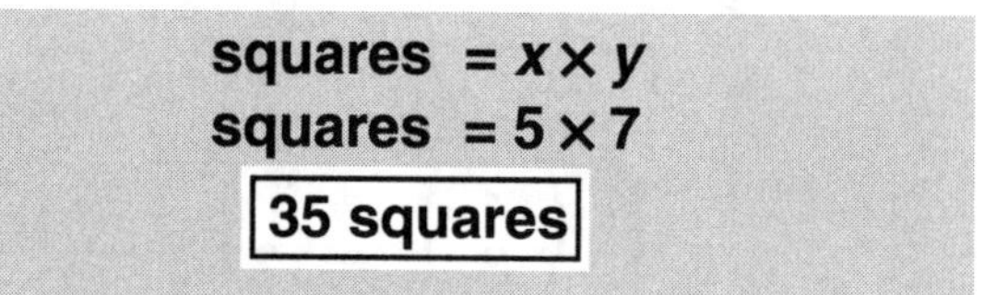

- Here's the whole answer: 35 squares.
- Remember, write the answer below your number equation and box it.

Teaching note: The coordinate system clearly represents the concept of area and nature of the units. The X and Y axes show the dimensions of the rectangle. The squares are shown as divisions inside the rectangle. The students can count the squares to confirm that the calculations are correct.

In Lesson 66, students work problems in which they find both the area and perimeter of rectangles shown on the coordinate system. The X and Y axes show unit names. Students write answers with unit names.

Here's a pair of problems from Lesson 66:

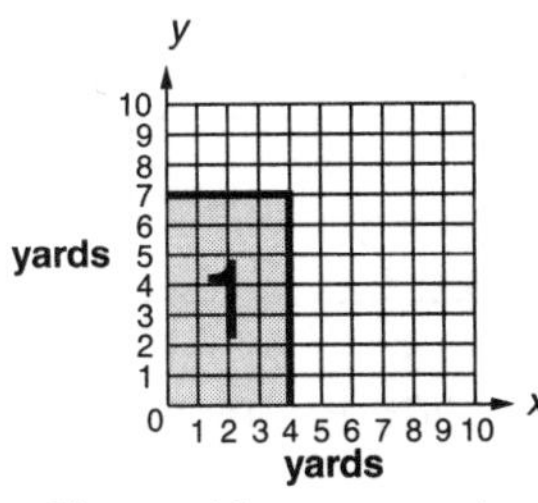

a. Figure out the **squares** for rectangle 1.

b. Figure out the **perimeter** for rectangle 1.

Teaching note: Students often have difficulty using the appropriate unit names. The problems are designed to make it easy for students to understand which unit name to use. If the problem asks about squares, students write the equation that deals with squares: squares = X × Y. Students then use the word **square** to describe the unit:

$$\textbf{squares} = x \times y$$
$$\textbf{squares} = 4 \times 7$$

28 square yards

If the problem asks about perimeter, it does not call for the equation involving squares, and it does not call for the word **square** in the answer.

If students have trouble using the appropriate unit names ask: "Are you finding squares or just finding the distance around the figure? . . . So will you have the name **squares** in your answer? . . . What's the unit name for this problem?"

In Lesson 69, students are introduced to the equation: **Area □ = base × height.** They will use this equation to work problems involving rectangles and other parallelograms. The base is the X axis. The height is the Y axis.

Here are the problems from Lesson 69:

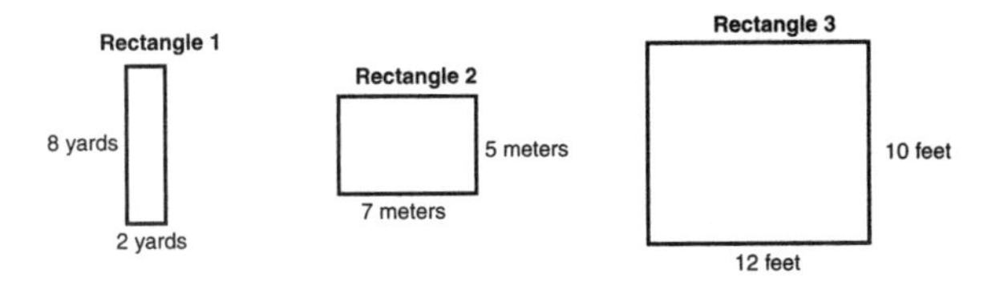

a. Find the area of rectangle 1.
b. Find the area of rectangle 2.
c. Find the perimeter of rectangle 3.
d. Find the area of rectangle 3.
e. Find the perimeter of rectangle 2.

Teaching note: If students get confused, remind them that the equation they are using for area involves the same steps they have taken in finding the number of squares. The unit name **square** is part of the unit name. "Remember, area refers to square units."

In Lesson 74, students find the area of triangles shown on the coordinate system. Students start with a right triangle, convert it into a rectangle by creating a second right triangle that is congruent with the first, and compute the area of the entire rectangle. The exercise demonstrates that the area of a triangle is one-half the area of a rectangle with the same base and height.

Students then use the equation:

$$\textbf{Area } \triangle = \frac{\textbf{base} \times \textbf{height}}{\textbf{2}}$$

Here's part of the introduction from Lesson 74:

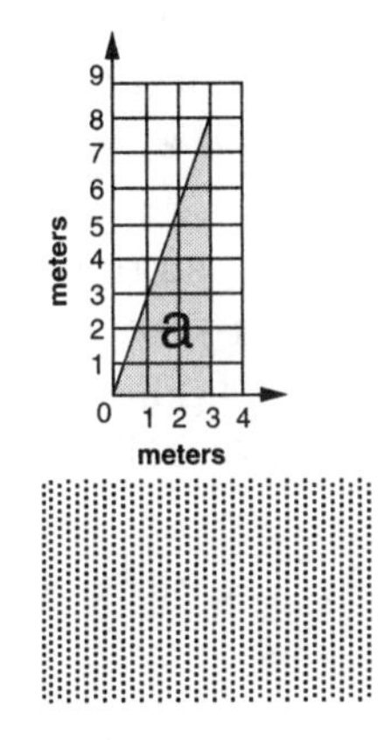

c. Problem A. First change the figure into a rectangle with the same base and height as the triangle. Raise your hand when you're finished.

- (Draw on the board:)

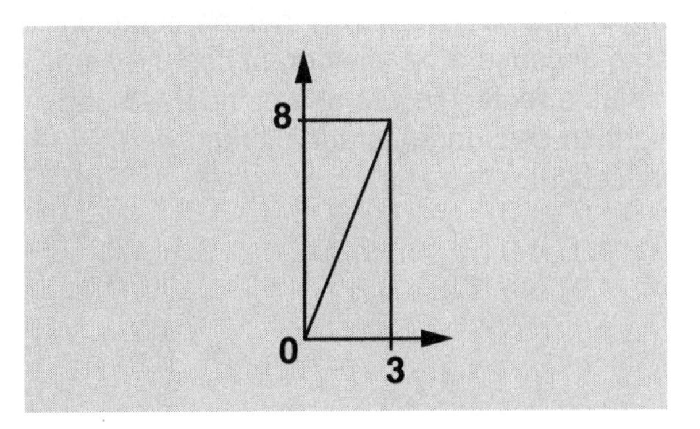

- Here's what you should have. Now write the equation for the area of a triangle. Work the problem and write the answer. Remember to write the unit name in the answer. Raise your hand when you're finished.
  (Observe students and give feedback.)
- (Write on the board:)

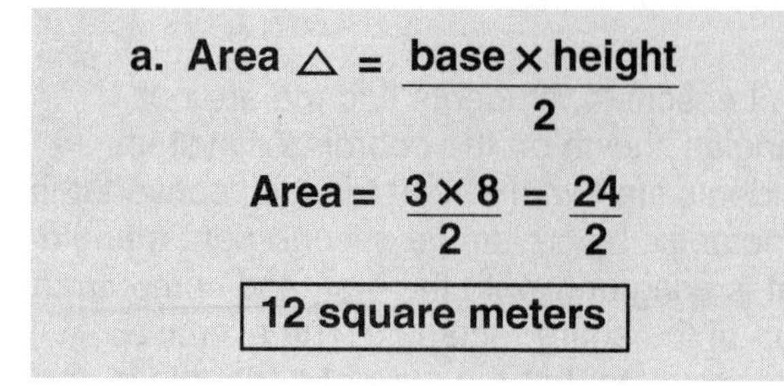

- Here's what you should have. The area of the rectangle you made is 3 times 8. That's 24. The area of the triangle is 1/2 of 24. The answer is 12 square meters. Raise your hand if you got everything right.

Teaching note: Make sure that students first write the complete equation for finding the area of the triangle. Below, they are to put in the numbers for the base and height and write the fractional answer. Below that equation, they write the complete answer—a whole number and a unit name.

In following lessons, students work problem sets that have triangles and rectangles. Students find the area of each figure. They are to start with the appropriate equation:

Area □ = base × height

or

Area △ = $\dfrac{\textbf{base} \times \textbf{height}}{\textbf{2}}$

In Lesson 79, students apply the equation for the area of a rectangle to figure out the area of parallelograms. They learn that the equation works because a parallelogram has the same area as a rectangle with the same base and height. In Lesson 80, students receive a verification of this fact.

Here are the steps in the demonstration:
Start with a rectangle.

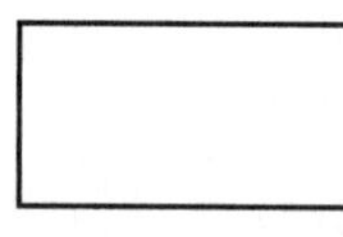

Make a diagonal line to create a right triangle.

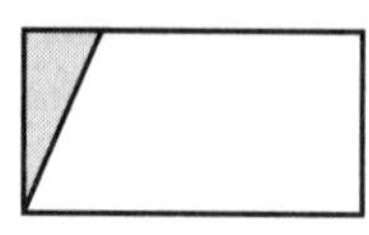

Move the triangle to the other side of the rectangle.

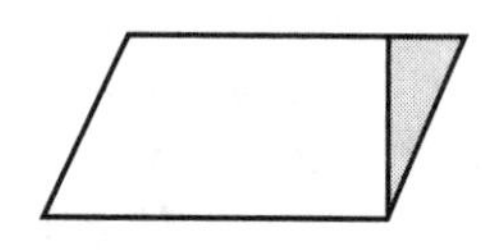

A parallelogram has been created using all the parts of the original rectangle and no additional parts. Therefore, the parallelogram has the same area as the rectangle.

In Lesson 83, students find the area and perimeter of the parallelograms not shown on the coordinate system. Finding the area of parallelograms is less difficult when they are shown on the coordinate system because the number for the height is given by the Y axis:

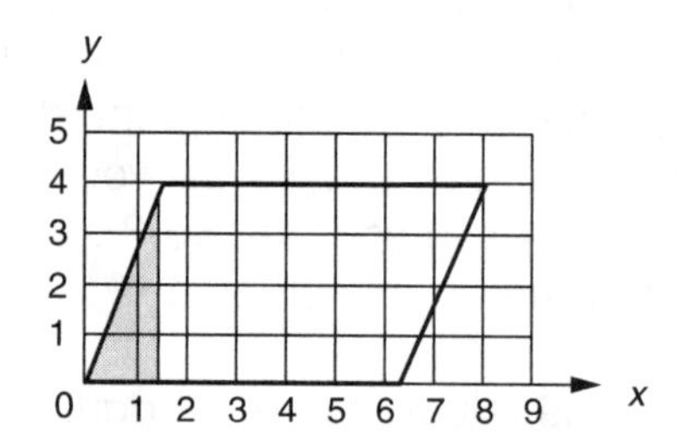

When parallelograms are not displayed on the coordinate system, students must discriminate between the **height of the figure** and the **length of the sides.** The height is not the length of any side.

Here's part of the introduction from Lesson 83:

a. Find part 3.
- (Teacher reference:)

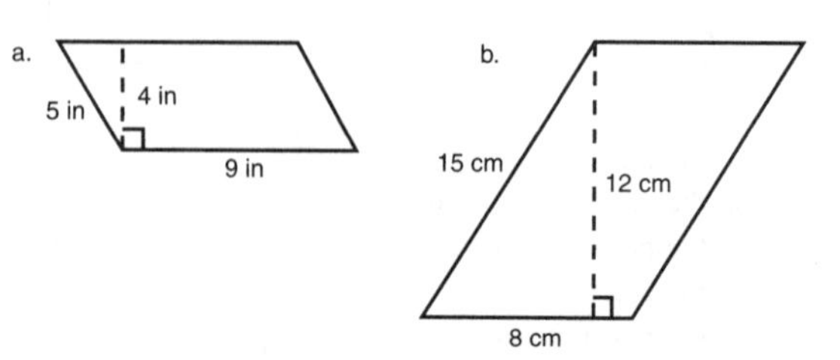

- These are parallelograms that are not on the coordinate system. The height is shown with a dotted line. Remember, that's not the length of any side. That line is the same height Y would show on the coordinate system.

b. Figure A. The length of the left side is shown. What's the length of that side? (Signal.) *5 inches.*

- The height is shown. What's the height? (Signal.) *4 inches.*
- Figure B. The length of the left side is shown. What's the length of that side? (Signal.) *15 centimeters.*
- The height is shown. What's the height? (Signal.) *12 centimeters.*

c. Go back to figure A. Find the area and the perimeter. Raise your hand when you're finished. (Observe students and give feedback.)

- (Write on the board:)

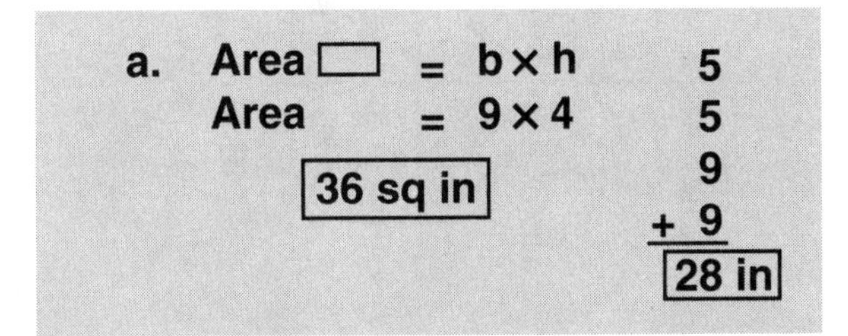

- Check your work. Here's what you should have. Raise your hand if you got everything right.

Teaching note: In step b, you present questions that require students to indicate the length of the left side and the height of the figure. Make sure that students are very firm when answering these questions. When students compute the perimeter, they use the length of the sides. When they work the area, they use the length of the base and the height.

In subsequent lessons, students work problems that require them to find the area and perimeter of rectangles, parallelograms, and triangles.

In Lesson 96, students compute the area of triangles that do not have a right angle:

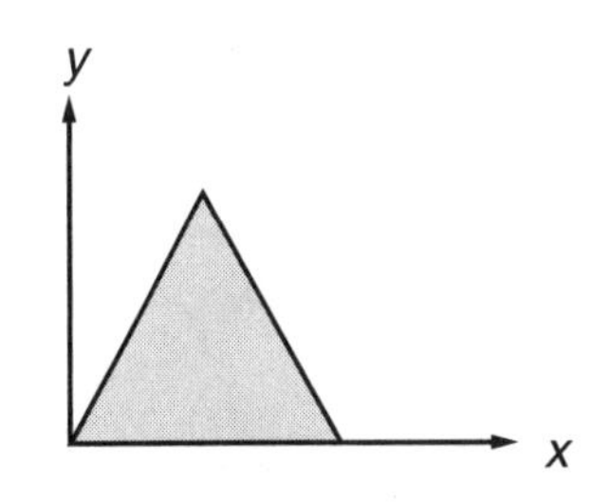

Students convert the triangle into a parallelogram with the same base and height as the triangle. To make this conversion, students construct a second triangle that is congruent with the triangle shown:

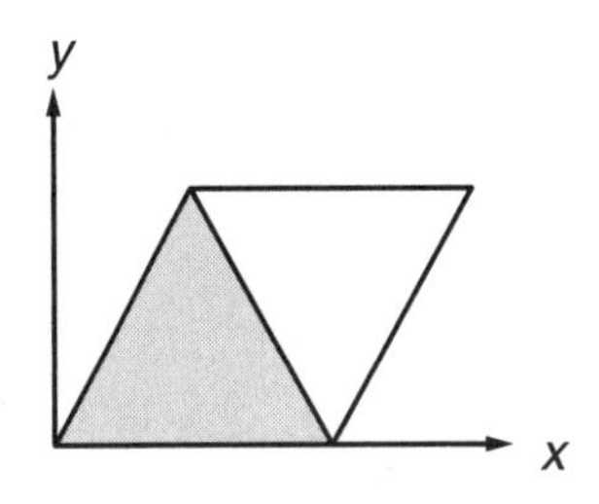

The resulting parallelogram is twice the area of the original triangle. Therefore, the equation

$$\textbf{Area} \triangle = \frac{\textbf{base} \times \textbf{height}}{2}$$

works for all triangles.

In Lesson 97, students work with non-right triangles that are not shown on the coordinate system. These triangles may present difficulties because no side shows the height of the figure. As with the parallelograms, the height is shown with a dotted line and a right-angle marker:

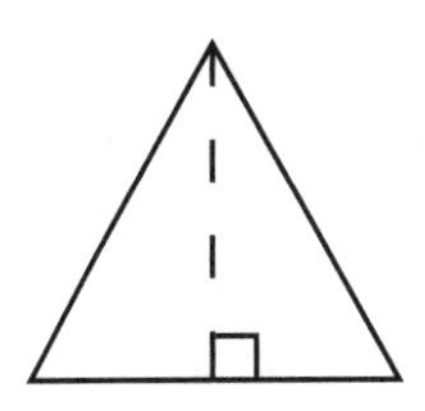

Here's part of the introduction from Lesson 97:

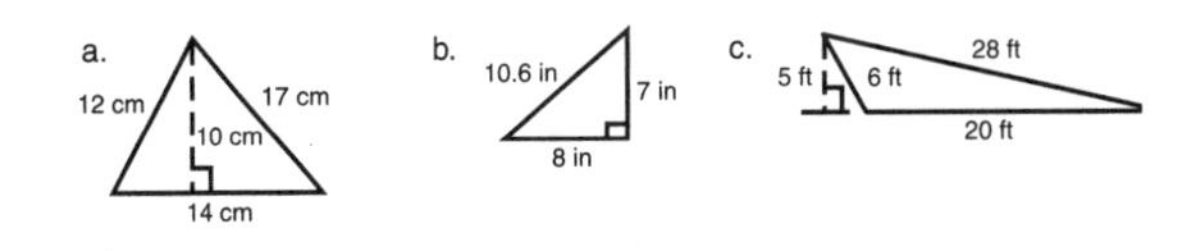

a. These are triangles that are not on the coordinate system. One triangle has a side that would be parallel to the Y axis. So the length of that side is the **height** of the figure. Everybody, which triangle is that? (Signal.) *B.*

- The other triangles do not have a side that shows the height. For those figures, the height is shown with a dotted line that goes straight up from the base.

b. Figure A. The height is shown with a dotted line. What's the height? (Signal.) *10 centimeters.*

- Figure B. The side that is 7 inches long is the height.
- Figure C. Is the length of any side the height of the figure? (Signal.) *No.*
- The height is shown with a dotted line. What's the height? (Signal.) *5 feet.*
- Remember, when you find the area, you always use the height.

c. Your turn: Work problem A. Find the area and find the perimeter. Remember, when you find the perimeter, you add the length of each side. In figure A, the height is not the length of a side. Raise your hand when you're finished. (Observe students and give feedback.)

- (Write on the board:)

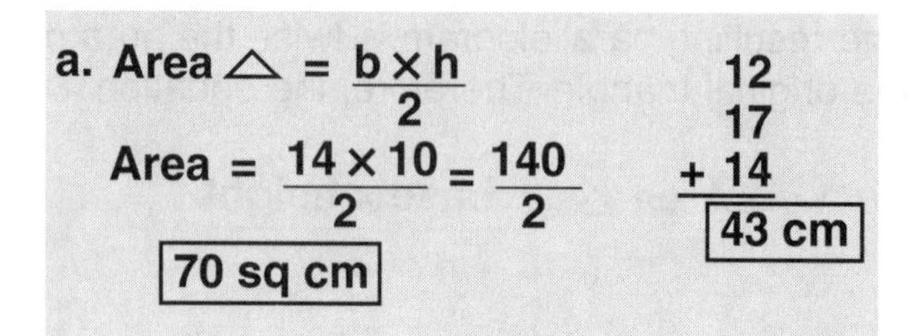

- Here's what you should have. The area is 70 square centimeters. The perimeter is 43 centimeters.

> ***Teaching note:*** Remind students of the basic procedure: "When you find the perimeter, you always use the numbers for the sides. When you find the area, you use the base and the height. The height may not be the length of any side."

In later lessons, students find the area and perimeter of the full range of triangles and parallelograms:

CIRCLES

In Level E, students learn to compute the **circumference** and **area** of circles. They also learn the component vocabulary: **diameter** and **radius.**

The work with circumference begins in Lesson 91. Students derive the value of pi by using the equation **diameter( )= circumference** for three different circles:

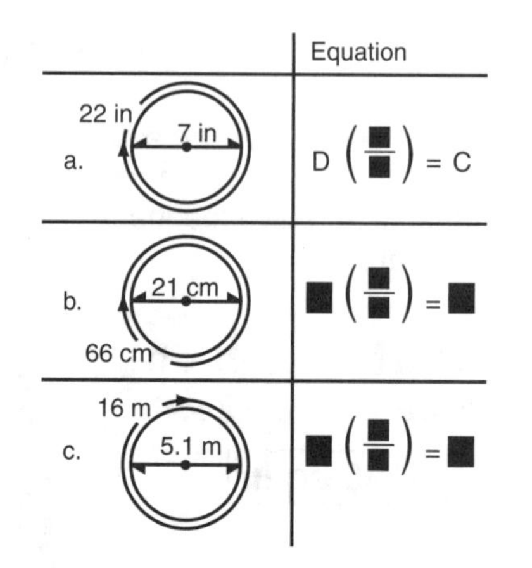

Students apply what they know about problems of this form to write the missing fraction, which equals:

$$\frac{\textbf{circumference}}{\textbf{diameter}}$$

Students use their calculator to work the division problem and round the answer to hundredths. For all three problems (22 divided by 7, 66 divided by 21, and 16 divided by 5.1), the answer is 3.14. This demonstration shows that for any circle, the ratio of circumference to diameter is a constant, 3.14, which is called pi.

In Lesson 92, students are introduced to the equation: $\pi \times D = C$. (***Note:*** The equation presents π first, not $D \times \pi = C$, because students can solve problems of the form: $3.14 \times (\ ) = C$. They cannot solve problems of the form: $(\ ) \times 3.14 = C$.)

In Lesson 92, students find the circumference of circles, given the diameter:

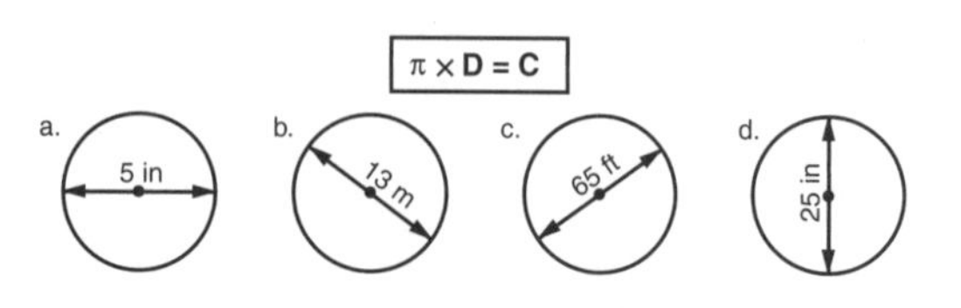

In Lesson 93, students also use the equation for the circumference of a circle to find the diameter of circles. The procedure to find the missing fraction is the same as that used to solve ratio problems.

For example, for item A above:

$$3.14\,(\blacksquare) = 12$$

Students write the missing fraction:

$$\left(\frac{12}{3.14}\right)$$

For diameter problems, students use their calculator to work the division problem: $12 \div 3.14$. They round the answer to two decimal places and complete the simple equation that tells what D equals: $D = 3.82$ in.

In Lesson 111, students learn that half the diameter is called the radius. Students then work problems that a) give the circumference and ask about the radius or b) give the radius and ask about the circumference.

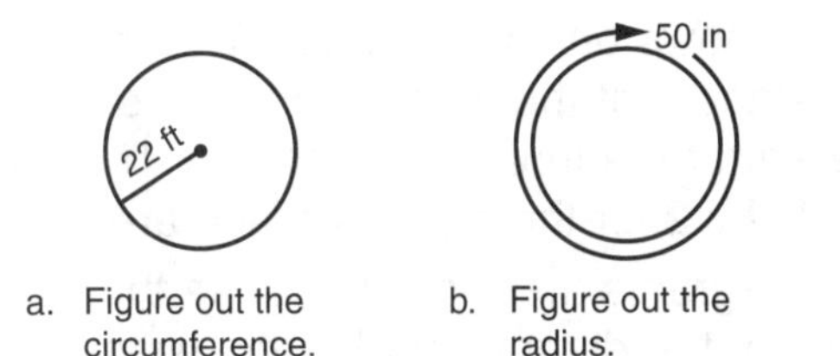

a. Figure out the circumference.
b. Figure out the radius.

To find the radius, students first find the diameter, then divide by 2. To find the circumference, students first multiply the radius by 2, then use the equation: $\pi \times D = C$.

In Lesson 113, students figure out the area of circles. They use the equation: Area $= \pi \times r \times r$. Lesson 113 provides a verification of the equation for finding area. **Radius** times **radius** is shown as a square whose sides are the length of the radius. The square is repeated 3.14 times, thus filling in all the parts of the circle with square units.

Students then apply the equation to work problems. Some problems give the diameter and ask about the area:

Other problems give the radius:

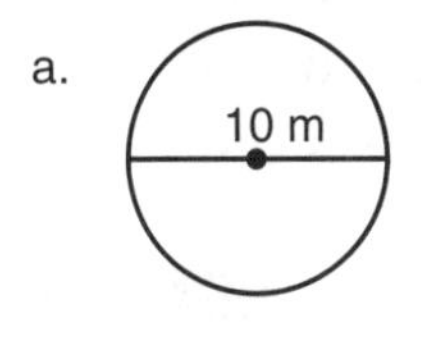

What's the area?

Students put the information from the problem in the equation, for example, Area $= 3.14 \times 5 \times 5$.

Here's part of the exercise from Lesson 113:

a. 10 m

b. (Write on the board:)

$$\mathbf{A = \pi \times r \times r}$$

- For each circle, you'll figure the area. Remember, the area equals pi times the radius times the radius.

c. Circle A. The radius is not shown, but the diameter is shown. What's the diameter? (Signal.) *10 meters.*

- So what's the radius? (Signal.) *5 meters.*
- The radius times the radius is 5 times 5. What's the answer? (Signal.) *25.*
- You multiply pi by that number and you'll have the area of the circle.
- Copy the equation for the area. Put in the number for pi and the number for the radius times the radius and figure out the area. Remember, the unit name is **square meters.** Raise your hand when you're finished.
- (Write to show:)

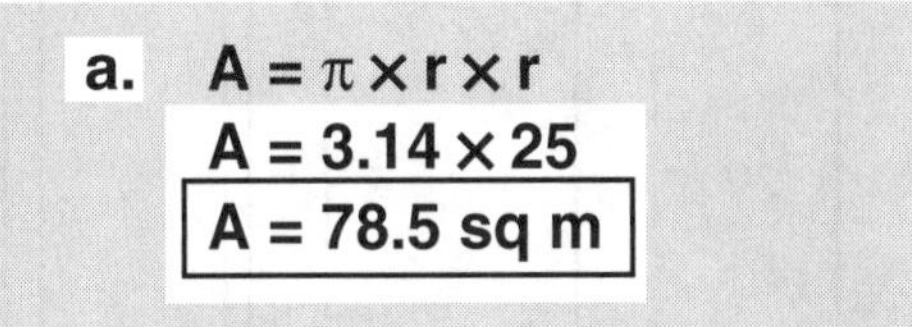

a. $A = \pi \times r \times r$
$A = 3.14 \times 25$
$A = 78.5$ sq m

- Here's what you should have, 3 and 14-hundredths times 25 equals 78 and 5/10. The area is 78 and 5/10. The area is 78 and 5/10 square meters.

Teaching note: Make sure that students write the complete equation: $A = p \times r \times r$. Some may show all the numbers that are multiplied: $3.14 \times 5 \times 5$. Others may show only π times the product (25); however, students must show the equation with a number for π and a numerical value for radius times radius.

They must also show the complete answer. It's somewhat arbitrary to require them to write the answer in the form: A = 78.5 sq m; however, if they write this equation, they will show the question they have answered. They are less likely to write an incorrect unit name. If students make a mistake on the unit name, ask, "What did you figure out? . . . Are the units for area square units or regular units?"

Note also that when students find the circumference, the diameter, or the radius, they write a simple equation:

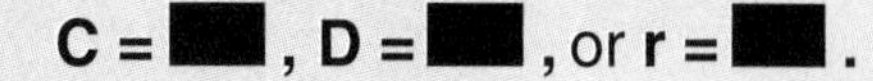

In the remaining lessons, students work problems that require them to find either the circumference or area of circles.

SURFACE AREA

Beginning in Lesson 94, students find the surface area of boxes. The initial set of examples shows color-coded boxes. The pairs of faces that have the same area are shown in the same color. The top and bottom are red, the front and back are yellow, and the two sides are blue. Students find the area of one red face, one yellow face and one blue face. Then students multiply by 2 to find the surface area of the entire box.

Here's part of the introduction from Lesson 94:

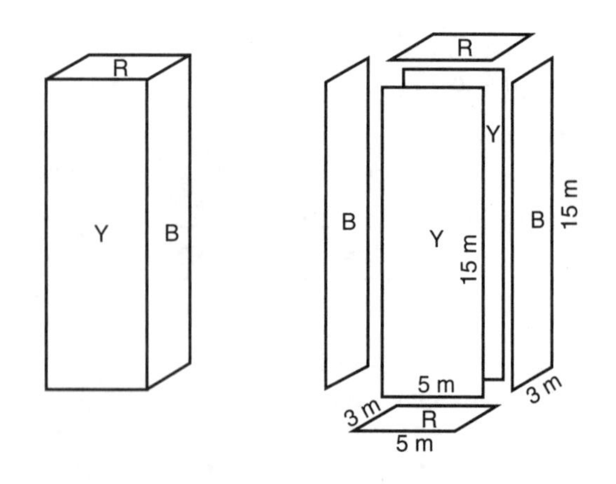

e. The first picture shows the box. The second picture shows the faces with spaces between them. Remember, the red faces are equal, the yellow faces are equal, and the blue faces are equal.

f. Figure out the area of one red face, one yellow face, and one blue face. Then add those areas. Raise your hand when you've done that much. (Observe students and give feedback.)

- (Write on the board:)

red	**15**
yellow	**75**
blue	**+ 45**
	135 sq m

- Here's the answer you should have. You've figured out half the area of the box. What do you do to figure the area of the entire box? (Signal.) *Multiply by 2.*
- Yes, multiply 135 by 2 and write the area of the entire box. Remember the unit name. Raise your hand when you're finished.
- Everybody, what's 135 times 2? (Signal.) *270.*
- The surface area of the whole box is 270 square meters.

g. Remember how to find the surface area of boxes.

In Lesson 97, students work similar problems that do not show an "exploded" diagram. The picture shows only three faces. The students understand that the faces are in pairs. They find the area for the three faces shown. Then they multiply by 2 for the entire surface area.

The diagrams are tricky because the units shown on the diagram for length, width, and height tell about two different faces:

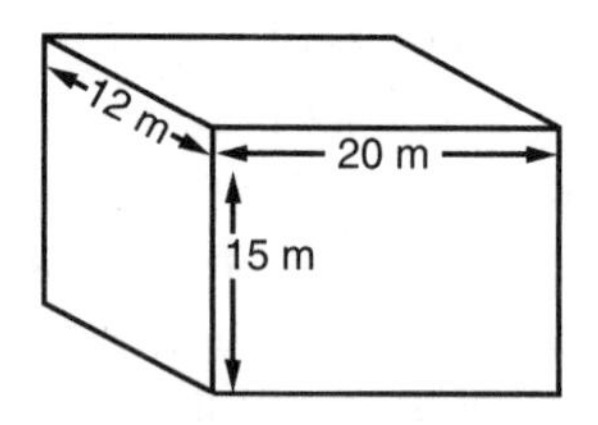

15 meters is a dimension of the front face and the side face. 20 meters is a dimension of the front face and the top face. 12 meters is a dimension of the side face and the top face. Expect students to have some difficulty applying the numbers appropriately. If they tend to make many mistakes, direct them to rework the problems.

In Lesson 99, pyramids are introduced. These pyramids have rectangular bases and two pairs of side faces:

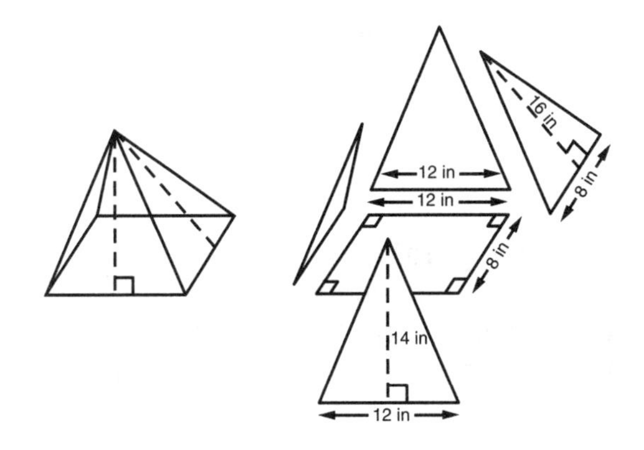

(The base is shown in red; front and back faces are yellow; side faces are blue.) Students add the surface area of one blue face and one yellow face. They multiply that area by 2. This gives the total area of all the faces that meet at the top of the figure. Then students add the surface area of the base.

A second kind of pyramid is introduced in Lesson 105. This type has a triangular base and three sides that have exactly the same area.

Here's part of the exercise from Lesson 102:

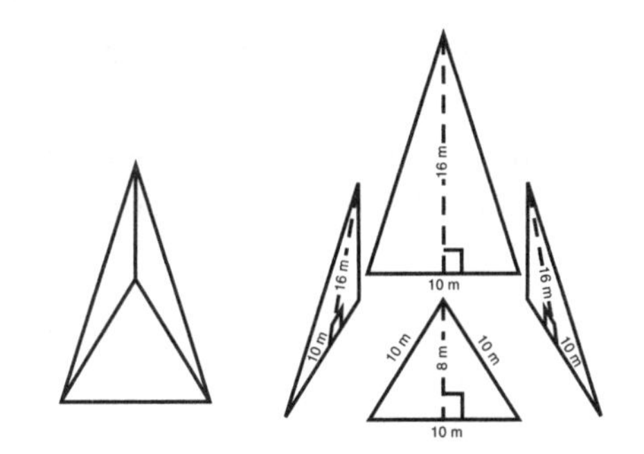

b. Figure A is a pyramid with a **triangular** base. All three sides that come to a point are the same color because they have the same area. The base is a different color because it has a different area.

- To find the area of the whole figure, you find the area of one blue face. Then what do you do with that number? (Signal.) *Multiply by 3.*
- Yes, multiply by 3 and you'll have the area of all blue faces. Then you add the area of the red base.

c. Everybody, figure out the total area of the blue faces. Raise your hand when you've done that much.

(Observe students and give feedback.)

- (Write on the board:)

blue	80
	× 3
	240 sq m

- Here's what you should have. One blue face has an area of 80 square meters. The total area for all the blue faces is 3 times 80 square meters. That's 240 square meters.

d. Everybody, figure out the area of the triangular base and add that to the total area for the blue faces. Raise your hand when you've written the area for the whole figure.

(Observe students and give feedback.)

- Check your work. The base of the figure is 40 square meters. The area of the whole figure is 280 square meters. Raise your hand if you got it right.

Teaching note: Students may have trouble with the idea that each face has a base (the base of the triangle), but that one of the faces is also referred to as the base (the base of the pyramid). You can make it simpler for the students if you refer to the color of the triangles. When referring to the base of the pyramid, call it the red base. Or say, "One of the faces is the base of this figure. What's the color of that face?" The red base has a height shown with a dotted line and another **side** referred to as the base. If you refer to the color of the face, you'll minimize the confusion. Also remind students of the overall strategy: "You're figuring out the area of each **face** and figuring out the total of all the **faces.**"

VOLUME

Volume begins in Lesson 104. Students use the equation: **Volume = area of base × height**. The area of the base gives square units. Multiplying by the height creates cubes. The unit name for volume is therefore expressed as cubic units. Students work first with six-sided boxes (rectangular base), then with five-sided boxes (triangular base).

Here's part of the introduction to six-sided boxes in Lesson 104:

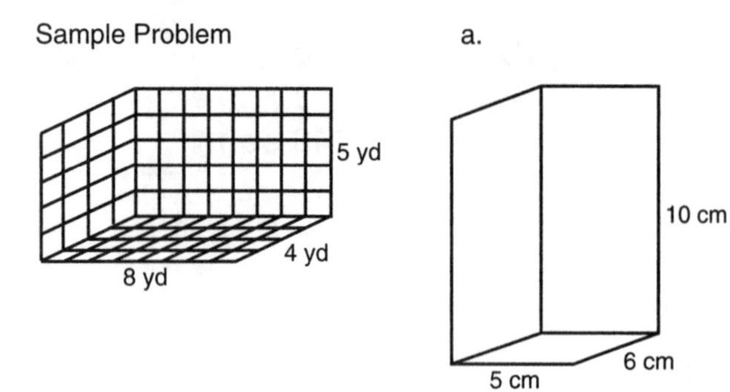

e. We'll work the sample problem together. We start with the equation for the volume of a box.

f. Everybody, what is that equation? (Signal.) *Volume equals area of base times height.*
(Repeat step f until firm.)

g. (Write on the board:)

V = Area of b × h

- Copy the equation for volume. Next to the equation, figure out the area of the base in the sample problem. Raise your hand when you've done that much.
- Everybody, what's the area of the base? (Signal.) *32 square yards.*
- Yes, the base is 8 times 4. That's 32 square yards.
- (Write to show:)

V = Area of b × h
V = 32 ×

- To find the volume, we multiply 32 times the height. Everybody, what's the height? (Signal.) *5 yards.*
- Find the volume. Remember, the unit name is **cubic yards.** Raise your hand when you're finished.
- (Write to show:)

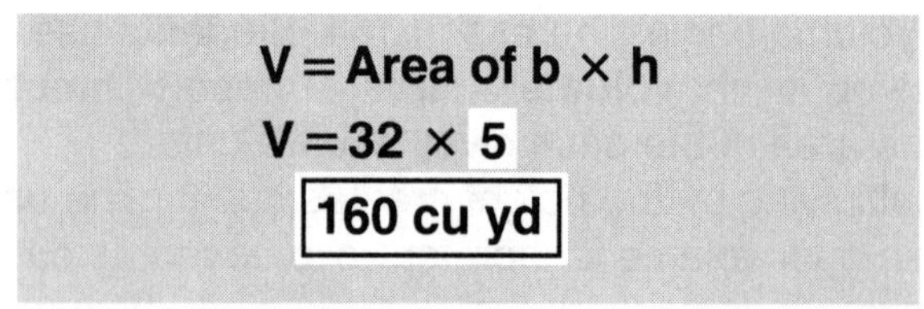

- Here's what you should have. You multiply 32 by 5. That's 160. The volume is 160 cubic yards. Raise your hand if you got it right.

h. Work problem A. Remember to start with the equation for volume. Find the area of the base. Then multiply by the height. Raise your hand when you've finished problem A.
(Observe students and give feedback.)

- (Write on the board:)

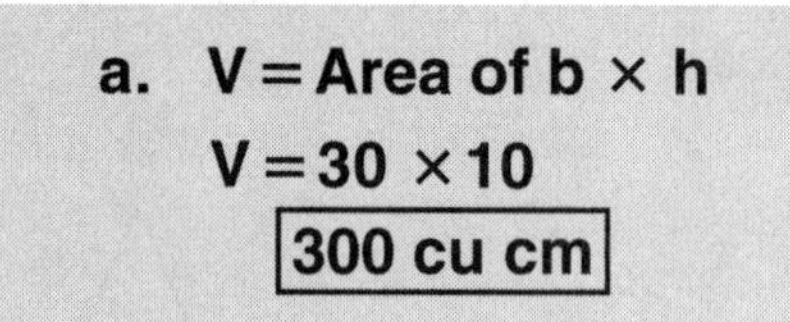

- Here's what you should have. Raise your hand if you got it right.

Teaching note: Students are expected to remember the equation for the volume of a box (Volume = area of base × height). When students work a volume problem, they are to start with this equation.

In Lesson 106, students find the volume of boxes that have a triangular base. The equation for finding the volume is the same: Volume = area of base × height. The only difference for finding the volume of a box with a triangular base is the procedure required to find the area of the base.

In Lesson 107, students work a mixed set of problems, finding the volume of both five- and six-sided boxes.

ANGLES AND LINES

In Level E, students learn the following information about angles:

1) Angles are measured in degrees and are shown with a curved arrow that goes from one line to the other:

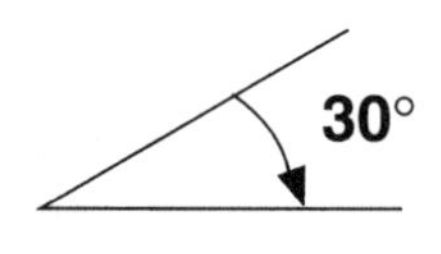

2) The arrow may be close to the point where the lines intersect or it may be farther from this point:

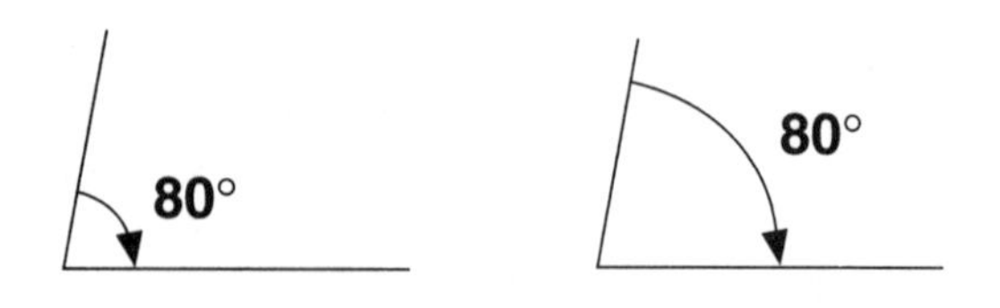

3) The curved arrow is part of a circle. The number of degrees for a whole circle is 360; the number for half a circle is 180.

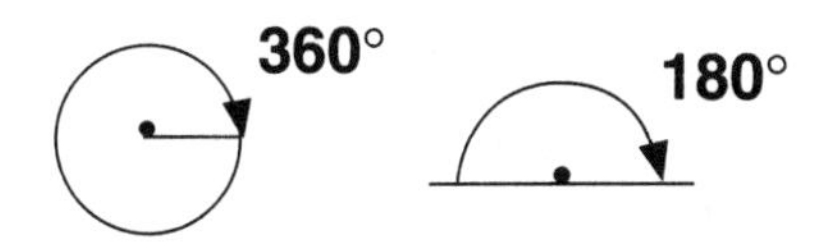

4) The number of degrees for a "corner" is 90:

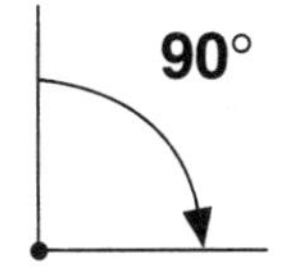

5) The same angle is the same portion of a circle, regardless of the spatial orientation. All these angles are 30 degrees:

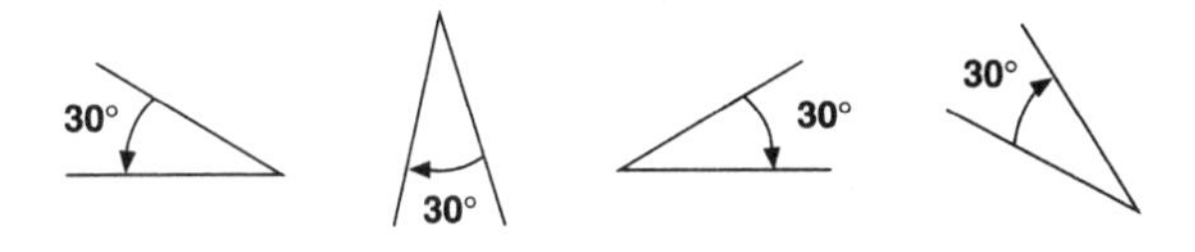

6) An angle that is divided into two parts can be shown as the big number in a number family; the two parts are the small numbers:

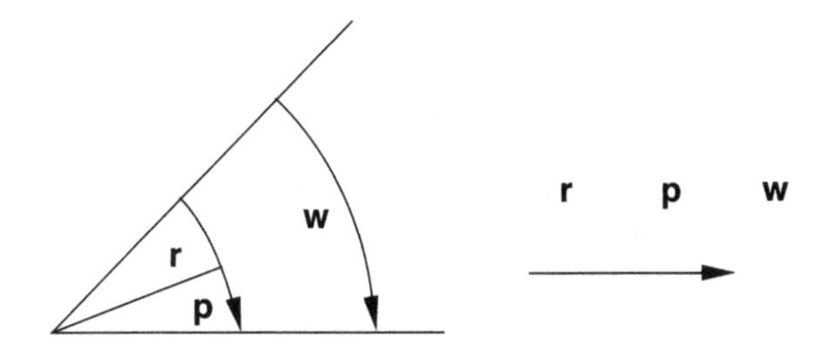

7) A line intersecting parallel lines creates the same angle at both lines (corresponding angles):

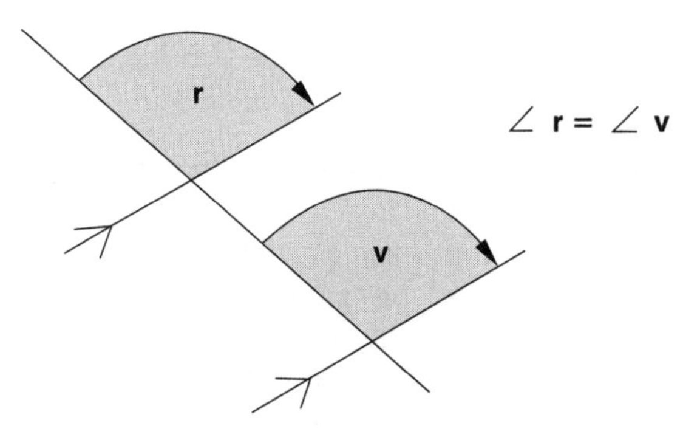

8) Opposite angles formed by intersecting lines are equal:

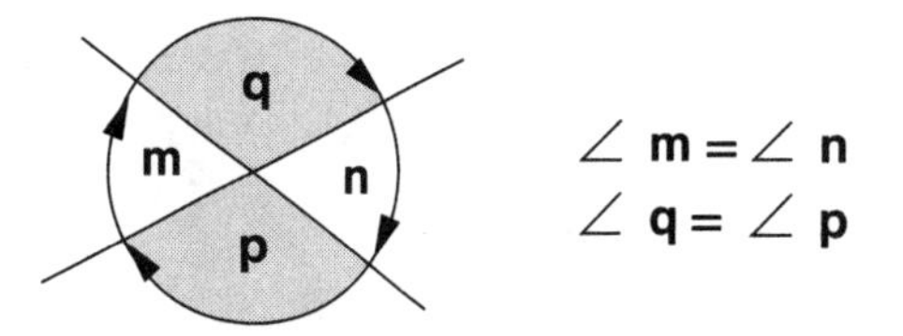

Students use this information to work a variety of problems.

The first exercises occur in Lesson 71. Students learn facts about angles: The angle for the corner of a rectangle is 90 degrees; the angle for half a circle is 180 degrees; the angle for a complete circle is 360 degrees.

Teaching note: Students are to memorize these facts. Students will use the information in later lessons to figure out the number of degrees in fractions of a circle, and will also work problems in which they draw inferences from angles on a "straight line" which forms half a circle (180 degrees):

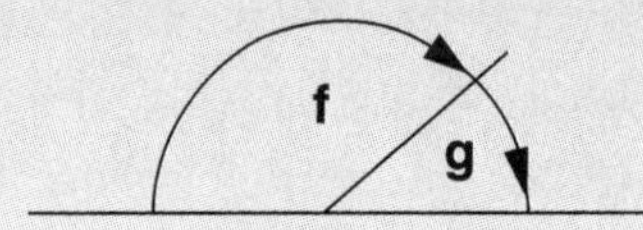

Here's the problem set from Lesson 71:

a. Write the degrees for the largest angle.
b. How many more degrees is angle p than angle r?
c. How many degrees are in a whole circle?
d. How many degrees are in half a circle?
e. What's the letter of the smallest angle?

In Lesson 72, students work with angles that are divided into two parts. Students make a number family to figure out the degrees in one of the angles shown (either one of the smaller angles or the entire angle).

Here's part of the exercise from Lesson 72:

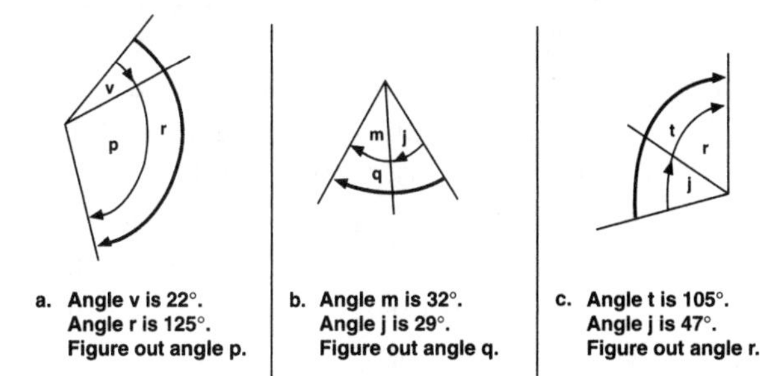

d. Problem A. Raise your hand when you know the letters for the two smaller angles that add up to the whole angle. √

- One smaller angle is V. Everybody, what's the letter for the other smaller angle? (Signal.) *P.*
- What's the letter for the whole angle? (Signal.) *R.*
- (Write on the board:)

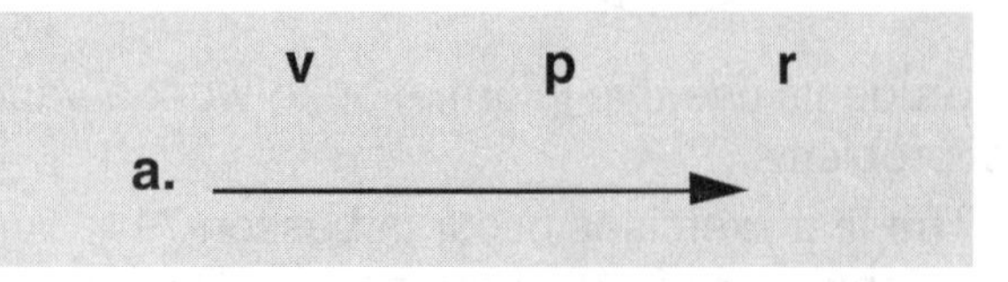

- Here's the number family with three letters.
- Your turn: Copy the number family. Then read problem A. Write the two numbers the problem gives and figure out the missing number. Write the answer for item A and box it. Remember the degree symbol. Raise your hand when you're finished. (Observe students and give feedback.)
- (Write to show:)

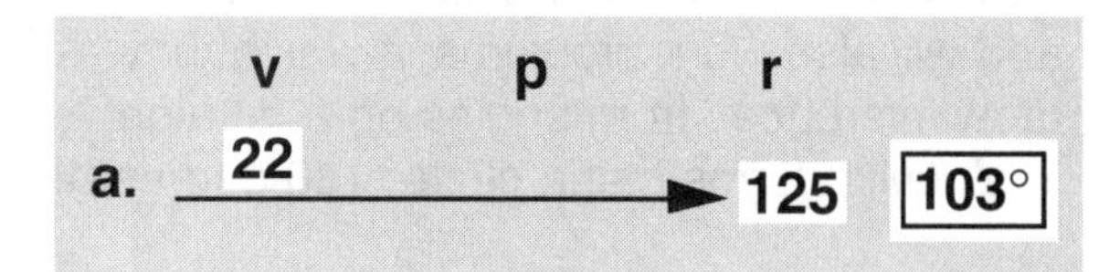

- The problem tells that angle V is 22 degrees and angle R is 125 degrees. The missing angle is P.
- Everybody, how many degrees is angle P? (Signal.) *103.*

Teaching note: This exercise should not be difficult for the students; however, it is very informative about the subtle properties of angles. Angles can be added, subtracted, and combined the way other parts of a whole can be added, subtracted, and combined. The total number of degrees is the big number. The number of degrees for the two component parts equals the degrees for the whole. Students often have trouble seeing that the total number of degrees in the two smaller angles actually equals the degrees in the larger angle. The color coding shows that this relationship exists. The total for V and P is the total for the white and the gray. The blue angle is also the total for the white and the gray.

If students have trouble understanding the relationship, have them outline with their finger the entire angle, and each of the smaller angles. Once they get the idea that the total angle is represented two ways (it's both the white and the gray angles combined, and it's the blue angle), they will have a good understanding of the basis for mathematical inferences involving combined angles.

In Lesson 74, students find the number of degrees in a fraction of a circle. Students learn that a fraction of a value is a fraction times that value. To complete the degrees in 4/5 of a circle, students translate 4/5 of a circle to 4/5 × 360. The answer is 288. So 4/5 of a circle is 288 degrees.

Students work similar problems that show angles that are less than 360 degrees:

b. How many degrees are in $\frac{7}{10}$ of a circle?

b. How many degrees are in $\frac{2}{9}$ of angle p?

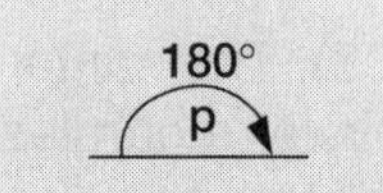

f. Work problem B. Raise your hand when you're finished.
(Observe students and give feedback.)

- (Write on the board:)

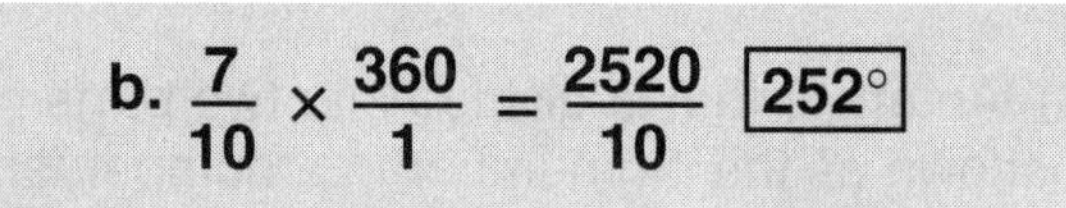

$$b.\ \frac{7}{10} \times \frac{360}{1} = \frac{2520}{10}\ \boxed{252°}$$

- Here's what you should have. 7/10 of a circle is 7/10 times 360. That's 252 degrees. Raise your hand if you got it right.

g. Problem C asks: How many degrees are in 2/9 of angle P? 2/9 of angle P is 2/9 times angle P. Write the equation with the degrees for angle P and box the answer. Raise your hand when you're finished. (Observe students and give feedback.)

- (Write on the board:)

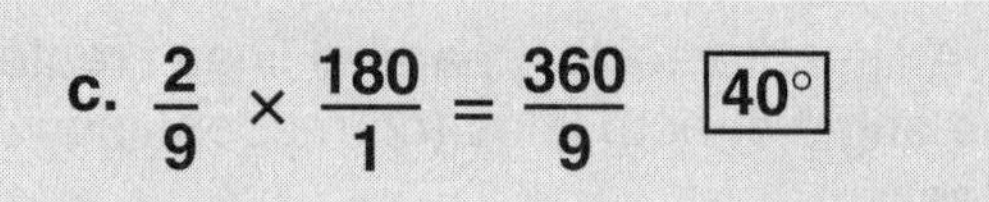

$$c.\ \frac{2}{9} \times \frac{180}{1} = \frac{360}{9}\ \boxed{40°}$$

- Here's what you should have. Angle p is 180 degrees. 2/9 times 180 is 40 degrees. Raise your hand if you got it right.

Teaching note: Make sure that students show their work. Do not accept abbreviated "equations" that have parts missing.

This problem type is different from a ratio problem because the entire ending fraction is the answer. (The numerator is not the answer, and the denominator is not the answer.) Students are not to box part of the ending fraction. They are to work the division problem for that fraction, write the answer with a degree marker, and box the answer. Students who are permitted to take shortcuts may later become greatly confused about whether they are finding the value that completes a fraction or whether they are figuring out a fraction and then simplifying that fraction.

For ratios, you're finding either the numerator or a denominator of a fraction:

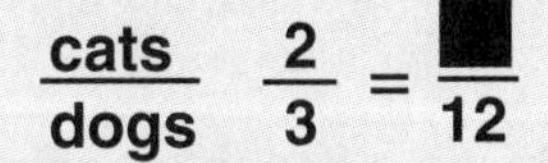

The answer to the question the problem asks is **part** of the fraction—either the numerator or denominator.

For fraction multiplication, the **whole** fraction is the answer:

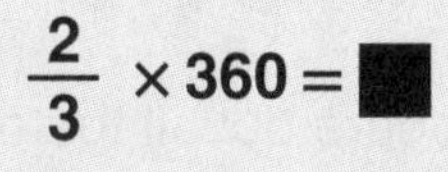

One reason that students are required to box their answers is to ensure that students understand the question the problem asks and understand the calculations that lead to that answer. If students take shortcuts and do not box their answers, they may not clearly see the difference between problem types.

In Lesson 81, students are introduced to problems that show an entire angle of 90 degrees or 180 degrees divided into two component angles. Students are shown that this angle marker:

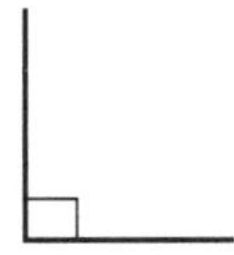

indicates 90 degrees. (The marker is like the corner of a rectangle.) The angles for half a circle show 180 degrees:

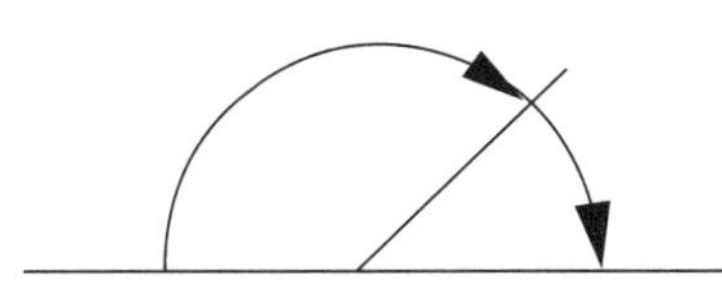

From the information about the whole angle, students are able to work problems that ask about one of the component angles.

Examples:

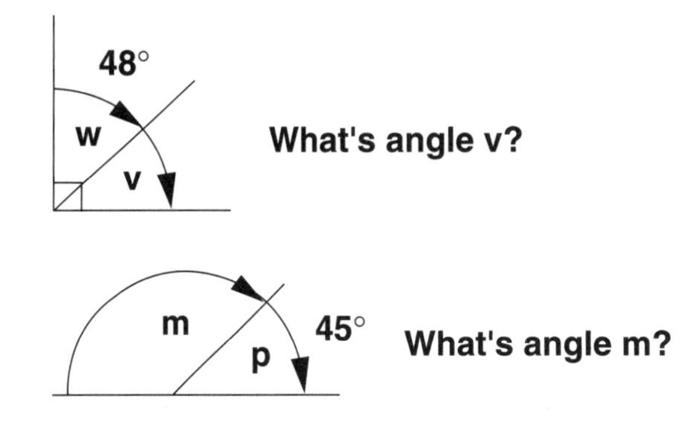

To work the problems, students make a number family and write the number of degrees for the big number (either 90 or 180). Students then put in the value for the other angle shown and figure out the third angle:

Teaching note: In the number family, there is no letter for the whole angle, merely the number of degrees.

In Lesson 83, students learn the rule about corresponding angles: A line intersecting parallel lines creates the same angle at each parallel line.

Here's part of the introduction from Lesson 83:

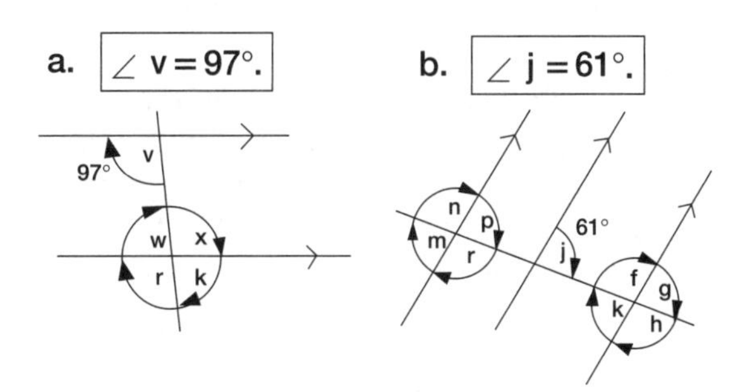

g. Problem A. The number of degrees is shown for one of the angles. The corresponding angle has the same number of degrees.

- (Write on the board:)

a. ∠ v = 97°

- Here's the statement for the angle that is shown. This says: Angle V equals 97 degrees.
- Copy this equation. Below, write the equation for the corresponding angle. Write the letter and the number of degrees. Don't forget the angle symbol. Raise your hand when you're finished.
- (Write to show:)

a. ∠ v = 97°
∠ r = 97°

- Here's what you should have. The corresponding angle is R. Angle R equals 97 degrees.
- Problem B. The number of degrees is shown for angle J. Write the equation for that angle. Then write the equation for each of the corresponding angles. Raise your hand when you're finished. (Observe students and give feedback.)
- (Write on the board:)

b. ∠ j = 61°
∠ p = 61°
∠ g = 61°

- Here are the three equations you should have. Angle J equals 61 degrees. Angle P equals 61 degrees. Angle G equals 61 degrees.

Teaching note: If students have trouble writing the correct equation, do this: Touch one of the angles in problem b. Tell the student to touch any angles that correspond to this angle. If the student makes a mistake, touch the corresponding angle or angles and repeat the task. Repeat with different angles. Don't try to use lengthy explanations about the relative position of the angles. Just require students to touch angles that correspond to the different angles that you touch.

In Lesson 86, students identify the number of degrees for all the angles that are shown in a diagram:

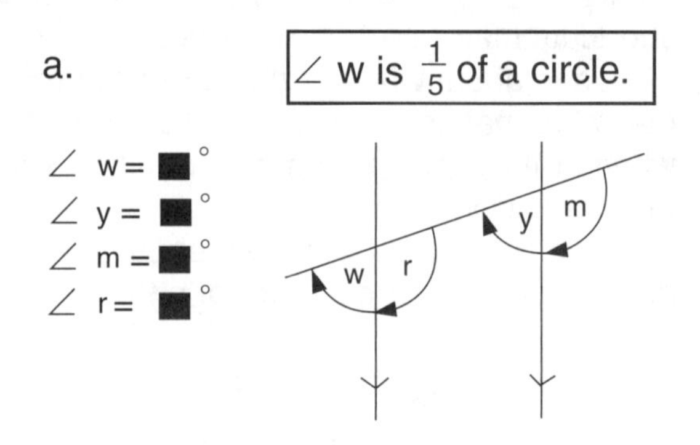

The diagram shows a line intersecting parallel lines. So pairs of angles are equal.

Students are provided with information about one of the angles: Angle w is 1/5 of a circle. Students use what they know to figure out the number of degrees in angle w:

∠ w = 72°

Then students figure out all the other angles. Together, angle w and angle r form half a circle. So angle r = 180 − 72. Angle r equals 108 degrees.

Angle y corresponds to angle w. So y also equals 72 degrees. Angle m corresponds to angle R, so angle M equals 108 degrees.

In Lesson 88, students work problems that involve vertically opposite angles.

Example:

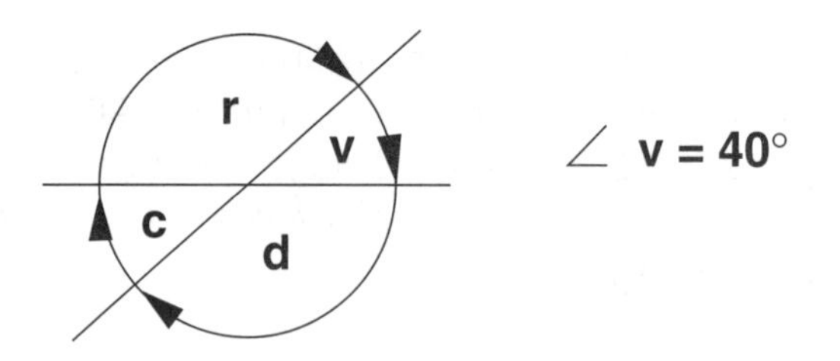

Students work these problems by using what they know about the degrees in half a circle.

Here's the procedure:

Angle v is given. They combine r with v.

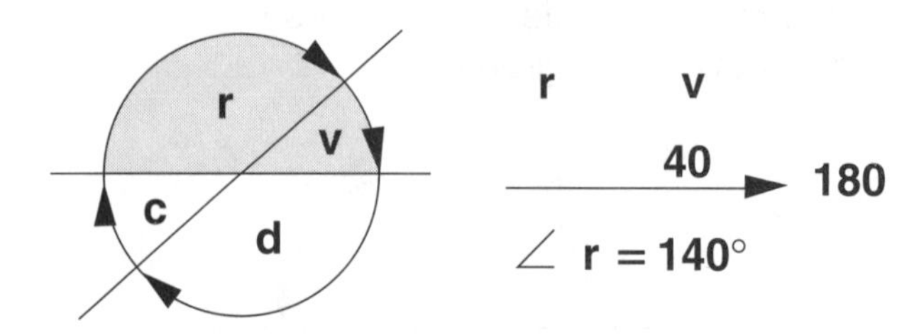

Then they combine r with c.

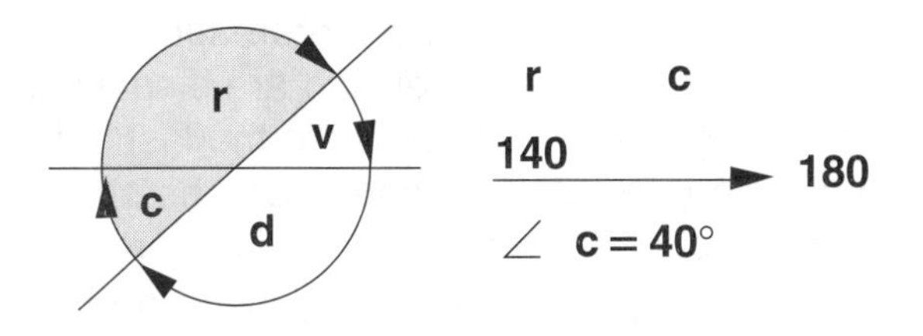

They discover that angle v and angle c are each 40 degrees. Finally, students figure out angle d. They do that by combining angle v with angle d.

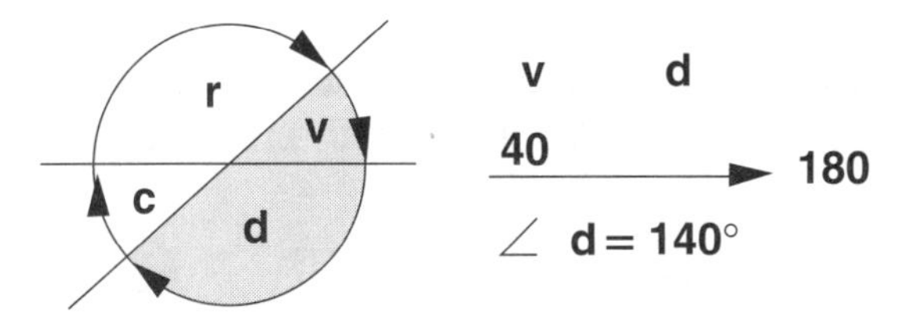

Angle d equals angle r.

In Lesson 91, students figure out the rule that vertically opposite angles are equal. Students are introduced to the expression, **opposite angles.** They apply the rule to work problems of this form:

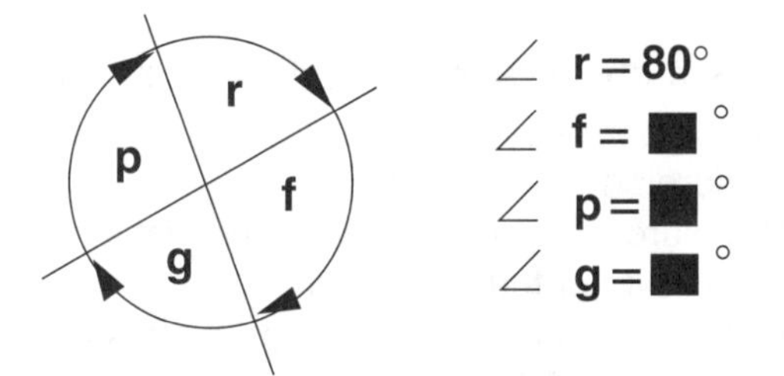

> ***Teaching note:*** With what students know about angles that make up half a circle, they are able to figure out all the angles without using the rule about opposite angles. However, the rule provides a fast way of figuring out all the angles.

In Lesson 92, students apply what they have learned about corresponding angles, opposite angles and angles that form half a circle to work problems of the form:

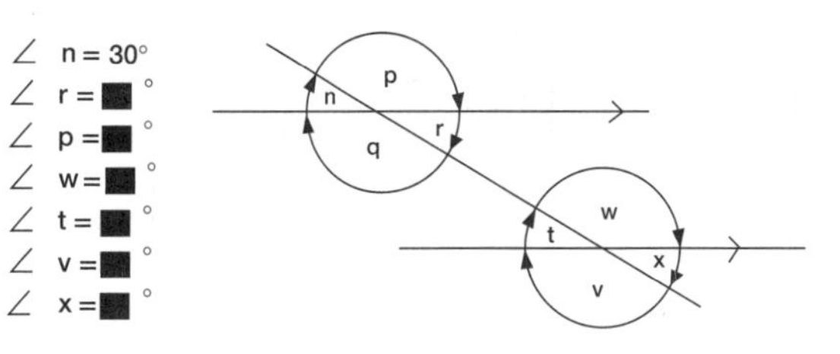

Projects

Projects presented in Level E extend what students have learned about circles, proportions, probability, averages, volume, area, and perimeter to activities that require gathering data and experimentation. Projects also require students to display data in new ways (bar graphs, pie graphs with proportional slices, frequency distributions, and scale models.)

The projects begin in Lesson 116 and continue through Lesson 125. The teacher presentation provides fairly detailed directions for each project. Before presenting these lessons, read the teacher presentation carefully and make sure that you have the materials students will need.

Here's a summary of the materials needed:

LESSON(S)	MATERIALS
116–117	Tape measure, masking tape or thumbtacks, construction paper, and scissors
118–120	Protractors
123	Two paper bags, two black cards and three not-black cards of the same size, four identical black objects and one not-black object of the same size
125	Paper cups and coins

For most of the projects, students work in teams or pairs.

On Lessons 116 and 117, students work in teams to construct a scale model of the solar system. First, students use information about the distance of Earth from the sun and about the "ratio numbers" for the other planets to figure out the distance of these planets from the sun.

Here's the table they use:

	Distance from the sun				
	Ratio number	Million km	Million mi	Model: inches	Model: rounded inches
Mercury	.39				
Venus	.72				
Earth	1.00	150	93	10.0	
Mars	1.52				
Jupiter	5.20				
Saturn	9.54				
Uranus	19.18				
Neptune	30.06				
Pluto	39.79				

Students first complete the column that indicates each distance in millions of kilometers. Students work the problems a fast way: If Mercury's distance is 39-hundredths of the Earth's distance, Mercury is .39 × 150 million kilometers from the sun.

Next, students complete the column for the distances in millions of miles using the value for Earth (93) as the basis for comparison. (If Earth's distance is 93 million miles, the distance for Mars is 1.52 × 93 million miles.)

In the next lesson, students complete the columns that show the distances for the model students will construct. Students indicate the number of inches each planet will be from the sun. They then round these values to the nearest inch:

	Distance from the sun				
	Ratio number	Million km	Million mi	Model: inches	Model: rounded inches
Mercury	.39	59	36	3.9	4
Venus	.72	108	67	7.2	7
Earth	1.00	150	93	10.0	10
Mars	1.52	228	141	15.2	15
Jupiter	5.20	780	484	52.0	52
Saturn	9.54	1431	887	95.4	95
Uranus	19.18	2877	1785	191.8	192
Neptune	30.06	4509	2796	300.6	301
Pluto	39.79	5969	3700	397.9	398
		Lesson 116		Lesson 117	

This extension activity demonstrates how the same ratio numbers can be used to compute a variety of proportions. Students use information about the Earth's distance from the sun to calculate the distance of other planets in kilometers, miles, and inches. The same ratio numbers are used for all calculations.

Following completion of the table, students work cooperatively to construct a **model** of the solar system. The planets are represented with circles 2 inches in diameter and are displayed according to the values shown in the last column of the table (Mercury, 4 inches from the sun; Venus, 7 inches from the sun; and so forth).

The project for Lesson 118 requires students to construct slices for a pie graph. For this project, students use information about hours to make slices that show the correct proportions.

Students first complete the table. The number of hours for each slice is converted into degrees. Students use a protractor to construct each slice of the pie graph. Expect students to have mechanical problems in using the protractor.

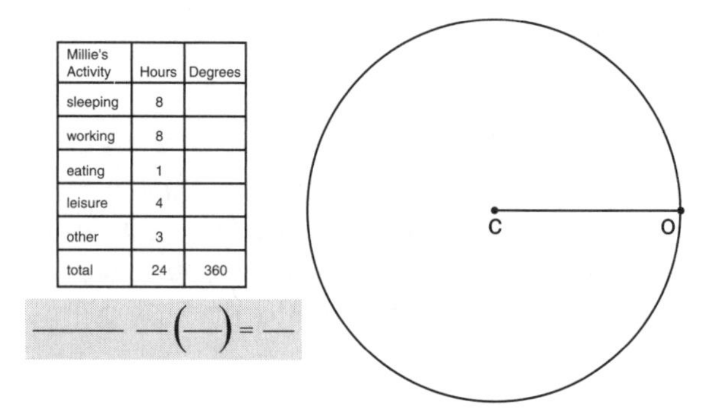

Here's a checklist of what they must do:

- Use the appropriate line as the baseline for the measurement.
- Make sure the center point for the circle is on the center point of the protractor.
- Make sure the baseline goes through zero degrees on the protractor.
- Make a dot on the circumference of the circle to mark the correct number of degrees for the slice. (If the slice is to be 50 degrees, make a dot where the 50-degree marker intersects the circumference of the circle.)
- Use a straight-edge to draw a line from the mark to the center of the circle.
- Use this line as the baseline for the next measurement.

In Lesson 119, students work in pairs. They conduct a survey to determine the two favorite colors of 15 respondents. Students display the data with tally marks, numbers, and degrees. The degrees indicate the size of the slice on the pie graph that they construct.

In Lesson 120, students do a similar project, conducting a survey for favorite geometric shapes. Students display the data two ways: in a bar graph and in a pie graph. The bar graph requires percent numbers.

Students complete this table:

We're conducting a survey about people's favorite shapes. Point to your favorite shape.

	Frequency	Number	%	Degree
○				
△				
□				
⏢				
▱				
✡				
Total	■	20	100	360

Students record tally marks in the column labeled **Frequency.** They show the numbers in the next column. They convert the numbers to percents for column 3. Students show the degrees in the last column. To construct the bar graph, students use the percent numbers. To construct the pie graph, they use the degree numbers.

In Lesson 121, students use the information from 10 different bar graphs to compute the average percents for the shapes. Students display the average percents on a bar graph.

In Lesson 122, students compare the surface area and volume of two cubes, one relatively large, one relatively small. Students discover that the larger cube is more "efficient" because it has less surface area for every cubic unit of volume. For the larger cube, the number for volume exceeds the number for surface area. For the smaller cube, the number for volume is less than the number for surface area. Students then figure out the size of a cube for which both the volume and surface area have the same number.

Lesson 123 presents a probability project. Students determine the contents of a bag by conducting an experiment. Students are told that there are 5 objects in the bag, at least one of which is black. To determine the number of black objects in the bag, students first indicate the expected outcomes for the various possible combinations if one took 30 trials:

COMPOSITION OF SET	EXPECTED OUTCOME
0 black, 5 not	0 out of 30
1 black, 4 not	6 out of 30
2 black, 3 not	12 out of 30
3 black, 2 not	18 out of 30
4 black, 1 not	24 out of 30
5 black, 0 not	30 out of 30

Students take 30 trials at pulling an object from the bag and recording the data. The results imply which bag was used. Students find the expected outcome that is closest to the actual outcome. The bag that produced that expected number is the bag that was used in the experiment.

Example: 16 is the outcome. The closest to 18. That implies the bag with 3 black objects.

In Lesson 124, students work a problem similar to that presented in Lesson 122. They find the size of a square for which both the perimeter and the area have the same number.

In Lesson 125, students work in pairs to conduct a probability experiment. They flip a coin 30 times and record the outcomes in sets of 6 trials. The expected number of heads for each set of trials is 3. Students record the actual number for each set. Then each pair of students reports the outcomes for their sets of data. The data for the entire class are summarized on the board. Then students use the summary to construct a frequency-distribution table.

For example:

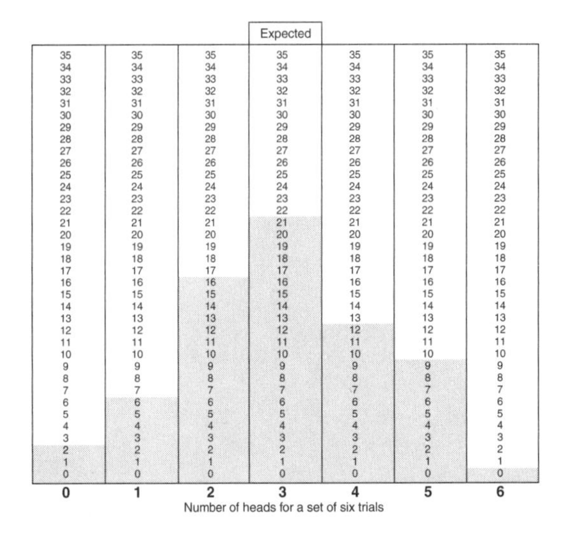

Students make a bar to the appropriate number for each column.

SUMMARY

Students who complete the projects presented in Level E will have learned new tool skills, used these skills in problem-solving contexts, and finally applied them to complex projects. The projects give you and the students an idea of the power the students have developed. As you do the projects, you and the students will identify other possible projects. If time permits, do them. The purpose of teaching core skills and operations is to apply them to real-life settings. Students who complete Level E have a repertoire of skills and the experiences required to meet the challenges presented as they move to higher levels of math and tackle even more difficult enterprises. Both you and your students will be impressed with their performance.

Appendix A

Connecting Math Concepts

Level E Cumulative Test 1 (Lessons 1–30)

EXERCISE 1

a. This is a test. You should only have your test and a sharpened pencil on your desk.
b. Find part 1.
c. Work parts 1 through 15.
- Raise your hand when you've finished part 15.
- (Observe students, but do not give feedback.)

CUMULATIVE TEST 1 PERCENT SUMMARY					
SCORE	%	SCORE	%	SCORE	%
113	100	101	89	89	79
112	99	100	88	88	78
111	98	98–99	87	87	77
110	97	97	86	86	76
109	96	96	85	85	75
107–108	95	95	84	84	74
106	94	94	83	83	73
105	93	93	82	81–82	72
104	92	92	81	80	71
103	91	90–91	80	79	70
102	90				

CUMULATIVE TEST 1 SCORING CHART						
PART	SCORE				POSSIBLE SCORE	PASSING SCORE
1	Working or not working each item 1	Total 6	Each correct answer 1	Total 3	9	8
2	1 for each item				4	3
3	2 for each item				6	6
4	Each cell 1	Total 4	Each question 2	Total 6	10	8
5	Only circled larger fraction 1	Total 3	Correct sign 2	Total 6	9	7
6	EACH ITEM: Problem 2	Answer 1	Total 3		6	5
7	2 for each item				6	6
8	3 for each item				6	6
9	2 for each item				6	6
10	3 for each item				9	6
11	1 for each item				3	3
12	2 for each item				10	8
13	2 for each item				6	Parts 13, 14 combined
14	1 for each missing number 1				8	12
15	Complete multiplication equation 1	Total 3			15	15
	Division Problem 1	Answer 1	Total 6			
	Fraction 1	Answer 1	Total 6			
				TOTAL	113	

CUMULATIVE TEST 1 REMEDIES	
PART	LESSON and (EXERCISE)
1	4 (4), 5 (3), 6 (1), 7 (1), 9 (3), 11 (1), 12 (1), 13 (2), 15 (4), 16 (1)
2	1 (5), 2 (1), 5 (4), 6 (7)
3	2 (6), 3 (7), 5 (5), 6 (4), 7 (3), 8 (5), 9 (6), 10 (2), 15 (3)
4	1 (4), 2 (2), 3 (3), 4 (2), 5 (6), 6 (5), 7 (4, 6), 8 (3), 9 (4), 11 (7), 12 (4), 13 (4), 14 (4), 15 (7), 16 (6), 17 (7)
5	25 (2), 26 (1), 27 (1), 28 (4), 29 (1)
6	1 (3), 2 (3), 3 (2), 4 (5), 15 (5), 16 (2), 17 (6), 18 (2), 19 (2), 21 (3), 22 (1), 23 (4)
7	22 (4), 23 (7), 24 (7), 25 (5)
8	1 (5), 2 (1), 5 (4), 6 (7), 14 (2), 15 (1)
9	1 (2), 2 (4, 8), 3 (6), 4 (7), 5 (2), 6 (2)
10	4 (6), 5 (7), 6 (6), 7 (5), 8 (4), 9 (7), 11 (8), 12 (2), 13 (3), 19 (4), 25 (6), 26 (4), 27 (3), 28 (3)
11	3 (4), 4 (1), 5 (1), 6 (3), 10 (1), 11 (3), 16 (3), 19 (3)
12	22 (5), 23 (2), 25 (1), 26 (3), 27 (2), 28 (5), 29 (2)
13	19 (5), 20 (2), 21 (4), 22 (2), 23 (1), 24 (3)
14	14 (3), 17 (3), 18 (1), 25 (4), 26 (5), 27 (5)
15	1 (6), 2 (7), 3 (5), 4 (8), 12 (6), 13 (5), 17 (5), 18 (5), 19 (7), 21 (7), 22 (6)

CUMULATIVE TEST 2 SCORING CHART						
PART	SCORE				POSSIBLE SCORE	PASSING SCORE
1	2 for each item				4	4
2	EACH ITEM: Answer 1	Only correct fraction circled 2		Total 3	6	5
3	2 for each question				10	8
4	EACH ITEM: Fraction with prime factors 2	Reduced fraction 2		Total 4	12	9
5	2 for each item				8	6
6	Only circled larger value 1	Total 4	Correct sign 2	Total 8	12	10
7	3 for each item				6	6
8	1 for each cell				4	4
9	1 for each item				4	3
10	1 for each missing number				8	7
11	Working or not working each item 1	Total 6	Each answer 1	Total 4	10	8
12	1 for each cell				6	5
13	2 for each item				4	4
14	2 for each item				6	6
			TOTAL		100	

Connecting Math Concepts

Level E Cumulative Test 2 (Lessons 1–60)

Note: Students may use calculators only on parts 13 and 14.

EXERCISE 1

a. This is a test. You should only have your test and a sharpened pencil on your desk.
b. Find part 1.
- After you work each item, you'll write the complete answer to each question. Remember, there's a number and a unit name.

c. Work parts 1 through 12.
- (Observe students, but do not give feedback.)
- (After students complete part 12, permit them to use calculators to complete parts 13 and 14. Observe students, but do not give feedback.)

CUMULATIVE TEST 2 REMEDIES	
PART	LESSON and (EXERCISE)
1	27 (4), 28 (6), 29 (3), 30 (2), 31 (5), 32 (2), 40 (2), 52 (2), 53 (4), 54 (1), 55 (4), 56 (4), 57 (1), 58 (2), 59 (2)
2	31 (4), 32 (3), 34 (3), 35 (1), 38 (4), 39 (1), 41 (2)
3 a, b	46 (1), 47 (3), 48 (2), 49 (1), 51 (3), 52 (5), 53 (2), 54 (5)
3 c	34 (2), 35 (2), 36 (2)
4	21 (1), 22 (5), 23 (2), 24 (2, 6), 25 (1, 3), 26 (3), 27 (2), 28 (5), 29 (2), 31 (6), 32 (5), 33 (4), 35 (5), 36 (3), 37 (2), 38 (2), 39 (3), 41 (1), 42 (1), 43 (4)
5	2 (6), 3 (7), 5 (5), 6 (4), 7 (3), 8 (5), 9 (6), 10 (2), 15 (3)
6	25 (2), 26 (1), 27 (1), 28 (4), 29 (1)
7	1 (5), 2 (1), 5 (4), 6 (7), 14 (2), 15 (1)
8	26 (6, a-d), 27 (6, a-c), 28 (7, a-c), 29 (6, a-d), 36 (2, a-d), 37 (5, a-d), 38 (3, a-d), 39 (5, a-d)
9	1 (5), 2 (1), 5 (4), 6 (7)
10	14 (3), 17 (3), 18 (1), 25 (4), 26 (5), 27 (5)
11	4 (4), 5 (3), 6 (1), 7 (1), 9 (3), 11 (1), 12 (1), 13 (2), 15 (4), 16 (1)
12	22 (4), 23 (7), 24 (7), 25 (5), 28 (2), 29 (5), 30 (3), 31 (2), 32 (6), 33 (5), 34 (5), 37 (6), 38 (6), 39 (6), 41 (7), 42 (5),
13	41 (4), 42 (3)
14	43 (6), 44 (1), 45 (5), 48 (5), 49 (4)

Connecting Math Concepts

Level E Cumulative Test 3 (Lessons 1–90)

Note: Students are not to use calculators for any part of the test.

a. This is a test. You should only have your test and a sharpened pencil on your desk.
b. Find part 1.
c. Do the test on your own.
- Raise your hand when you're finished.

CUMULATIVE TEST 3 PERCENT SUMMARY					
SCORE	%	SCORE	%	SCORE	%
113	100	101	89	89	79
112	99	100	88	88	78
111	98	98–99	87	87	77
110	97	97	86	86	76
109	96	96	85	85	75
107–108	95	95	84	84	74
106	94	94	83	83	73
105	93	93	82	81–82	72
104	92	92	81	80	71
103	91	90–91	80	79	70
102	90				

CUMULATIVE TEST 3 SCORING CHART			
PART	SCORE	POSSIBLE SCORE	PASSING SCORE
1	3 for each question	6	6
2	3 for each item	3	3
3	2 for each item	10	8
4	EACH ITEM: Problem for perimeter 1; Answer and unit name 1; Problem for area 1; Answer and unit name 1; Total 4	12	10
5	3 for each item	6	6
6	2 for each item	4	4
7	2 for each item	6	6
8	3 for each item	6	6
9	1 for each item	7	6
10	1 for each item	3	3
11	3 for each item	6	6
12	Problem 1; Answer 1; Total 2	4	4
13	Prime factors for each number 1; Total 6; Least common multiple for item 2; Total 4	12	10
14	1 for each item	4	3
15	Only circled larger value 1; Total 4; Correct sign 2; Total 8	12	10
16	2 for each item	6	6
17	1 for each missing cell	6	5
	TOTAL	113	

CUMULATIVE TEST 3 REMEDIES	
PART	LESSON and (EXERCISE)
1	47 (3), 48 (2), 49 (1), 64 (2), 65 (2), 66 (4), 67 (1), 68 (2), 69 (2)
2	27 (4), 28 (6), 29 (3), 30 (2), 31 (5), 32 (2)
3 a, b, c	74 (5), 75 (4)
3 d, e	71 (4), 72 (3), 73 (3), 77 (2), 78 (5), 79 (4)
4	58 (1), 59 (1), 61 (4), 62 (3), 63 (3), 64 (3), 65 (5), 66 (3), 68 (1), 69 (3), 70 (1), 72 (2), 74 (6), 75 (7), 76 (3), 77 (6), 79 (3), 80 (1), 81 (6), 82 (6), 83 (3), 85 (2), 86 (2)
5	74 (4), 75 (3), 76 (4), 77 (5), 79 (1), 80 (2), 81 (3), 84 (1), 85 (3), 86 (4), 87 (2)
6	31 (1), 73 (6), 75 (1), 78 (2)
7	59 (5), 61 (6), 62 (7), 63 (5), 64 (6), 65 (6), 66 (7)
8	43 (2), 44 (6), 45 (2), 46 (4, 6), 47 (6), 48 (6), 66 (2, 5), 67 (2, 5), 68 (3), 69 (5), 71 (5), 72 (4)
9	55 (2), 81 (4), 82 (4), 83 (5), 84 (6), 85 (6), 86 (6), 88 (5), 89 (6)
10	71 (1), 72 (1), 73 (1), 74 (2), 76 (2), 77 (1), 78 (3), 79 (2)
11	34 (2), 35 (2), 36 (4), 37 (1), 38 (5), 39 (2), 41 (3), 42 (2), 43 (1), 44 (3), 45 (3), 46 (3), 47 (5), 48 (3)
12	81 (2), 82 (2)
13	65 (3), 66 (6), 67 (3)
14	1 (5), 2 (1), 5 (4), 6 (7)
15	25 (2), 26 (1), 27 (1), 28 (4), 29 (1)
16	1 (2), 2 (4, 8), 3 (6), 4 (7), 5 (2), 6 (2)
17	22 (4), 23 (7), 24 (7), 25 (5), 28 (2), 29 (5), 30 (3), 31 (2), 32 (6), 33 (5), 34 (5), 37 (6), 38 (6), 39 (6), 41 (7), 42 (5)

Connecting Math Concepts

Level E Final Cumulative Test (Lessons 1–120)

Note: Students are not to use calculators for any part of the test.

a. This is a test. You should only have your test and a sharpened pencil on your desk.
b. Find part 1. Do the test on your own.
- Raise your hand when you're finished.

FINAL CUMULATIVE TEST PERCENT SUMMARY					
SCORE	%	SCORE	%	SCORE	%
248	100	221–223	89	196–198	79
246–247	99	219–220	88	194–195	78
244–245	98	216–218	87	191–193	77
241–243	97	214–215	86	189–190	76
239–240	96	211–213	85	186–188	75
236–238	95	209–210	84	184–185	74
234–235	94	206–208	83	182–183	73
231–233	93	204–205	82	179–181	72
229–230	92	201–203	81	177–178	71
226–228	91	199–200	80	174–176	70
224–225	90				

FINAL CUMULATIVE TEST SCORING CHART			
PART	SCORE	POSSIBLE SCORE	PASSING SCORE
1	3 for each item	18	15
2	2 for each question	6	4
3	EACH ITEM: Correct function 2; Each Y value 1; Total 5	10	8
4	2 for each item	14	12
5	3 for each item	12	12
6	3 for each item	15	12
7	EACH ITEM: Each missing cell 1; Total 2	6	5
8	3 for each item	15	12
9	3 for each item	9	8
10	EACH ITEM: Perimeter 2; Area 2; Total 4	12	10
11	EACH ITEM: Each question 2; Total 4	12	10
12	2 for each item	8	8
13	2 for each item	6	4
14	Each complete equation 1; Total 3; Each simple equation 2; Total 4	7	6
15	1 for each angle	10	8
16	2 for each item	4	4
17	EACH ITEM: Each missing cell 1; Total 3	12	10
18	2 for each item	8	6
19	2 for each item	6	4
20	Area 2; Volume 2; Unit name for each answer 1	6	5
21	2 for each question	8	6
22	EACH ITEM: Each missing cell 1; Total 2	8	8

FINAL CUMULATIVE TEST SCORING CHART *(cont'd)*

PART	SCORE	POSSIBLE SCORE	PASSING SCORE
23	2 for each item	8	8
24	1 for each item	2	2
25	2 for each item	6	4
26	EACH ITEM: Problem 1, Answer 1, Unit Name 1, Total 3	12	10
27	2 for each answer	8	8
	TOTAL	**248**	

FINAL CUMULATIVE TEST REMEDIES

PART	LESSON and (EXERCISE)
1 a, b	2 (6), 3 (7), 5 (5), 6 (4), 7 (3), 8 (5), 9 (6), 10 (2), 103 (3), 104 (6), 105 (4)
1 c	97 (6), 98 (7), 99 (6), 101 (7), 102 (6), 103 (1), 104 (2), 105 (3), 123 (2)
1 d	2 (6), 3 (7)
1 e	25 (6), 26 (4), 27 (3), 28 (3), 123 (2)
1 f	43 (2), 44 (6), 45 (2), 46 (4, 6), 47 (6), 48 (6), 49 (6), 51 (2), 52 (4), 53 (5), 57 (6), 58 (4), 59 (3), 61 (2), 62 (6), 63 (6), 64 (5), 65 (7), 66 (5), 67 (5), 68 (3), 69 (5), 71 (5), 72 (4), 86 (1), 89 (4)
2	1 (4), 2 (2), 3 (3), 4 (2), 5 (6), 6 (5), 7 (4, 6), 8 (3), 9 (4), 11 (7), 12 (4), 13 (4), 14 (4), 15 (7), 16 (6), 17 (7), 26 (6), 27 (6), 28 (7), 29 (6), 33 (1, 2), 34 (4), 35 (6), 36 (2), 37 (5), 38 (3), 39 (5)
3	114 (4), 115 (4), 117 (1), 118 (1)
4 a, g	74 (4), 75 (3), 76 (4), 77 (5), 79 (1), 80 (2), 81 (3), 84 (1), 85 (3), 86 (4), 87 (2)
4 b, f	63 (7), 64 (4), 65 (3, 4), 66 (6), 67 (3, 4), 68 (5), 69 (1), 70 (2), 71 (2), 73 (5), 74 (3), 75 (6), 78 (4)
4 c, d, e	4 (4), 5 (3), 6 (1), 7 (1), 9 (3), 11 (1), 12 (1), 13 (2), 15 (4), 16 (1)
5 a, c	27 (4), 28 (6), 29 (3), 30 (2), 31 (5), 32 (2)
5 b	55 (3), 56 (5), 57 (4), 58 (3, 6), 59 (4, 6), 60 (1, 2), 61 (5), 62 (5), 63 (2)
5 d	108 (1), 109 (5), 111 (4), 112 (5)
6	21 (1), 22 (5), 23 (2), 24 (2, 6), 25 (1, 3), 26 (3), 27 (2), 28 (5), 29 (2), 31 (6), 32 (5), 33 (4), 35 (5), 36 (3), 37 (2), 38 (2), 39 (3), 41 (1, 6), 42 (1), 43 (4)
7	22 (4), 23 (7), 24 (7), 25 (5), 28 (2), 29 (5), 30 (3), 31 (2), 32 (6), 33 (5), 34 (5), 37 (6), 38 (6), 39 (6), 41 (7), 42 (5)
8 a	9 (3), 11 (1), 71 (3), 72 (5), 73 (4)
8 b	74 (5), 75 (4)
8 c	105 (6), 106 (6), 107 (5), 108 (5), 109 (2), 111 (2)

FINAL CUMULATIVE TEST REMEDIES *(cont'd)*

PART	LESSON and (EXERCISE)
8 d, e	25 (2), 26 (1), 27 (1), 28 (4), 29 (1), 111 (3), 112 (6)
9	35 (7), 36 (5), 102 (5), 103 (6), 104 (4)
10	58 (1), 59 (1), 61 (4), 62 (3), 63 (3), 64 (3), 65 (5), 66 (3), 68 (1), 69 (3), 70 (1), 72 (2), 74 (6), 75 (7), 76 (3), 77 (6), 79 (3), 80 (1), 81 (6), 82 (6), 83 (3), 85 (2), 86 (2), 96 (6), 97 (3), 98 (2)
11	52 (2), 53 (4), 54 (1), 55 (4), 56 (4), 57 (1), 58 (2), 59 (2), 61 (3), 62 (2), 63 (4), 64 (2), 65 (2), 66 (4), 82 (3), 83 (4), 84 (4), 87 (3), 88 (4), 106 (2), 107 (1), 108 (4), 109 (3), 110 (1), 111 (6), 114 (6)
12	112 (1), 113 (2 steps a–e), 117 (4 part 7), 119 (4 part 4)
13 a	12 (3), 13 (1), 14 (1), 15 (2), 16 (2)
13 b	34 (2), 35 (2), 36 (4), 37 (1), 38 (5), 39 (2), 41 (3), 42 (2), 43 (1), 44 (3), 45 (3), 46 (3), 47 (5), 48 (3)
13 c	93 (1), 94 (1), 95 (2), 96 (2), 97 (4)
14	17 (1), 18 (3), 19 (1), 21 (6), 22 (7), 23 (5)
15 a	71 (4), 72 (3), 73 (3), 74 (5), 75 (4), 77 (2), 78 (5), 79 (4), 81 (4), 82 (4)
15 b	83 (5), 84 (6), 85 (6), 86 (6), 88 (5), 89 (6), 91 (2), 92 (5), 93 (2)
16	113 (2), 114 (1), 115 (2), 116 (2)
17	92 (6), 93 (6), 94 (6), 95 (4), 96 (5), 97 (5), 98 (6), 99 (5), 101 (4), 103 (2)
18	19 (5), 20 (2), 21 (4), 23 (1), 24 (3), 39 (3), 41 (6), 44 (5), 45 (6)
19	85 (1), 86 (5), 87 (5), 89 (2)
20	94 (2), 95 (3), 96 (4), 97 (1), 98 (5), 104 (1), 105 (5), 108 (6)
21	71 (7), 72 (7), 73 (7)
22	71 (1), 72 (1), 73 (1), 74 (2), 76 (2), 77 (1), 78 (3), 79 (2)
23	66 (3), 68 (1), 69 (3), 104 (1), 105 (5)
24	71 (1), 72 (1), 73 (1), 74 (2)
25 a	104 (3), 105 (2), 106 (4), 107 (2), 108 (2)
25 b	109 (1), 110 (2), 111 (5)
25 c	112 (3), 114 (2), 124 (1), 125 (1)
26	71 (6), 72 (6), 73 (2), 76 (5), 81 (5), 82 (5), 83 (1), 84 (5), 85 (5), 98 (1), 99 (4), 100 (3), 115 (1), 116 (1)
27	91 (1), 92 (2), 93 (4), 94 (3), 95 (6), 111 (1), 112 (2), 113 (1), 114 (3), 115 (3), 117 (2)

CONNECTING MATH CONCEPTS
LEVEL E CUMULATIVE TEST 1
LESSONS 1–30

NAME ____________________

DATE ____________________

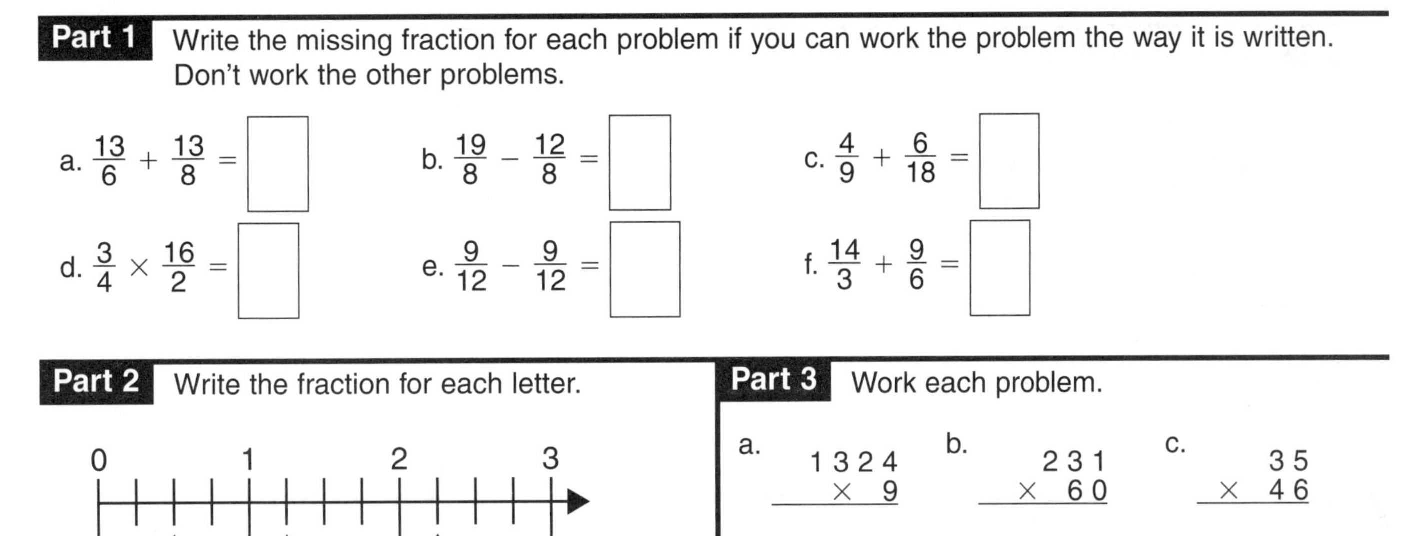

Part 1 Write the missing fraction for each problem if you can work the problem the way it is written. Don't work the other problems.

a. $\frac{13}{6} + \frac{13}{8} = \square$ b. $\frac{19}{8} - \frac{12}{8} = \square$ c. $\frac{4}{9} + \frac{6}{18} = \square$

d. $\frac{3}{4} \times \frac{16}{2} = \square$ e. $\frac{9}{12} - \frac{9}{12} = \square$ f. $\frac{14}{3} + \frac{9}{6} = \square$

Part 2 Write the fraction for each letter.

Part 3 Work each problem.

a. 1324×9 b. 231×60 c. 35×46

Part 4 Complete the table. Answer each question.

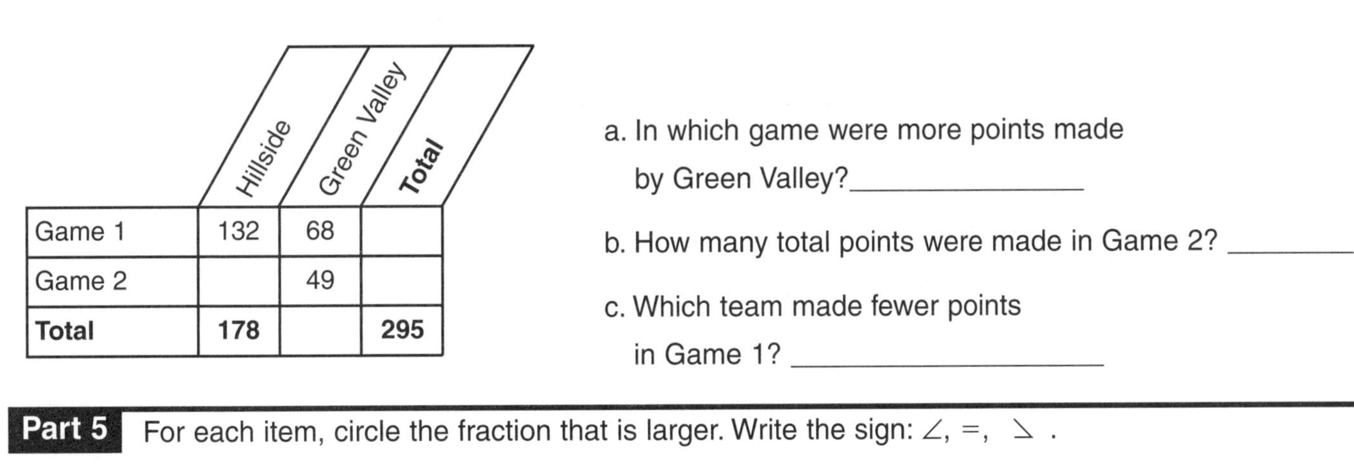

	Hillside	Green Valley	Total
Game 1	132	68	
Game 2		49	
Total	**178**		**295**

a. In which game were more points made by Green Valley? ____________

b. How many total points were made in Game 2? ________

c. Which team made fewer points in Game 1? ____________

Part 5 For each item, circle the fraction that is larger. Write the sign: $<$, $=$, $>$.

a. $\frac{6}{6}$ $\frac{6}{7}$ b. $\frac{4}{5}$ $\frac{6}{5}$ c. $\frac{15}{3}$ $\frac{16}{4}$

© SRA/McGraw-Hill. Permission is granted to reproduce for school use.

NAME ____________________

DATE ____________________

Part 6 Write a column problem and answer the question for each item.

a. Toby had some money. Then he spent $15. He ended up with $164. How much did he start out with?

____

b. There were some fleas on a dog. 36 more fleas jumped onto the dog. Now there are 116 fleas on the dog. How many fleas were on the dog to begin with? ________

Part 7 Complete the table.

	Decimal	Mixed Number
a.	7.06	
b.		$4\frac{5}{100}$
c.	3.2	

Part 8 For each item, write the equation for the pair of equivalent fractions shown in each diagram.

a.
0 1 2

0 1 2

b.

b. ☐ = ☐

a. ☐ = ☐

© SRA/McGraw-Hill. Permission is granted to reproduce for school use.

NAME ______________________

DATE ______________________

Part 9 Complete the equation to show the place-value addition (number expansion).

a. 792 =

b. 48 =

c. 208 =

Part 10 Work each problem. Write the complete answer.

a. $6\overline{)39}$

b. $4\overline{)26}$

c. $5\overline{)129}$

Part 11 Write the fraction for each description.

a. The fraction is more than 1. The numbers are 13 and 20. ☐

b. The denominator is 7. The fraction equals 6 whole units. ☐

c. The fraction is less than 1. The numbers are 8 and 17. ☐

Part 12 Complete each multiplication fact. Next to the fact, write the equation with prime factors.

a. ___ × ___ = 8 ______________

b. ___ × ___ = 6 ______________

c. ___ × ___ = 70 ______________

d. ___ × ___ = 33 ______________

e. ___ × ___ = 48 ______________

Part 13 For each item, complete the equation to show the mixed number and the fraction it equals.

a. $6\frac{4}{9} = \square$

b. $3\frac{2}{4} = \square$

c. $1\frac{8}{12} = \square$

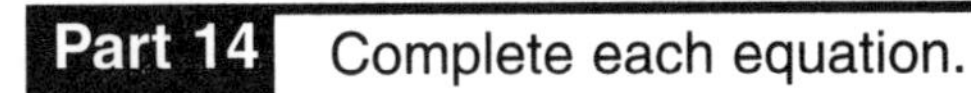

Part 14 Complete each equation.

a. $6 = \frac{\quad}{4} = \frac{\quad}{2} = \frac{\quad}{5} = \frac{\quad}{8}$

b. $4 = \frac{\quad}{4} = \frac{\quad}{2} = \frac{\quad}{5} = \frac{\quad}{8}$

© SRA/McGraw-Hill. Permission is granted to reproduce for school use.

NAME ______________________

DATE ______________________

Part 15 Copy the table and complete it. A sample item is worked.

	Multiplication	Division	Fraction Equation
Sample	$8 \times \boxed{14} = 112$	$8\overline{)112}$ with quotient 14	$\frac{112}{8} = 14$
a.	$3 \times \boxed{} = 219$		
b.	$6 \times \boxed{} = 384$		
c.	$7 \times \boxed{} = 301$		

© SRA/McGraw-Hill. Permission is granted to reproduce for school use.

NAME ______________________

DATE ______________________

Part 1 Write complete answers to the questions.

In a class, there were 2 boys for every 3 girls. There were 15 girls in the class.

1. How many students were in the class? ______________________

2. How many boys were in the class? ______________________

Part 2 Complete each equation. Circle the first fraction or the last fraction to show which is larger.

a. $\frac{4}{9} \times \frac{3}{4} = \square$

b. $\frac{8}{3} \times \frac{14}{13} = \square$

Part 3 Answer the questions.

a. There were 22 bluebirds and 18 robins.

1. What fraction of the birds were robins? ________

2. What fraction of the birds were bluebirds? ________

b. $\frac{2}{6}$ of the bears were black.

1. What fraction of the bears were not black? ________

2. What's the fraction for all the bears? ________

c. A bakery had some muffins. 14 muffins were sold. There were still 86 muffins in the bakery.

How many muffins were in the bakery to begin with? ________

© SRA/McGraw-Hill. Permission is granted to reproduce for school use.

NAME ____________________

DATE ____________________

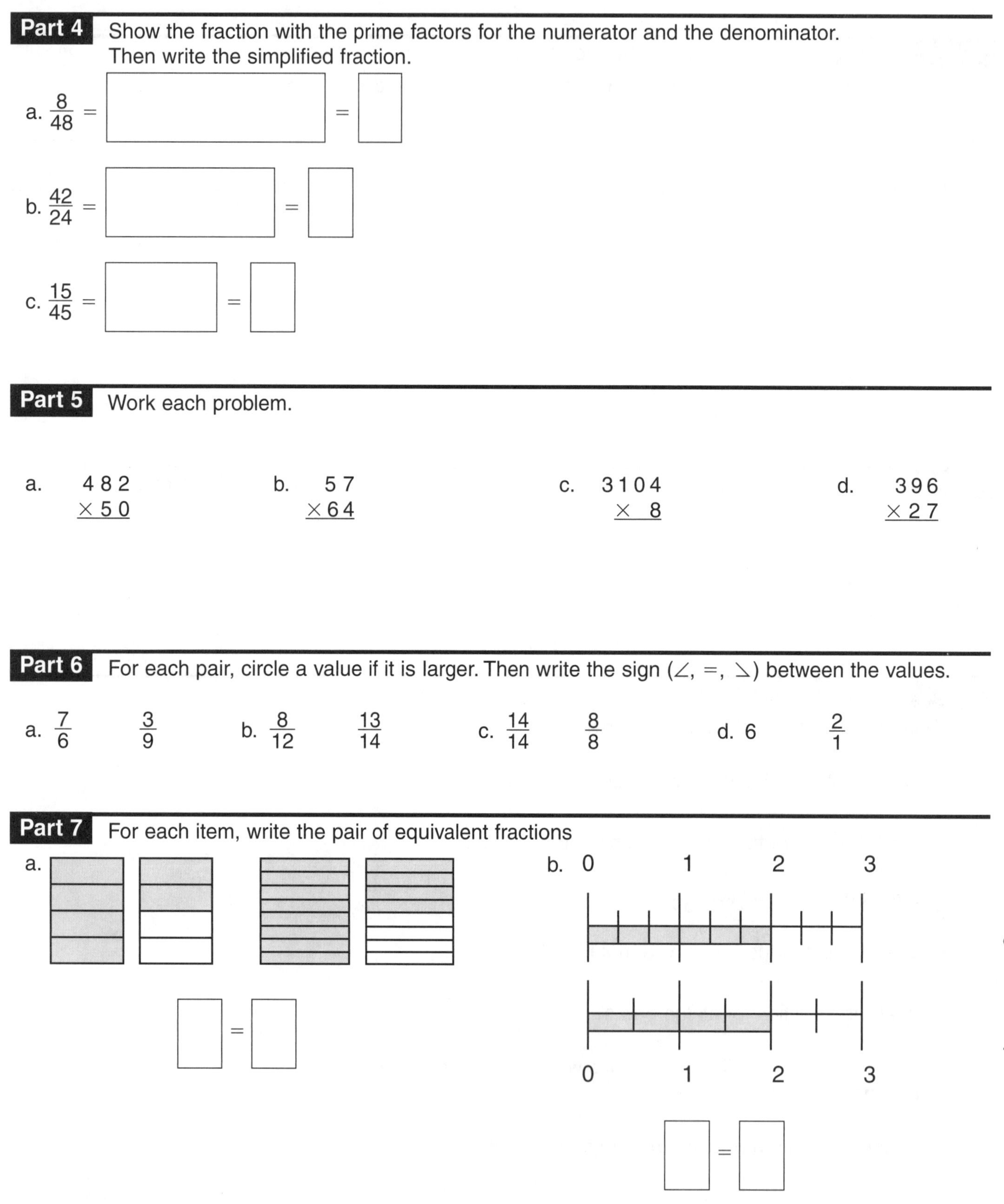

© SRA/McGraw-Hill. Permission is granted to reproduce for school use.

NAME ____________________

DATE ____________________

Part 8 The facts tell about four numbers in the table. Put those numbers in the table. Do not figure out the rest of the numbers.

This table is supposed to show the number of snakes and fish at Bob's Pets and at Petland.

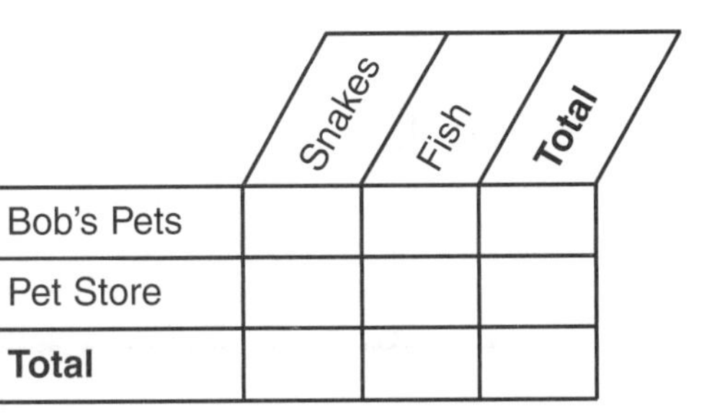

	Snakes	Fish	**Total**
Bob's Pets			
Pet Store			
Total			

The total number of snakes and fish at Petland is 142. Bob's Pets has 31 snakes. There are 12 more snakes at Petland than at Bob's Pets. The total number of fish for both stores is 178.

Part 9 Write the fraction for each letter.

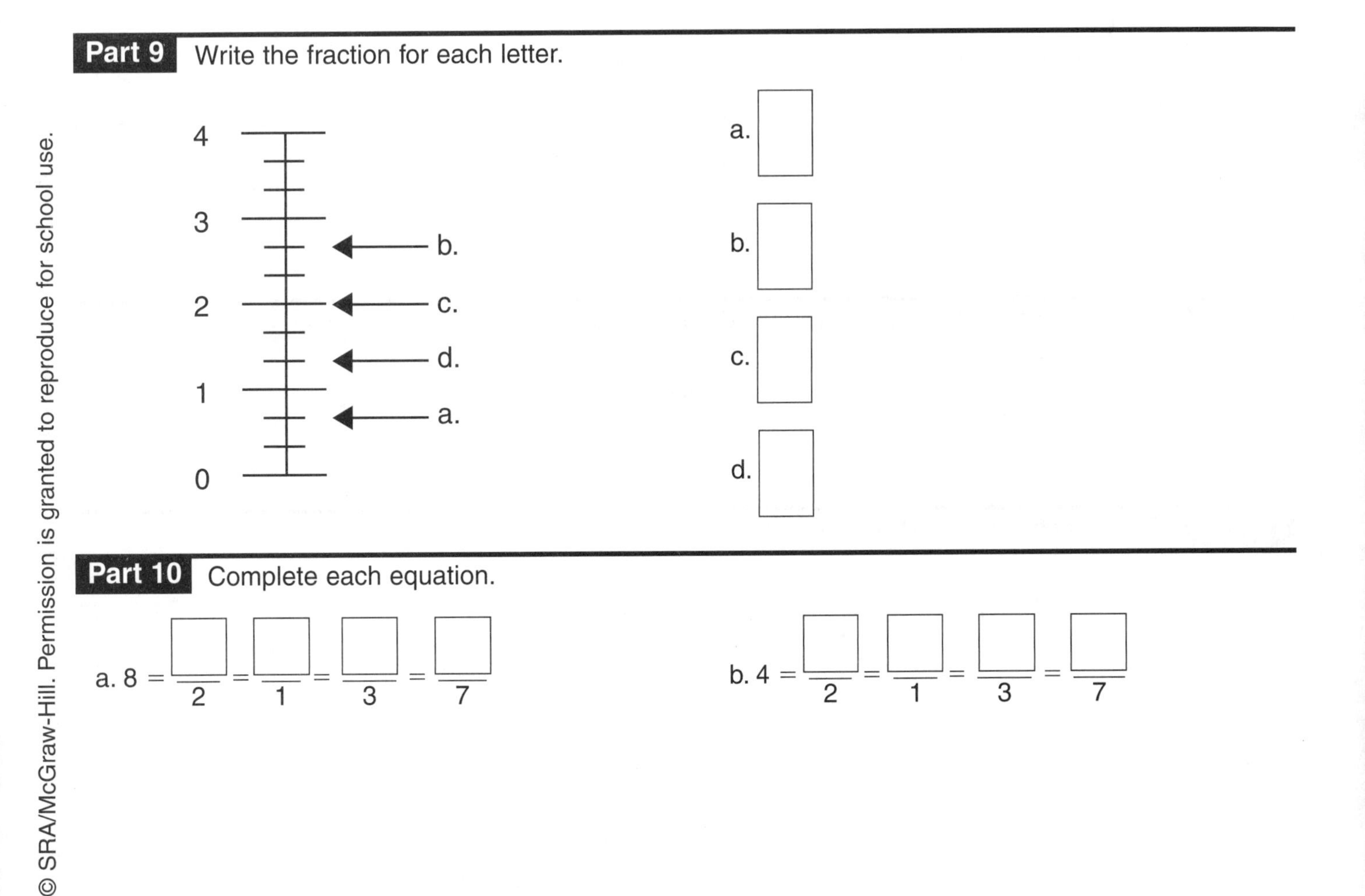

Part 10 Complete each equation.

a. $8 = \frac{\square}{2} = \frac{\square}{1} = \frac{\square}{3} = \frac{\square}{7}$

b. $4 = \frac{\square}{2} = \frac{\square}{1} = \frac{\square}{3} = \frac{\square}{7}$

© SRA/McGraw-Hill. Permission is granted to reproduce for school use.

NAME ____________________

DATE ____________________

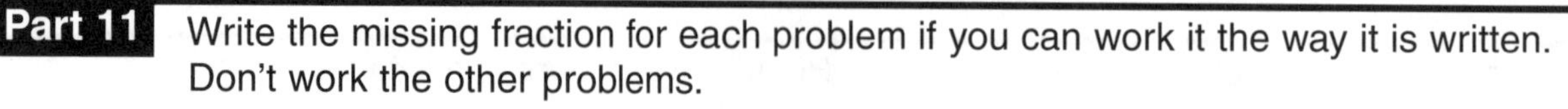

Part 11 Write the missing fraction for each problem if you can work it the way it is written. Don't work the other problems.

a. $\frac{5}{7} + \frac{3}{8} =$ ☐

b. $\frac{12}{17} - \frac{3}{17} =$ ☐

c. $\frac{8}{12} - \frac{8}{14} =$ ☐

d. $\frac{8}{1} \times \frac{40}{10} =$ ☐

e. $\frac{9}{4} + \frac{6}{4} =$ ☐

f. $\frac{8}{3} \times \frac{6}{2} =$ ☐

Part 12 Copy and complete the table. The sample is worked.

	Mixed Number	Fraction	Decimal
Sample	$7\frac{218}{1000}$	$\frac{7218}{1000}$	7.218
a.		$\frac{13}{10}$	
b.			7.56
c.	$3\frac{4}{10}$		

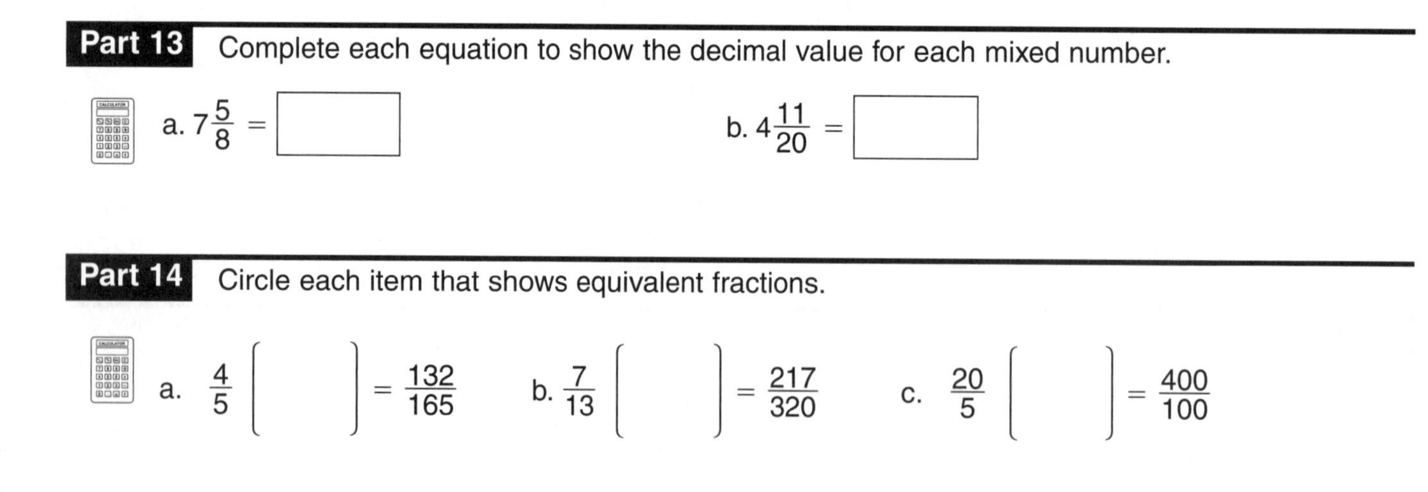

Part 13 Complete each equation to show the decimal value for each mixed number.

a. $7\frac{5}{8} =$ ☐

b. $4\frac{11}{20} =$ ☐

Part 14 Circle each item that shows equivalent fractions.

a. $\frac{4}{5}\left[\quad\right] = \frac{132}{165}$

b. $\frac{7}{13}\left[\quad\right] = \frac{217}{320}$

c. $\frac{20}{5}\left[\quad\right] = \frac{400}{100}$

© SRA/McGraw-Hill. Permission is granted to reproduce for school use.

CONNECTING MATH CONCEPTS
LEVEL E CUMULATIVE TEST 3
LESSONS 1–90

NAME ______________________

DATE ______________________

Part 1 Work the problem and answer the questions.

a. $\frac{3}{8}$ of the players scored at least one point. 10 players did not score any points.

1. How many players scored?

2. How many players were there in all?

Part 2 Work the problem.

a. For every 3 cans of tomato soup you buy, you get a can of chicken noodle soup free. Yesterday, the store gave away 21 cans of chicken noodle soup. How many cans of tomato soup were bought yesterday?

Part 3 Answer the questions.

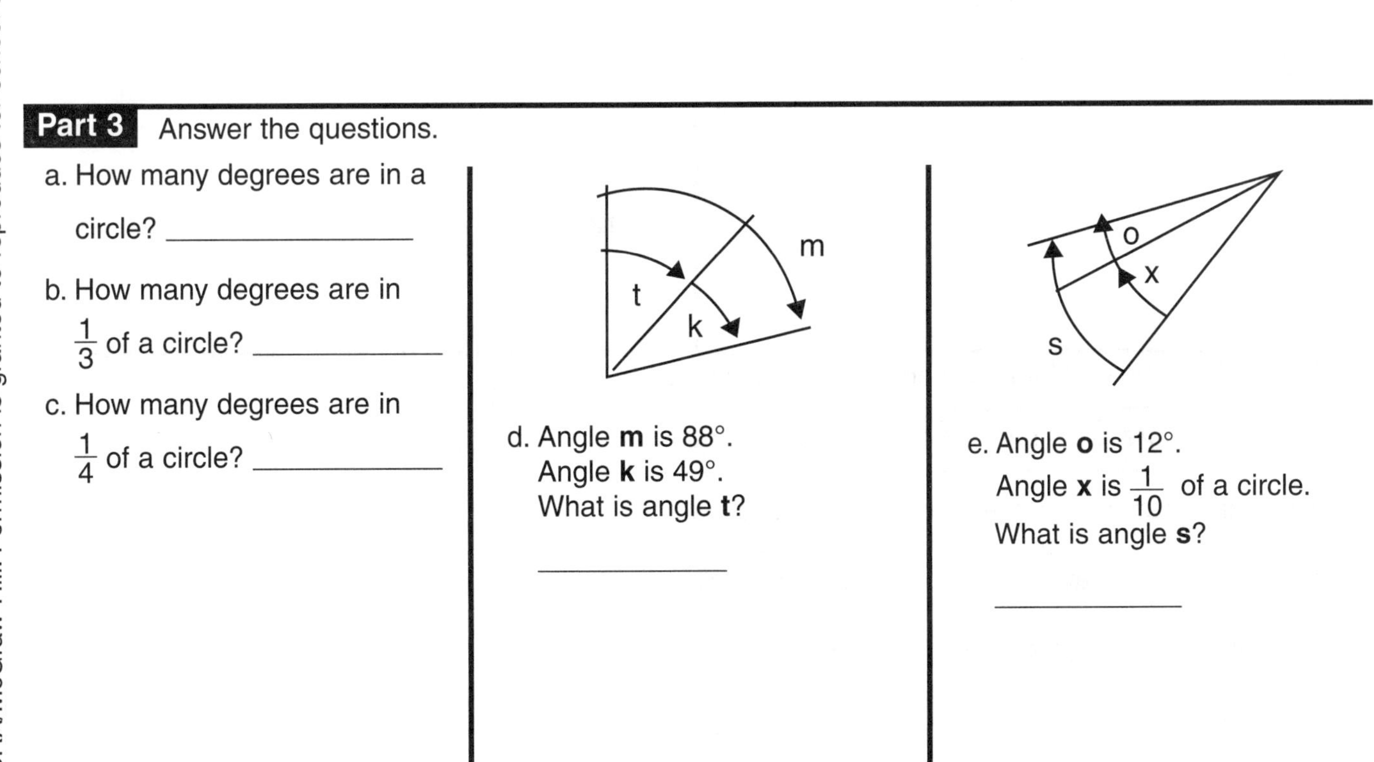

a. How many degrees are in a circle? ______________

b. How many degrees are in $\frac{1}{3}$ of a circle? ______________

c. How many degrees are in $\frac{1}{4}$ of a circle? ______________

d. Angle **m** is 88°.
Angle **k** is 49°.
What is angle **t**?

____

e. Angle **o** is 12°.
Angle **x** is $\frac{1}{10}$ of a circle.
What is angle **s**?

____

© SRA/McGraw-Hill. Permission is granted to reproduce for school use.

NAME ______________________

DATE ______________________

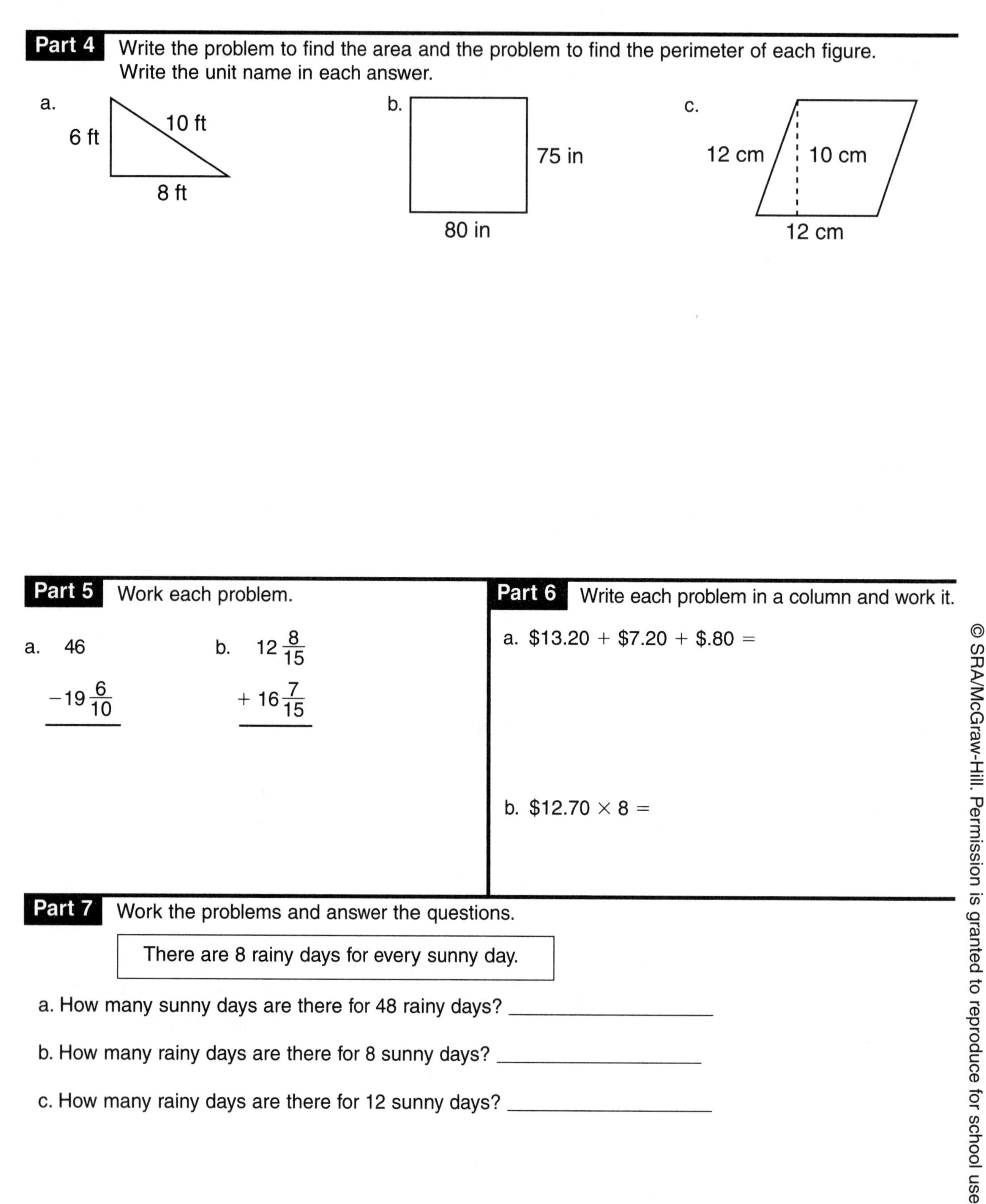

Part 4 Write the problem to find the area and the problem to find the perimeter of each figure. Write the unit name in each answer.

Part 5 Work each problem.

a. $46 - 19\frac{6}{10}$

b. $12\frac{8}{15} + 16\frac{7}{15}$

Part 6 Write each problem in a column and work it.

a. $13.20 + $7.20 + $.80 =

b. $12.70 × 8 =

Part 7 Work the problems and answer the questions.

There are 8 rainy days for every sunny day.

a. How many sunny days are there for 48 rainy days? ______________

b. How many rainy days are there for 8 sunny days? ______________

c. How many rainy days are there for 12 sunny days? ______________

© SRA/McGraw-Hill. Permission is granted to reproduce for school use.

NAME ____________________

DATE ____________________

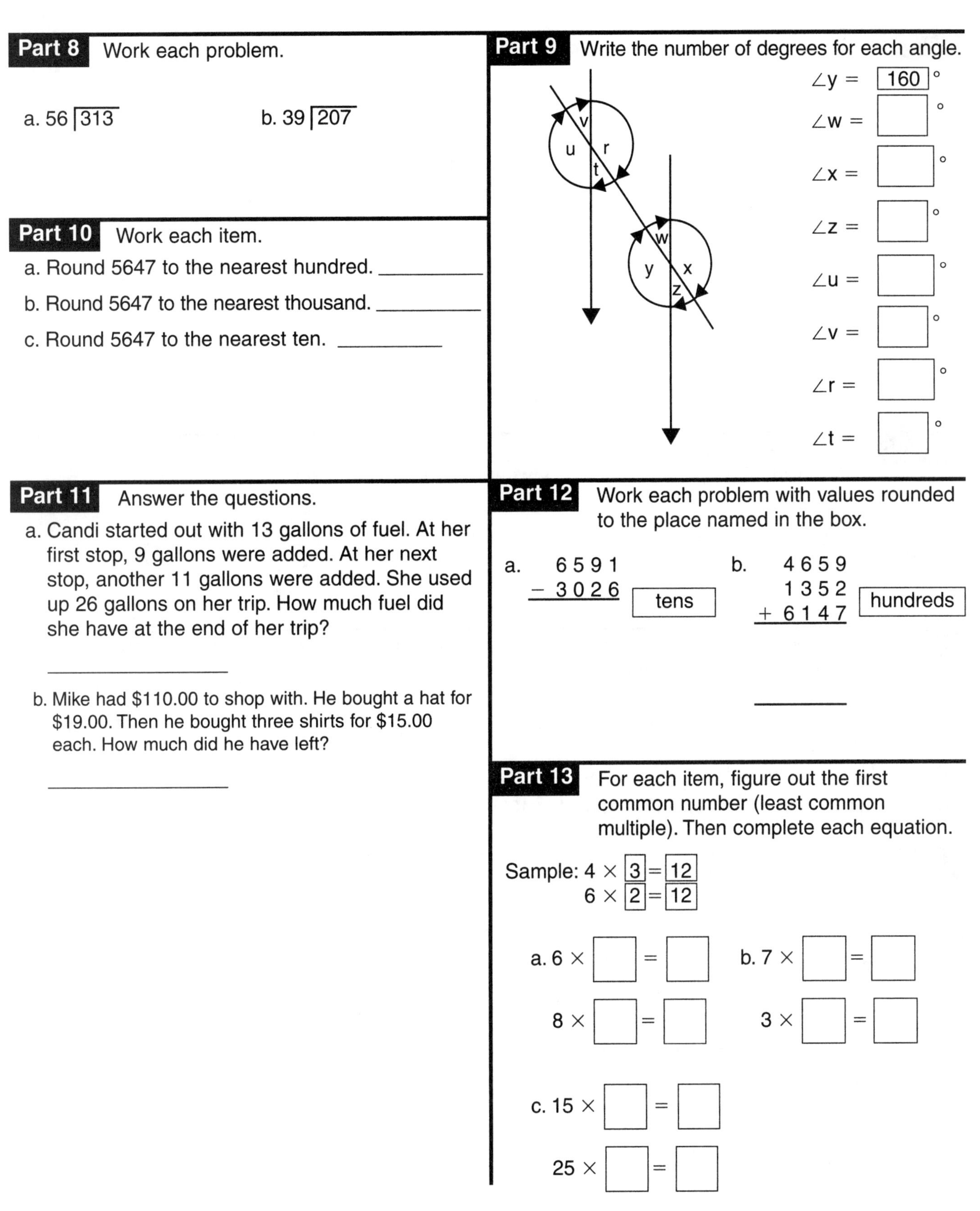

Part 8 Work each problem.

a. 56 $\overline{)313}$ b. 39 $\overline{)207}$

Part 9 Write the number of degrees for each angle.

∠y = 160 °

∠w = ____ °

∠x = ____ °

∠z = ____ °

∠u = ____ °

∠v = ____ °

∠r = ____ °

∠t = ____ °

Part 10 Work each item.

a. Round 5647 to the nearest hundred. ________

b. Round 5647 to the nearest thousand. ________

c. Round 5647 to the nearest ten. ________

Part 11 Answer the questions.

a. Candi started out with 13 gallons of fuel. At her first stop, 9 gallons were added. At her next stop, another 11 gallons were added. She used up 26 gallons on her trip. How much fuel did she have at the end of her trip?

____

b. Mike had $110.00 to shop with. He bought a hat for $19.00. Then he bought three shirts for $15.00 each. How much did he have left?

____

Part 12 Work each problem with values rounded to the place named in the box.

a.
```
  6591
- 3026
```
tens

b.
```
  4659
  1352
+ 6147
```
hundreds

____

Part 13 For each item, figure out the first common number (least common multiple). Then complete each equation.

Sample: 4 × 3 = 12
6 × 2 = 12

a. 6 × ☐ = ☐
8 × ☐ = ☐

b. 7 × ☐ = ☐
3 × ☐ = ☐

c. 15 × ☐ = ☐
25 × ☐ = ☐

© SRA/McGraw-Hill. Permission is granted to reproduce for school use.

NAME ______________________

DATE ______________________

Part 14 Write the fraction for each letter.

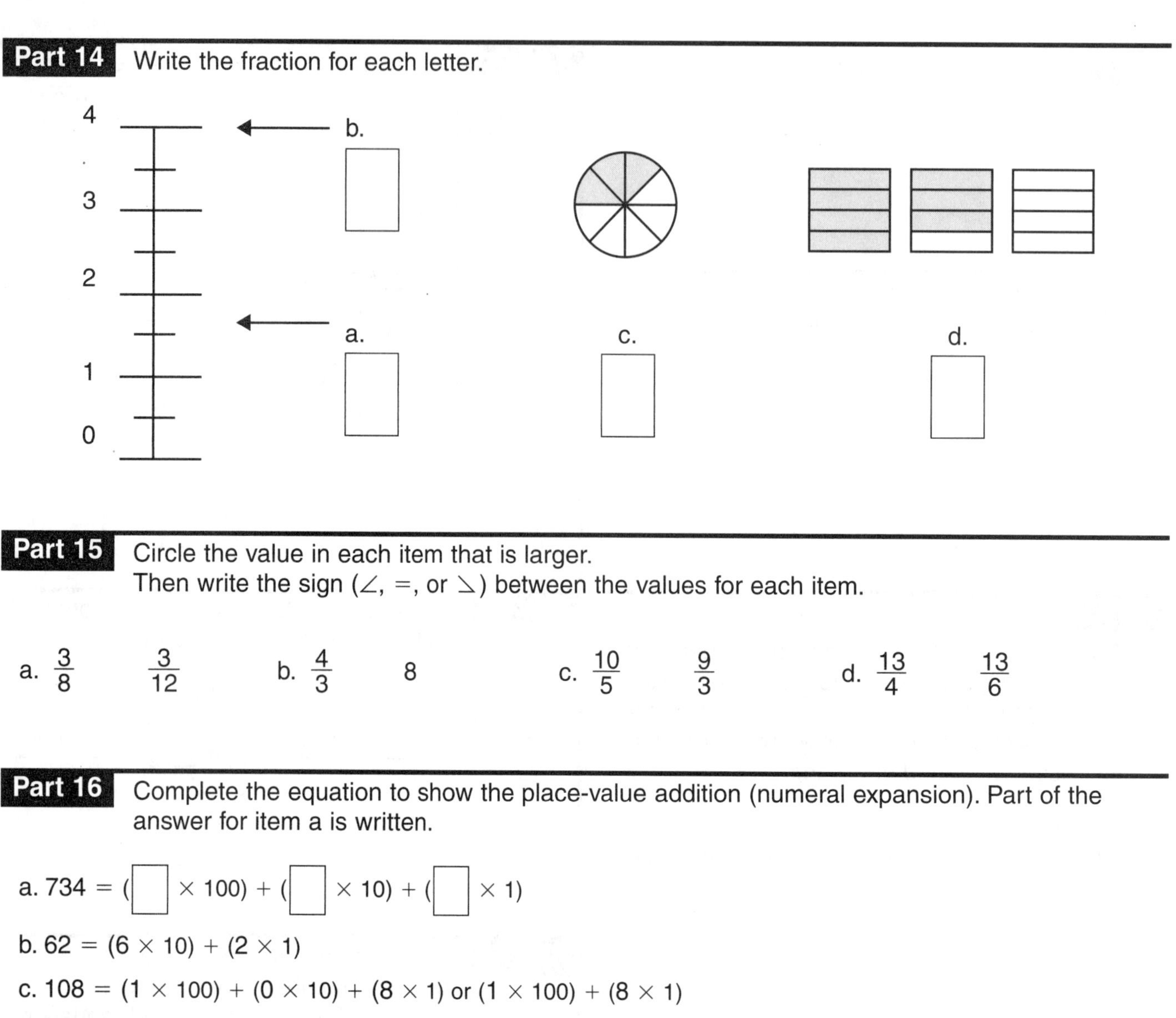

Part 15 Circle the value in each item that is larger.
Then write the sign (∠, =, or ⦣) between the values for each item.

a. $\frac{3}{8}$ $\frac{3}{12}$ b. $\frac{4}{3}$ 8 c. $\frac{10}{5}$ $\frac{9}{3}$ d. $\frac{13}{4}$ $\frac{13}{6}$

Part 16 Complete the equation to show the place-value addition (numeral expansion). Part of the answer for item a is written.

a. 734 = (☐ × 100) + (☐ × 10) + (☐ × 1)

b. 62 = (6 × 10) + (2 × 1)

c. 108 = (1 × 100) + (0 × 10) + (8 × 1) or (1 × 100) + (8 × 1)

Part 17 Complete the table. A sample item is shown.

	Decimal	Fraction	Mixed Number
Sample	7.218	$\frac{7218}{1000}$	$7\frac{218}{1000}$
a.	12.7		
b.		$\frac{206}{100}$	
c.			$4\frac{2}{1000}$

© SRA/McGraw-Hill. Permission is granted to reproduce for school use.

CONNECTING MATH CONCEPTS
LEVEL E FINAL CUMULATIVE TEST
LESSONS 1–125

NAME ______________________

DATE ______________________

Part 1 Work each item.

a. 250×1.9

c. $81 \overline{)437.4}$

e. $8 \overline{).248}$

b. 4.7×5.3

d. 857×30

f. $53 \overline{)402}$

Part 2 Make a table. Answer each question.

Mary and Sue collected buttons and bows. Mary had 142 bows. Sue had 85 buttons. Both girls had a total of 198 buttons. Sue had 38 fewer bows than Mary.

a. What was the total number of buttons and bows in Sue's collection? ____________

b. Who had more buttons, Mary or Sue? ____________

c. How many bows did Sue have? ____________

Part 3

Figure out the function. (The function is the rule that converts ***x*** values into ***y*** values.) Complete each table.

x	function x	y
5		15
6		18
8		
3		
2		

x	function x	y
9		
22		20
15		13
30		
24		

© SRA/McGraw-Hill. Permission is granted to reproduce for school use.

NAME ____________________

DATE ____________________

Part 4 Work each problem. Simplify your answers when possible.

a. $2 - 1\frac{1}{4}$

b. $\frac{7}{6} + \frac{2}{3}$

c. $\frac{3}{1} \times \frac{6}{9} \times \frac{2}{7} =$

d. $\frac{9}{3} - \frac{6}{3} =$

e. $\frac{2}{8} \times \frac{3}{8} =$

f. $\frac{8}{15} - \frac{3}{10}$

g. $4\frac{2}{5} + 1\frac{3}{5}$

Part 5 Work each item. Simplify your answer when possible.

a. If 7 shelves hold 84 books, how many books do 9 shelves hold? ____________

b. Each pound of seed costs $15. How many pounds of seed could you buy with $100? ____________

c. The boys and girls that play basketball are in the ratio of 3 to 2.
54 girls play basketball. How many boys play basketball? ____________

d. The low temperatures recorded on different days are as follows:

Days	Degrees
Monday	11
Tuesday	0
Wednesday	15
Thursday	7
Friday	12

What was the average low temperature? ____________

© SRA/McGraw-Hill. Permission is granted to reproduce for school use.

NAME ____________________

DATE ____________________

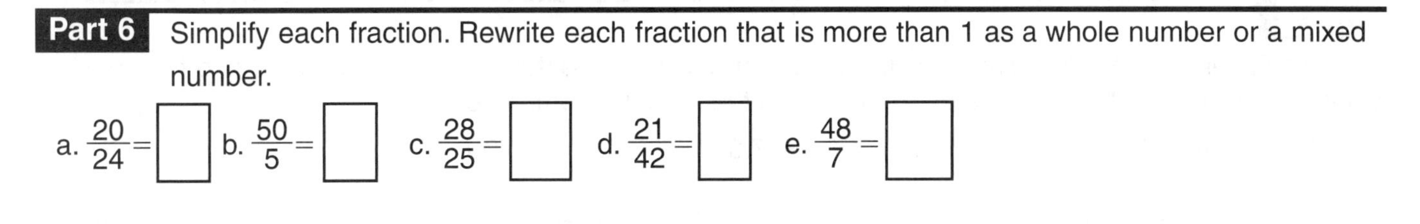

Part 6 Simplify each fraction. Rewrite each fraction that is more than 1 as a whole number or a mixed number.

a. $\frac{20}{24}$ = ☐ b. $\frac{50}{5}$ = ☐ c. $\frac{28}{25}$ = ☐ d. $\frac{21}{42}$ = ☐ e. $\frac{48}{7}$ = ☐

Part 7 Complete the table. The sample has been worked.

	Mixed Number	Fraction	Decimal
Sample	$7\frac{218}{1000}$	$\frac{7218}{1000}$	7.218
a.		$\frac{246}{100}$	
b.			1.017
c.	$8\frac{4}{100}$		

Part 8 Work each item. Simplify answers when possible.

a. What is $\frac{3}{8}$ of 92? ____________

b. How many degrees are in $\frac{8}{9}$ of a circle? ________

c. Which is more, 72 inches or 5 feet? ____________

d. Which is more, $\frac{6}{5}$ or $\frac{4}{3}$? ____________

e. Which is more, $\frac{10}{12}$ or $\frac{38}{48}$ ____________

© SRA/McGraw-Hill. Permission is granted to reproduce for school use.

NAME ______________________________

DATE ______________________________

Part 9

For each item, write the decimal numbers in order of size. Write the largest value on top and the smallest value on the bottom. If the values are equal, write them on the same line.

a. .999, 1.009, 1.9

____

____

____

b. 27.3, 2.73, 7.37

____

____

____

c. 5.700, 5.7, 5.71

____

____

____

Part 10

Figure out the perimeter and area of each figure. Remember the unit name.

a.

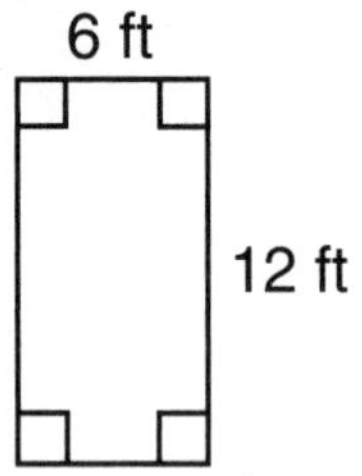

Perimeter ______________

Area ______________

b.

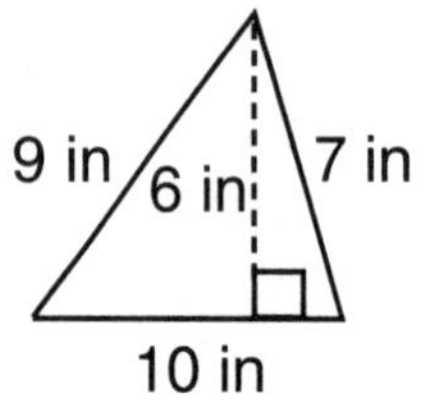

Perimeter ______________

Area ______________

c.

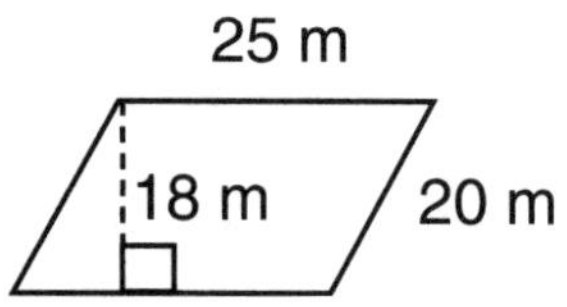

Perimeter ______________

Area ______________

© SRA/McGraw-Hill. Permission is granted to reproduce for school use.

NAME ____________________

DATE ____________________

Part 11 Answer each question.

a. 75% of the cars in the lot are white. There are 24 cars that are not white.

1. How many white cars are in the lot? ____________________

2. How many cars are in the lot altogether? ____________________

b. Andrew collected $\frac{7}{5}$ times as much money as Ben collected. Ben collected $25.

1. How much money did Andrew collect? ________

2. How much more money did Andrew collect than Ben collected? ________

c. The sale price is 80% of the regular price. The regular price is $25.

1. How much is the sale price? ________

2. How much less than the regular price is the sale price? ________

Part 12 For each bag, write the fraction for your chances of drawing a circle.

a. b. 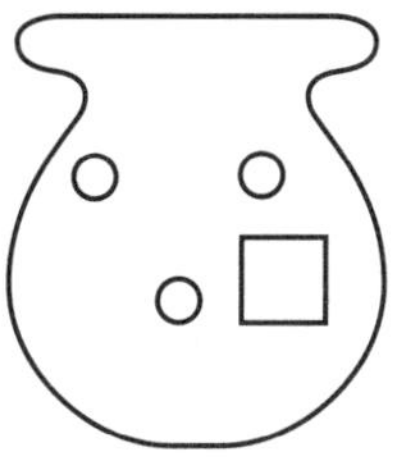 c.  d.

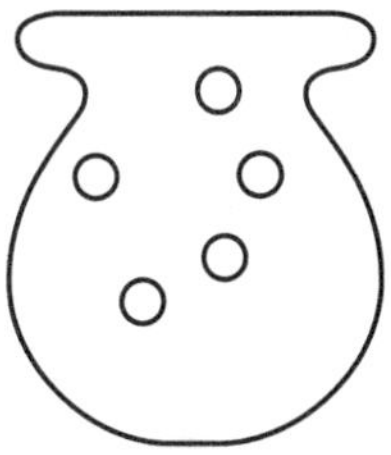

© SRA/McGraw-Hill. Permission is granted to reproduce for school use.

NAME ______________________

DATE ______________________

Part 13 Work each item.

a. The apartment building is 62 feet taller than the church. The apartment building is 104 feet tall. How tall is the church? __________

b. A boat set sail with 275 passengers on board. At the first stop, 52 passengers got off and 37 passengers got on. At the second stop, 28 passengers got on and 12 passengers got off. How many passengers were left on board? ________________

c. Yesterday, Linda earned some money. Today, she earned another \$52. In all, she earned \$105 for the two days. How much did she earn yesterday? ________

Part 14 Complete each equation. If the fractions shown are equivalent, write a simple equation below.

a. $\frac{3}{8}\left(\frac{\ }{\ }\right) = \frac{15}{40}$

b. $\frac{7}{2}\left(\frac{\ }{\ }\right) = \frac{63}{18}$

c. $\frac{9}{5}\left(\frac{\ }{\ }\right) = \frac{45}{20}$

© SRA/McGraw-Hill. Permission is granted to reproduce for school use.

NAME ______________________

DATE ______________________

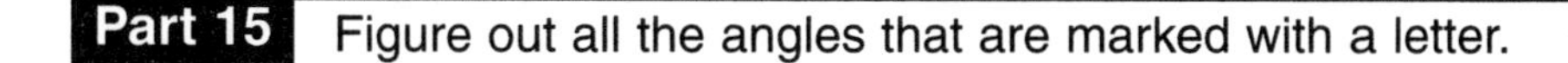

Part 15 Figure out all the angles that are marked with a letter.

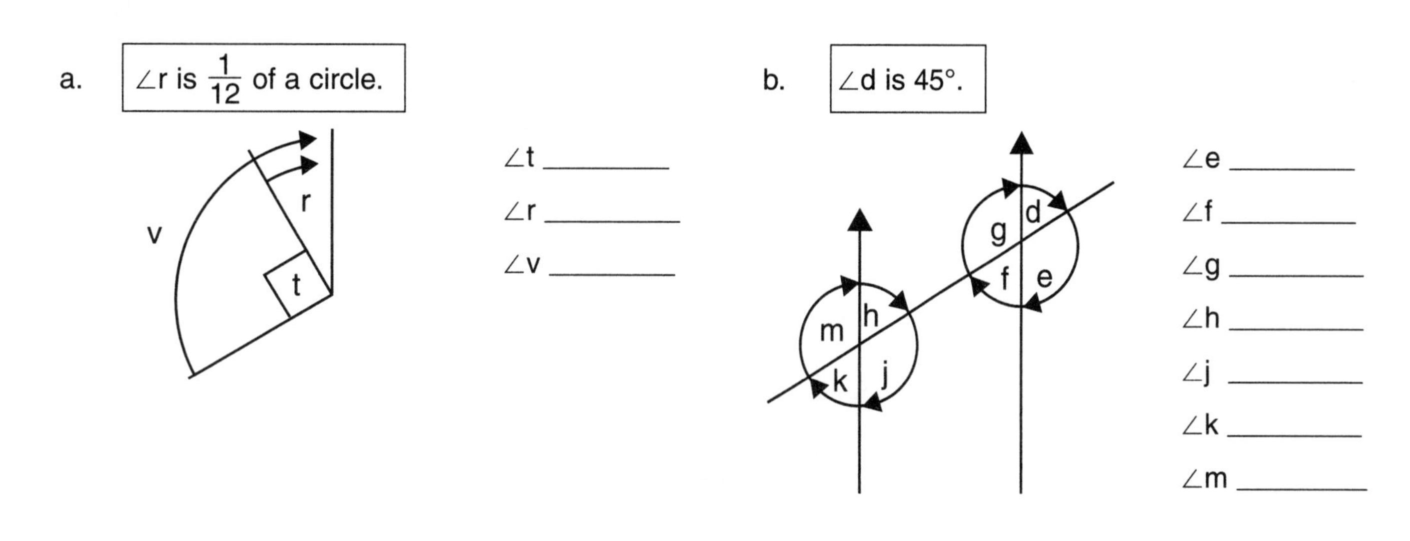

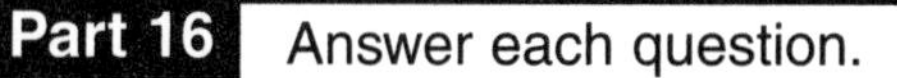

Part 16 Answer each question.

You take 80 trials at pulling an object from the bag, replacing the object back in the bag after each trial.

1. About how many times would you expect to pull out an X? ________

2. About how many times would you expect to pull out an object that is not an X? ________

© SRA/McGraw-Hill. Permission is granted to reproduce for school use.

NAME ______________________

DATE ______________________

Part 17 Complete the table. The sample problem has been worked.

		$\frac{\square}{100}$	%	Decimal
Sample	$\frac{23}{10}$	$\frac{230}{100}$	23%	2.35
a.	$\frac{4}{5}$			
b.	$\frac{7}{2}$			
c.	$\frac{20}{50}$			
d.	$\frac{6}{8}$			

Part 18 Complete the table.

	Mixed number	Fraction
a.	$5\frac{8}{10}$	
b.		$\frac{67}{4}$
c.		$\frac{21}{6}$
d.	$10\frac{3}{5}$	

Part 19 Rewrite each problem as a column problem and work it.

a. 14.08 − .975 = ________ b. 8 + 12.92 + 105.9 = ________ c. 48 − 25.4 = ________

© SRA/McGraw-Hill. Permission is granted to reproduce for school use.

CONNECTING MATH CONCEPTS
LEVEL E FINAL CUMULATIVE TEST (CONT'D)
LESSONS 1–125

NAME ____________________

DATE ____________________

Part 20 Figure out the surface area and volume of the box.

Surface area ____________________

Volume ____________________

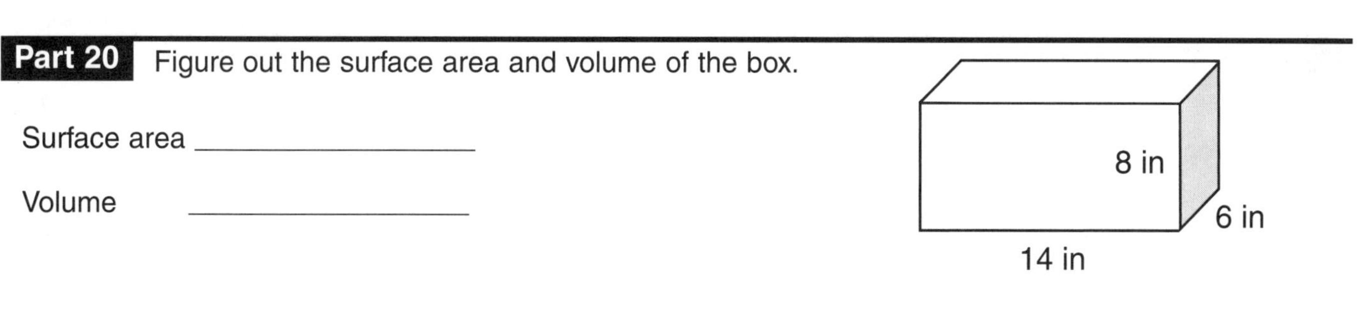

Part 21 Use the coordinate system to answer each question.

The line on this coordinate system shows the tons of paper made by a factory.

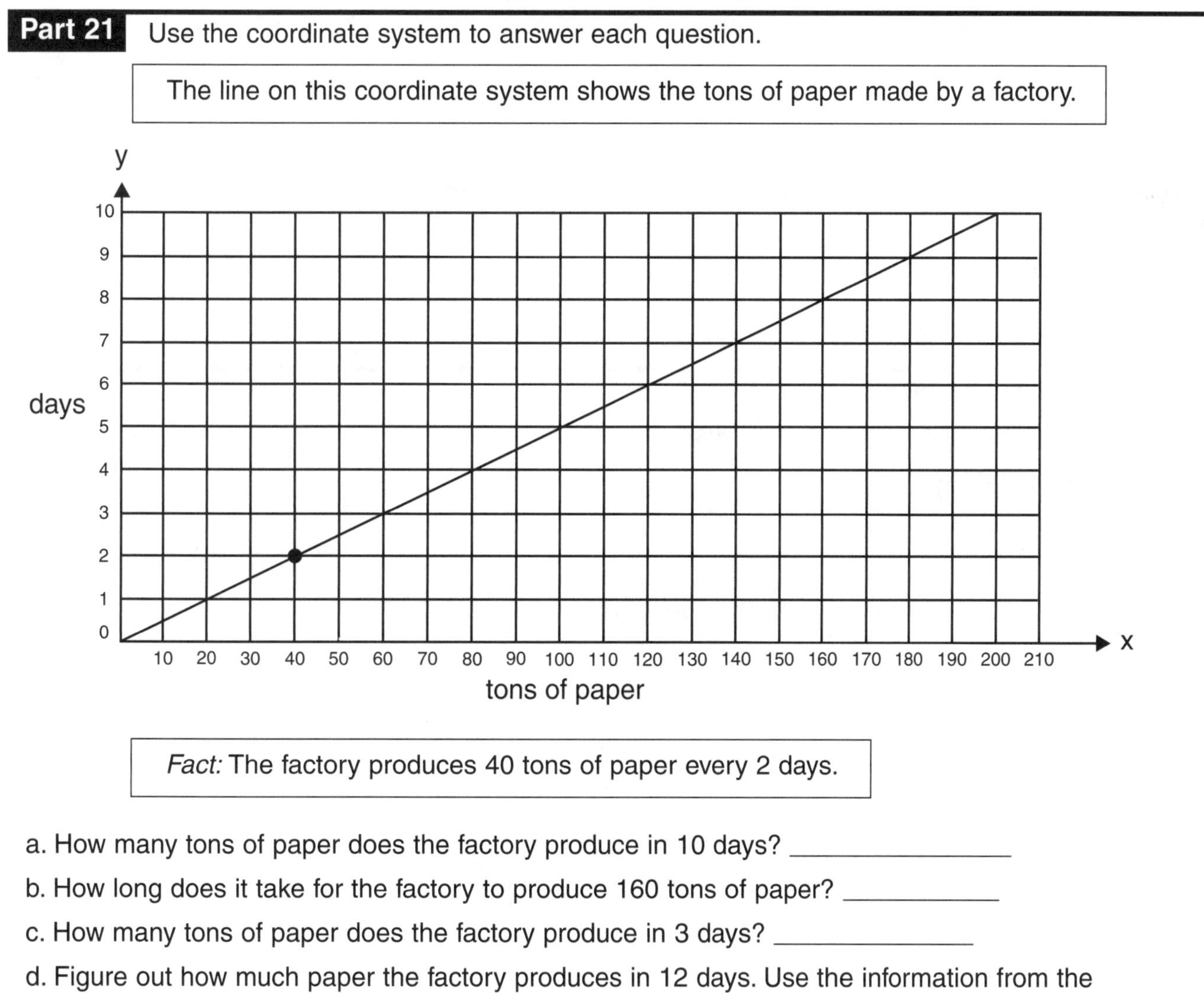

Fact: The factory produces 40 tons of paper every 2 days.

a. How many tons of paper does the factory produce in 10 days? ____________________

b. How long does it take for the factory to produce 160 tons of paper? ____________________

c. How many tons of paper does the factory produce in 3 days? ____________________

d. Figure out how much paper the factory produces in 12 days. Use the information from the fact to work this problem. ____________________

© SRA/McGraw-Hill. Permission is granted to reproduce for school use.

NAME ______________________

DATE ______________________

Part 22 Complete the table. Round each number to the nearest 10 and the nearest 100.

		nearest 10	nearest 100
a.	5425		
b.	11609		
c.	552		
d.	2321		

Part 23 Write whether each measurement could be for the **perimeter, area,** or **volume** of a figure.

a. 20 square feet ______________

b. 15 inches ______________

c. 12 cubic meters ______________

d. 45 feet ______________

Part 24 Write the number for each description.

a. forty thousand three hundred seven ______________

b. four thousand seventy five ______________

Part 25 Figure out the mystery number.

a. The mystery number is the starting number.

Complete the equations:

$\overset{?}{\square} \times 5 = \square$

$\square - 62 = 88$

b. You start with a number and add 235. Then you divide by 6.

You end up with 150. What number do you start with? ______

c. If you start with Mr. Jones' age and triple it, then subtract 20, then divide by 2, you end up with 29.

How old is Mr. Jones? _____

© SRA/McGraw-Hill. Permission is granted to reproduce for school use.

Part 26 Work each multiplication or division problem. Answer the questions.

a. Each book costs $15. How much do 12 books cost? ________

b. Bob goes to the store with $90 to buy books. Each book costs $12. When Bob leaves the store how many books could he be carrying? ____________

c. If 30 identical stones weigh 390 grams, how much does each stone weigh? ________

d. A cake weighs 60 ounces. It is divided into 9 pieces that are the same weight. How much does each piece weigh? ________________________________

Part 27 Work each item. Use the equation for the circumference of a circle or for the area of a circle. Show your answer as hundredths. Remember the unit name.

a.

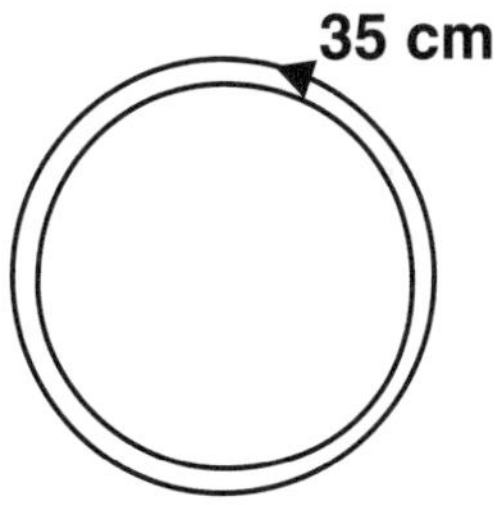

35 cm

Diameter = ______________

Radius = ______________

b.

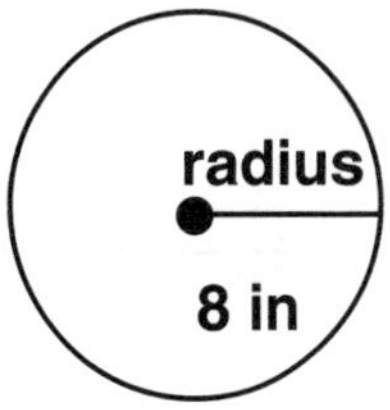

radius

8 in

Circumference = ______________

Area = __________________

© SRA/McGraw-Hill. Permission is granted to reproduce for school use.

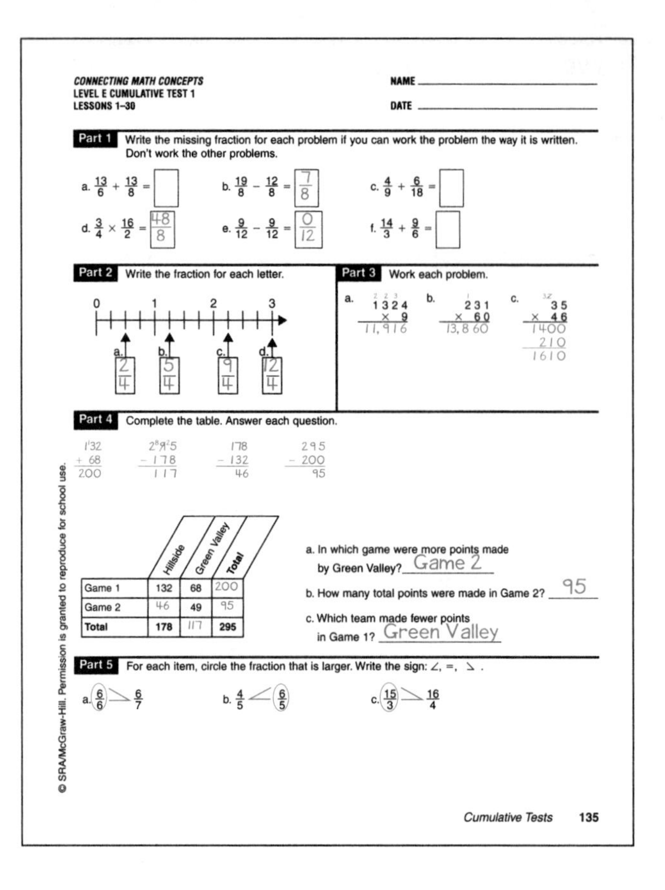

CONNECTING MATH CONCEPTS
LEVEL E CUMULATIVE TEST 1
LESSONS 1–30

NAME ____________

DATE ____________

Part 1 Write the missing fraction for each problem if you can work the problem the way it is written. Don't work the other problems.

a. $\frac{13}{6} + \frac{13}{8} = \square$ b. $\frac{19}{8} - \frac{12}{8} = \frac{7}{8}$ c. $\frac{4}{9} + \frac{6}{18} = \square$

d. $\frac{3}{4} \times \frac{16}{2} = \frac{48}{8}$ e. $\frac{9}{12} - \frac{9}{12} = \frac{0}{12}$ f. $\frac{14}{3} + \frac{9}{6} = \square$

Part 2 Write the fraction for each letter.

0 1 2 3

a. $\frac{2}{4}$ b. $\frac{5}{4}$ c. $\frac{9}{4}$ d. $\frac{12}{4}$

Part 3 Work each problem.

a. $1324 \times 9 = 11{,}916$ b. $231 \times 60 = 13{,}860$ c. 35×46: $1400 + 210 = 1610$

Part 4 Complete the table. Answer each question.

$132 + 68 = 200$ $295 - 178 = 117$ $178 - 132 = 46$ $295 - 200 = 95$

	Hillside	Green Valley	Total
Game 1	132	68	200
Game 2	46	49	95
Total	178	117	295

a. In which game were more points made by Green Valley? Game 2

b. How many total points were made in Game 2? 95

c. Which team made fewer points in Game 1? Green Valley

Part 5 For each item, circle the fraction that is larger. Write the sign: <, =, >.

a. $\frac{6}{6} > \frac{6}{7}$ b. $\frac{4}{5} < \frac{6}{5}$ c. $\frac{15}{3} > \frac{16}{4}$

© SRA/McGraw-Hill. Permission is granted to reproduce for school use.

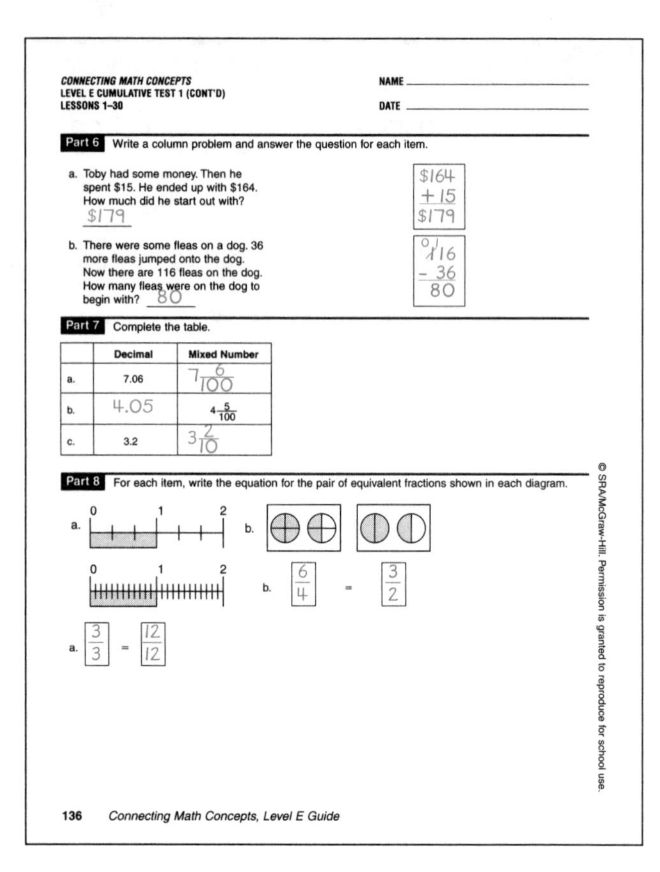

CONNECTING MATH CONCEPTS
LEVEL E CUMULATIVE TEST 1 (CONT'D)
LESSONS 1–30

NAME ____________

DATE ____________

Part 6 Write a column problem and answer the question for each item.

a. Toby had some money. Then he spent $15. He ended up with $164. How much did he start out with? $179

$164 + 15 = $179

b. There were some fleas on a dog. 36 more fleas jumped onto the dog. Now there are 116 fleas on the dog. How many fleas were on the dog to begin with? 80

$116 - 36 = 80$

Part 7 Complete the table.

	Decimal	Mixed Number
a.	7.06	$7\frac{6}{100}$
b.	4.05	$4\frac{5}{100}$
c.	3.2	$3\frac{2}{10}$

Part 8 For each item, write the equation for the pair of equivalent fractions shown in each diagram.

a. $\frac{3}{3} = \frac{12}{12}$

b. $\frac{6}{4} = \frac{3}{2}$

© SRA/McGraw-Hill. Permission is granted to reproduce for school use.

CONNECTING MATH CONCEPTS
LEVEL E CUMULATIVE TEST 1 (CONT'D)
LESSONS 1–30

NAME ____________

DATE ____________

Part 9 Complete the equation to show the place-value addition (number expansion).

a. 792 = 700 + 90 + 2

b. 48 = 40 + 8

c. 208 = 200 + 8

Part 10 Work each problem. Write the complete answer.

a. $39 \div 6$ = 6 R3 b. $26 \div 4$ = 6 R2

c. $129 \div 5$ = 25 R4

Part 11 Write the fraction for each description.

a. The fraction is more than 1. The numbers are 13 and 20. $\frac{20}{13}$

b. The denominator is 7. The fraction equals 6 whole units. $\frac{42}{7}$

c. The fraction is less than 1. The numbers are 8 and 17. $\frac{8}{17}$

Part 12 Complete each multiplication fact. Next to the fact, write the equation with prime factors.

a. $2 \times 4 = 8$ $2 \times 2 \times 2 = 8$

b. $2 \times 3 = 6$ $3 \times 2 = 6$

c. $7 \times 10 = 70$ $5 \times 7 \times 2 = 70$

d. $3 \times 11 = 33$ $3 \times 11 = 33$

e. $6 \times 8 = 48$ $2 \times 2 \times 2 \times 2 \times 3 = 48$

Factors may be in any order.

Part 13 For each item, complete the equation to show the mixed number and the fraction it equals.

a. $6\frac{4}{9} = \frac{58}{9}$ b. $3\frac{2}{4} = \frac{14}{4}$ c. $1\frac{8}{12} = \frac{20}{12}$

Part 14 Complete each equation.

a. $6 = \frac{24}{4} = \frac{12}{2} = \frac{30}{5} = \frac{48}{8}$

b. $4 = \frac{16}{4} = \frac{8}{2} = \frac{20}{5} = \frac{32}{8}$

© SRA/McGraw-Hill. Permission is granted to reproduce for school use.

CONNECTING MATH CONCEPTS
LEVEL E CUMULATIVE TEST 1 (CONT'D)
LESSONS 1–30

NAME ____________

DATE ____________

Part 15 Copy the table and complete it. A sample item is worked.

	Multiplication	Division	Fraction Equation
Sample	$8 \times 14 = 112$	$112 \div 8 = 14$	$\frac{112}{8} = 14$
a.	$3 \times 73 = 219$	$219 \div 3 = 73$	$\frac{219}{3} = 73$
b.	$6 \times 64 = 384$	$384 \div 6 = 64$	$\frac{384}{6} = 64$
c.	$7 \times 43 = 301$	$301 \div 7 = 43$	$\frac{301}{7} = 43$

© SRA/McGraw-Hill. Permission is granted to reproduce for school use.

CONNECTING MATH CONCEPTS
LEVEL E CUMULATIVE TEST 2
LESSONS 1–60

NAME ______________________

DATE ______________________

Part 1 Write complete answers to the questions.

In a class, there were 2 boys for every 3 girls. There were 15 girls in the class.

1. How many students were in the class? 25 students
2. How many boys were in the class? 10 boys

Boys	2	10
Girls	3	15
Students	5	25

$\frac{\text{Girls}}{\text{Students}} \quad \frac{3}{5} \quad \frac{5}{5} = \frac{15}{25}$

Part 2 Complete each equation. Circle the first fraction or the last fraction to show which is larger.

a. $\frac{4}{9} \times \frac{3}{4} = \frac{12}{36}$ b. $\frac{8}{3} \times \frac{14}{13} = \frac{112}{39}$

$14 \times 8 = 112$

Part 3 Answer the questions.

a. There were 22 bluebirds and 18 robins.

1. What fraction of the birds were robins? $\frac{18}{40}$
2. What fraction of the birds were bluebirds? $\frac{22}{40}$

Bluebirds $\frac{22}{40}$ Robins $\frac{18}{40}$ Birds $\frac{40}{40}$

b. $\frac{2}{6}$ of the bears were black.

1. What fraction of the bears were not black? $\frac{4}{6}$
2. What's the fraction for all the bears? $\frac{6}{6}$

Black $\frac{2}{6}$ Non Black $\frac{4}{6}$ Bears $\frac{6}{6}$

c. A bakery had some muffins. 14 muffins were sold. There were still 86 muffins in the bakery.

How many muffins were in the bakery to begin with? 100

End Up 86 Out 14 In □

$86 + 14 = 100$

© SRA/McGraw-Hill. Permission is granted to reproduce for school use.

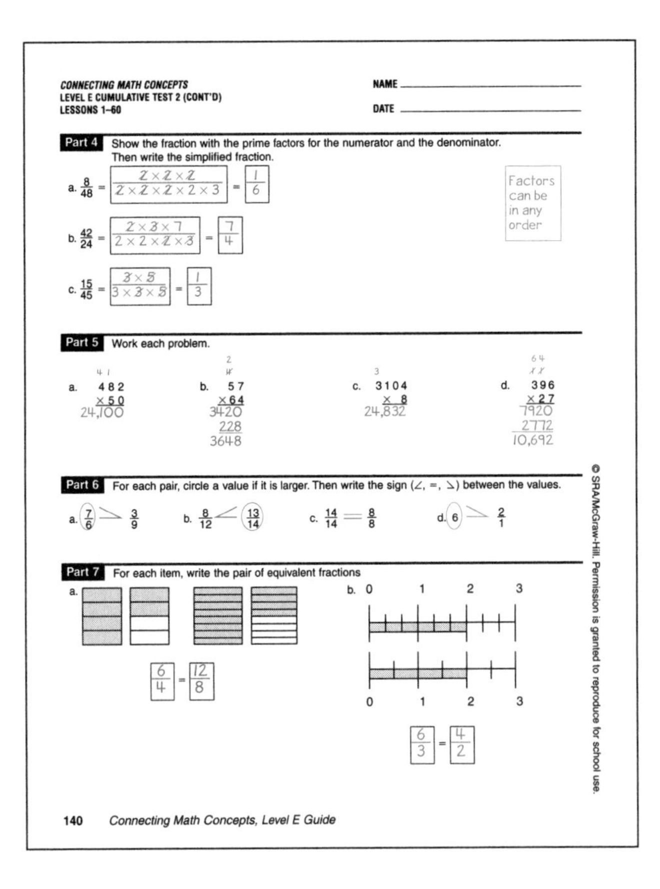
CONNECTING MATH CONCEPTS
LEVEL E CUMULATIVE TEST 2 (CONT'D)
LESSONS 1–60

NAME ______________________

DATE ______________________

Part 4 Show the fraction with the prime factors for the numerator and the denominator. Then write the simplified fraction.

a. $\frac{8}{48} = \frac{2 \times 2 \times 2}{2 \times 2 \times 2 \times 2 \times 3} = \frac{1}{6}$

b. $\frac{42}{24} = \frac{2 \times 3 \times 7}{2 \times 2 \times 2 \times 3} = \frac{7}{4}$

c. $\frac{15}{45} = \frac{3 \times 5}{3 \times 3 \times 5} = \frac{1}{3}$

Factors can be in any order

Part 5 Work each problem.

a. $482 \times 50 = 24{,}100$

b. 57×64: 3420 + 228 = 3648

c. $3104 \times 8 = 24{,}832$

d. 396×27: 7920 + 2772 = 10,692

Part 6 For each pair, circle a value if it is larger. Then write the sign (<, =, >) between the values.

a. $\frac{7}{6} > \frac{3}{9}$ b. $\frac{8}{12} < \frac{13}{14}$ c. $\frac{14}{14} = \frac{8}{8}$ d. $6 > \frac{2}{1}$

Part 7 For each item, write the pair of equivalent fractions

a. $\frac{6}{4} = \frac{12}{8}$

b. 0 1 2 3

$\frac{6}{3} = \frac{4}{2}$

© SRA/McGraw-Hill. Permission is granted to reproduce for school use.

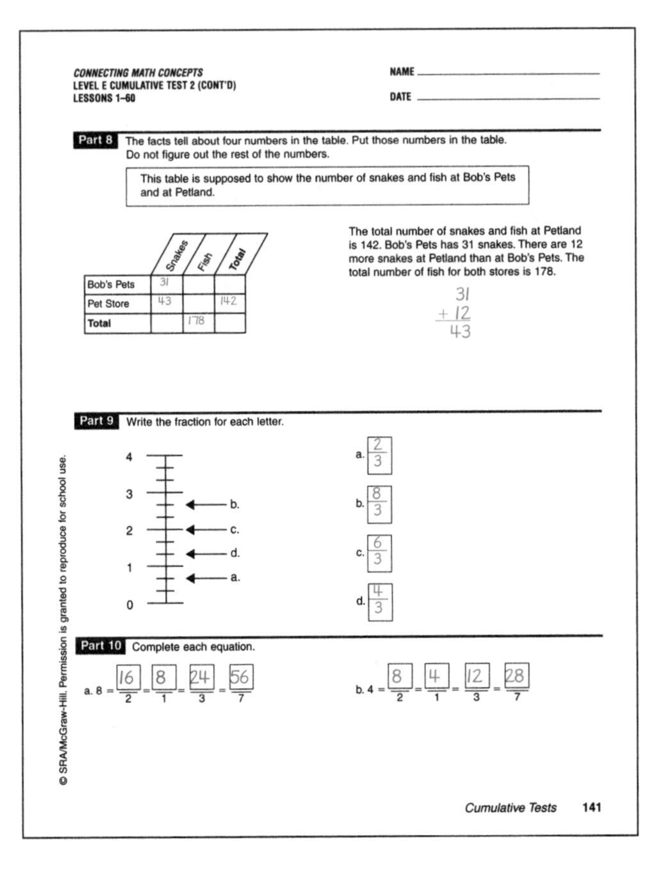
CONNECTING MATH CONCEPTS
LEVEL E CUMULATIVE TEST 2 (CONT'D)
LESSONS 1–60

NAME ______________________

DATE ______________________

Part 8 The facts tell about four numbers in the table. Put those numbers in the table. Do not figure out the rest of the numbers.

This table is supposed to show the number of snakes and fish at Bob's Pets and at Petland.

	Snakes	Fish	Total
Bob's Pets	31		
Pet Store	43		142
Total		178	

The total number of snakes and fish at Petland is 142. Bob's Pets has 31 snakes. There are 12 more snakes at Petland than at Bob's Pets. The total number of fish for both stores is 178.

$31 + 12 = 43$

Part 9 Write the fraction for each letter.

a. $\frac{2}{3}$ b. $\frac{8}{3}$ c. $\frac{6}{3}$ d. $\frac{4}{3}$

Part 10 Complete each equation.

a. $8 = \frac{16}{2} = \frac{8}{1} = \frac{24}{3} = \frac{56}{7}$

b. $4 = \frac{8}{2} = \frac{4}{1} = \frac{12}{3} = \frac{28}{7}$

© SRA/McGraw-Hill. Permission is granted to reproduce for school use.

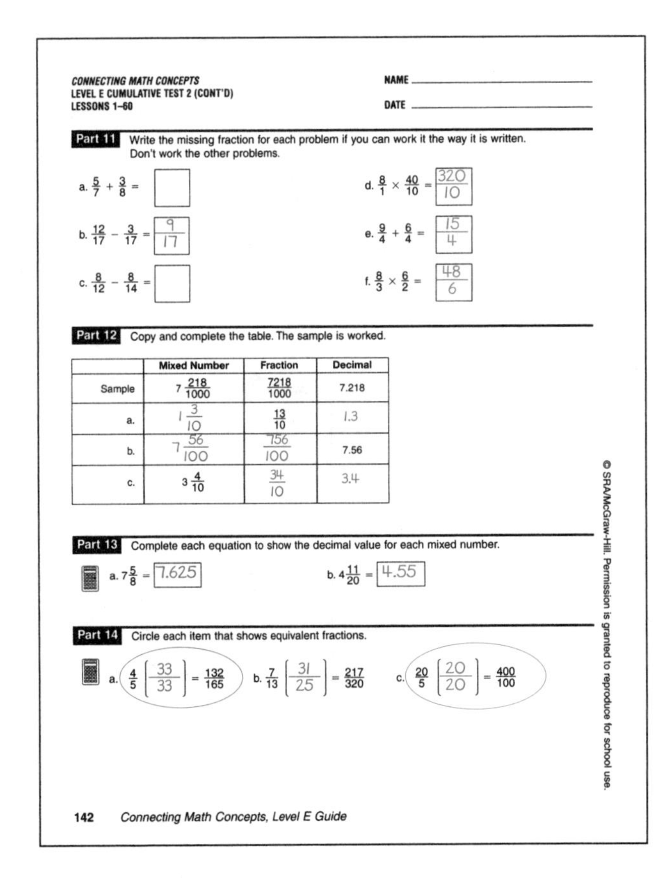
CONNECTING MATH CONCEPTS
LEVEL E CUMULATIVE TEST 2 (CONT'D)
LESSONS 1–60

NAME ______________________

DATE ______________________

Part 11 Write the missing fraction for each problem if you can work it the way it is written. Don't work the other problems.

a. $\frac{5}{7} + \frac{3}{8} =$ □

b. $\frac{12}{17} - \frac{3}{17} = \frac{9}{17}$

c. $\frac{8}{12} - \frac{8}{14} =$ □

d. $\frac{8}{1} \times \frac{40}{10} = \frac{320}{10}$

e. $\frac{9}{4} + \frac{6}{4} = \frac{15}{4}$

f. $\frac{8}{3} \times \frac{6}{2} = \frac{48}{6}$

Part 12 Copy and complete the table. The sample is worked.

	Mixed Number	Fraction	Decimal
Sample	$7\frac{218}{1000}$	$\frac{7218}{1000}$	7.218
a.	$1\frac{3}{10}$	$\frac{13}{10}$	1.3
b.	$7\frac{56}{100}$	$\frac{756}{100}$	7.56
c.	$3\frac{4}{10}$	$\frac{34}{10}$	3.4

Part 13 Complete each equation to show the decimal value for each mixed number.

a. $7\frac{5}{8} = 7.625$ b. $4\frac{11}{20} = 4.55$

Part 14 Circle each item that shows equivalent fractions.

a. $\frac{4}{5}\left[\frac{33}{33}\right] = \frac{132}{165}$ b. $\frac{7}{13}\left[\frac{31}{25}\right] = \frac{217}{320}$ c. $\frac{20}{5}\left[\frac{20}{20}\right] = \frac{400}{100}$

© SRA/McGraw-Hill. Permission is granted to reproduce for school use.

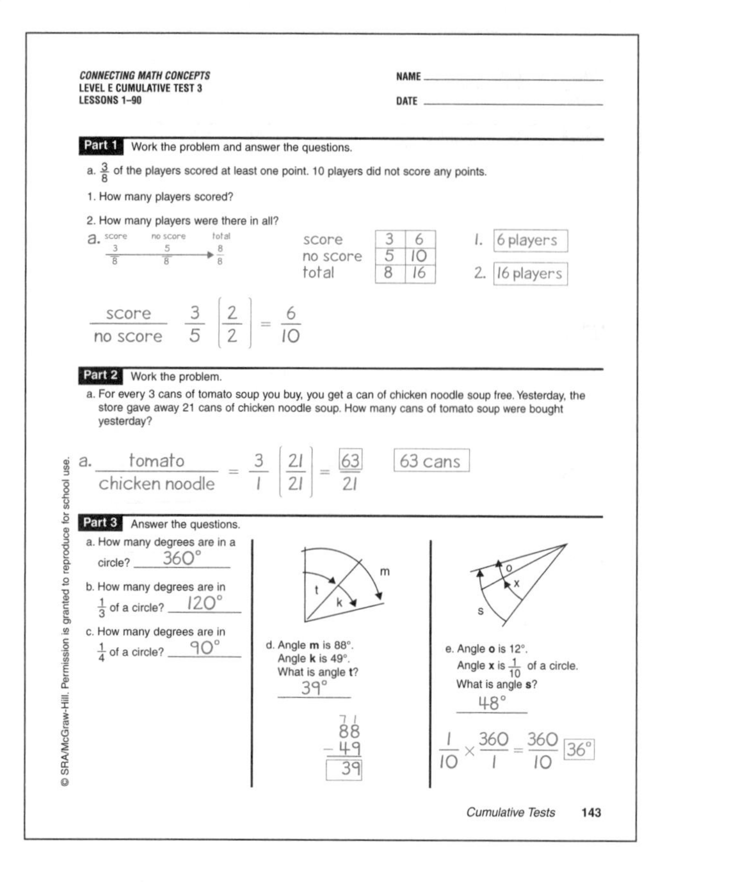

CONNECTING MATH CONCEPTS
LEVEL E CUMULATIVE TEST 3
LESSONS 1–90

NAME ____________
DATE ____________

Part 1 Work the problem and answer the questions.

a. $\frac{3}{8}$ of the players scored at least one point. 10 players did not score any points.

1. How many players scored?

2. How many players were there in all?

a. score $\frac{3}{8}$, no score $\frac{5}{8}$, total $\frac{8}{8}$

score	3	6
no score	5	10
total	8	16

1. 6 players
2. 16 players

$\frac{\text{score}}{\text{no score}} \quad \frac{3}{5}\left(\frac{2}{2}\right) = \frac{6}{10}$

Part 2 Work the problem.

a. For every 3 cans of tomato soup you buy, you get a can of chicken noodle soup free. Yesterday, the store gave away 21 cans of chicken noodle soup. How many cans of tomato soup were bought yesterday?

a. $\frac{\text{tomato}}{\text{chicken noodle}} \quad \frac{3}{1}\left(\frac{21}{21}\right) = \frac{63}{21}$ 63 cans

Part 3 Answer the questions.

a. How many degrees are in a circle? 360°

b. How many degrees are in $\frac{1}{3}$ of a circle? 120°

c. How many degrees are in $\frac{1}{4}$ of a circle? 90°

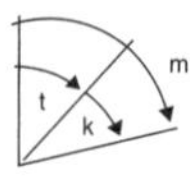

d. Angle **m** is 88°. Angle **k** is 49°. What is angle **t**? 39°

88 − 49 = 39

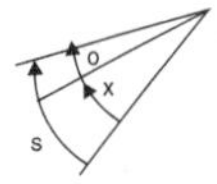

e. Angle **o** is 12°. Angle **x** is $\frac{1}{10}$ of a circle. What is angle **s**? 48°

$\frac{1}{10} \times \frac{360}{1} = \frac{360}{10}$ 36°

© SRA/McGraw-Hill. Permission is granted to reproduce for school use.

CONNECTING MATH CONCEPTS
LEVEL E CUMULATIVE TEST 3 (CONT'D)
LESSONS 1–90

NAME ____________
DATE ____________

Part 4 Write the problem to find the area and the problem to find the perimeter of each figure. Write the unit name in each answer.

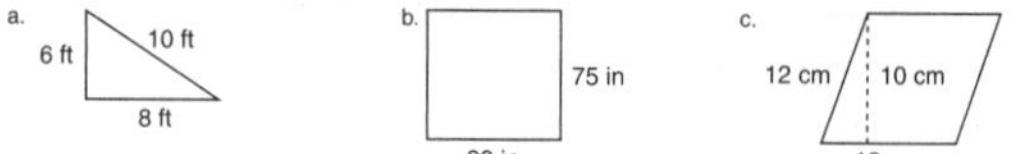

a. Area = $\frac{b \times h}{2}$; Area = $\frac{8 \times 6}{2} = \frac{48}{2}$; 24 sq. ft.; 6 + 10 + 8 = 24 feet

b. Area = b × h; Area = 80 × 75; 6000 sq. in.; 75 × 80 = 600; 80 + 80 + 75 + 75 = 310 in.

c. Area = b × h; Area = 12 × 10; 120 sq. cm; 12 + 12 + 12 + 12 = 48 cm

Part 5 Work each problem.

a. $46\frac{10}{10} - 19\frac{6}{10} = 26\frac{4}{10}$

b. $12\frac{8}{15} + 16\frac{7}{15} = 28\frac{15}{15} = 29$

Part 6 Write each problem in a column and work it.

a. \$13.20 + \$7.20 + \$.80 = \$21.20

b. \$12.70 × 8 = \$101.60

Part 7 Work the problems and answer the questions.

There are 8 rainy days for every sunny day.

a. How many sunny days are there for 48 rainy days? 6 sunny days

b. How many rainy days are there for 8 sunny days? 64 rainy days

c. How many rainy days are there for 12 sunny days? 96 rainy days

		a.	b.	c.
rainy	8	48	64	96
sunny	1	6	8	12

© SRA/McGraw-Hill. Permission is granted to reproduce for school use.

CONNECTING MATH CONCEPTS
LEVEL E CUMULATIVE TEST 3 (CONT'D)
LESSONS 1–90

NAME ____________
DATE ____________

Part 8 Work each problem.

a. 56 ⟌313 = 5 r 33 (−280 = 33)

b. 39 ⟌207 = 5 r 12 (−195 = 12)

Part 9 Write the number of degrees for each angle.

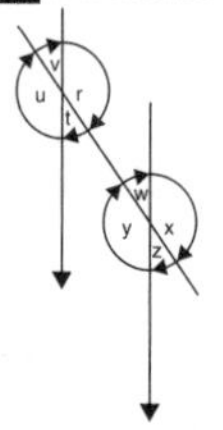

∠y = 160°
∠w = 20°
∠x = 160°
∠z = 20°
∠u = 160°
∠v = 20°
∠r = 160°
∠t = 20°

Part 10 Work each item.

a. Round 5647 to the nearest hundred. 5600

b. Round 5647 to the nearest thousand. 6000

c. Round 5647 to the nearest ten. 5650

Part 11 Answer the questions.

a. Candi started out with 13 gallons of fuel. At her first stop, 9 gallons were added. At her next stop, another 11 gallons were added. She used up 26 gallons on her trip. How much fuel did she have at the end of her trip? 7 gallons

b. Mike had \$110.00 to shop with. He bought a hat for \$19.00. Then he bought three shirts for \$15.00 each. How much did he have left? \$46.00

a. end up, out, in: 13 + 9 + 11 = 33; 33 − 26 = 7 gallons

b. out, in: 19 + 15 + 15 + 15 = 64; \$110 − 64 = \$46

Part 12 Work each problem with values rounded to the place named in the box.

a. 6591 − 3026 (tens): 6590 − 3030 = 3560

b. 4659 + 1352 + 6147 (hundreds): 4700 + 1400 + 6100 = 12,200

Part 13 For each item, figure out the first common number (least common multiple). Then complete each equation.

Sample: 4 × 3 = 12; 6 × 2 = 12

a. 6 × 4 = 24; 8 × 3 = 24

b. 7 × 3 = 21; 3 × 7 = 21

c. 15 × 5 = 75; 25 × 3 = 75

© SRA/McGraw-Hill. Permission is granted to reproduce for school use.

CONNECTING MATH CONCEPTS
LEVEL E CUMULATIVE TEST 3 (CONT'D)
LESSONS 1–90

NAME ____________
DATE ____________

Part 14 Write the fraction for each letter.

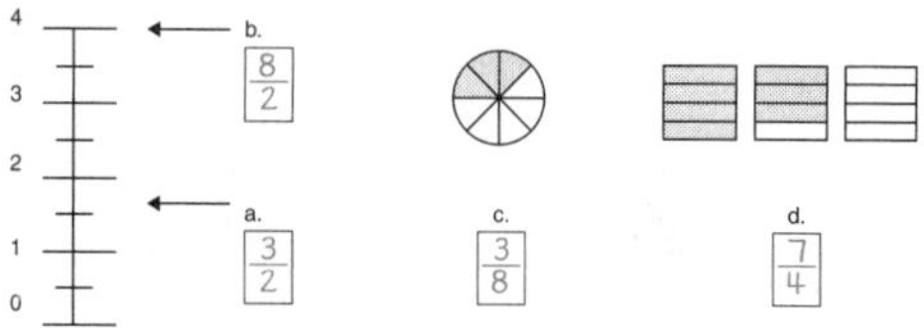

a. $\frac{3}{2}$ b. $\frac{8}{2}$ c. $\frac{3}{8}$ d. $\frac{7}{4}$

Part 15 Circle the value in each item that is larger. Then write the sign (<, =, or >) between the values for each item.

a. $\frac{3}{8} > \frac{3}{12}$ b. $\frac{4}{3} < 8$ c. $\frac{10}{5} < \frac{9}{3}$ d. $\frac{13}{4} > \frac{13}{6}$

Part 16 Complete the equation to show the place-value addition (numeral expansion). Part of the answer for item a is written.

a. 734 = (7 × 100) + (3 × 10) + (4 × 1)

b. 62 = (6 × 10) + (2 × 1)

c. 108 = (1 × 100) + (0 × 10) + (8 × 1) or (1 × 100) + (8 × 1)

Part 17 Complete the table. A sample item is shown.

	Decimal	Fraction	Mixed Number
Sample	7.218	$\frac{7218}{1000}$	$7\frac{218}{1000}$
a.	12.7	$\frac{127}{10}$	$12\frac{7}{10}$
b.	2.06	$\frac{206}{100}$	$2\frac{6}{100}$
c.	4.002	$\frac{4002}{1000}$	$4\frac{2}{1000}$

© SRA/McGraw-Hill. Permission is granted to reproduce for school use.

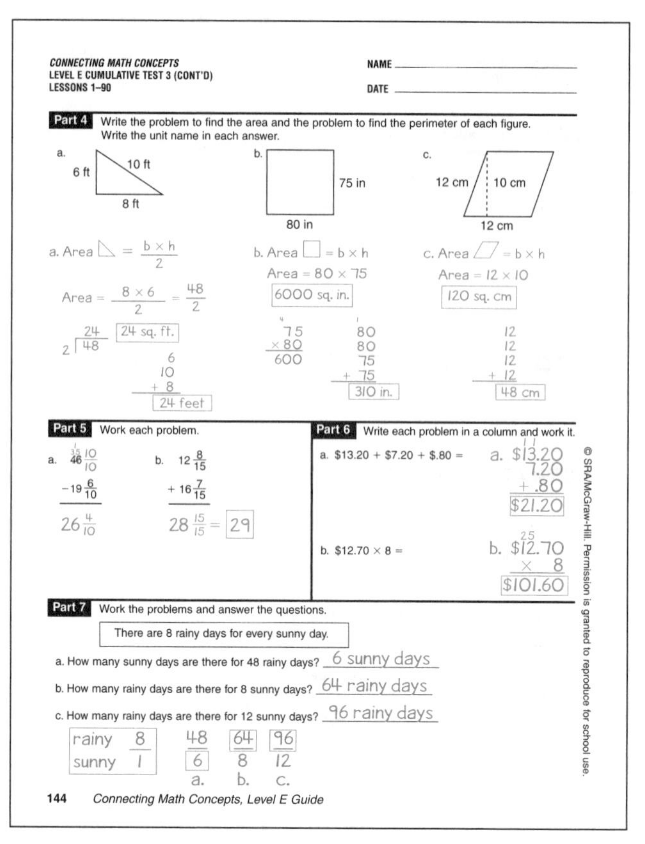

CONNECTING MATH CONCEPTS
LEVEL E FINAL CUMULATIVE TEST
LESSONS 1–125

NAME ______________________

DATE ______________________

Part 1 Work each item.

a. 250 × 1.9 = 2250 + 2500 = 475.0

b. 4.7 × 5.3 = 141 + 2350 = 24.91

c. 81 ⟌437.4 = 5.4 (− 405, 324, − 324, 0)

d. 857 × 30 = 25,710

e. 8 ⟌.248 = .031 (− 24, 08, − 8, 0)

f. 53 ⟌402 = $7\frac{31}{53}$ (− 371, 31)

Part 2 Make a table. Answer each question.

Mary and Sue collected buttons and bows. Mary had 142 bows. Sue had 85 buttons. Both girls had a total of 198 buttons. Sue had 38 fewer bows than Mary.

	Buttons	Bows	Total
Sue	85	104	189
Mary	113	142	255
Total	198	246	444

a. What was the total number of buttons and bows in Sue's collection? 189

b. Who had more buttons, Mary or Sue? Mary

c. How many bows did Sue have? 104

Dif 38, S, M 142; 142 − 38 = 104

198 − 85 = 113; 142 + 104 = 246; 113 + 142 = 255; 85 + 104 = 189; 198 + 246 = 444

Part 3

Figure out the function. (The function is the rule that converts *x* values into *y* values.) Complete each table.

x	function: x(3)	y
5	5 (3)	15
6	6 (3)	18
8	8 (3)	24
3	3 (3)	9
2	2 (3)	6

x	function: x − 2	y
9	9 − 2	7
22	22 − 2	20
15	15 − 2	13
30	30 − 2	28
24	24 − 2	22

© SRA/McGraw-Hill. Permission is granted to reproduce for school use.

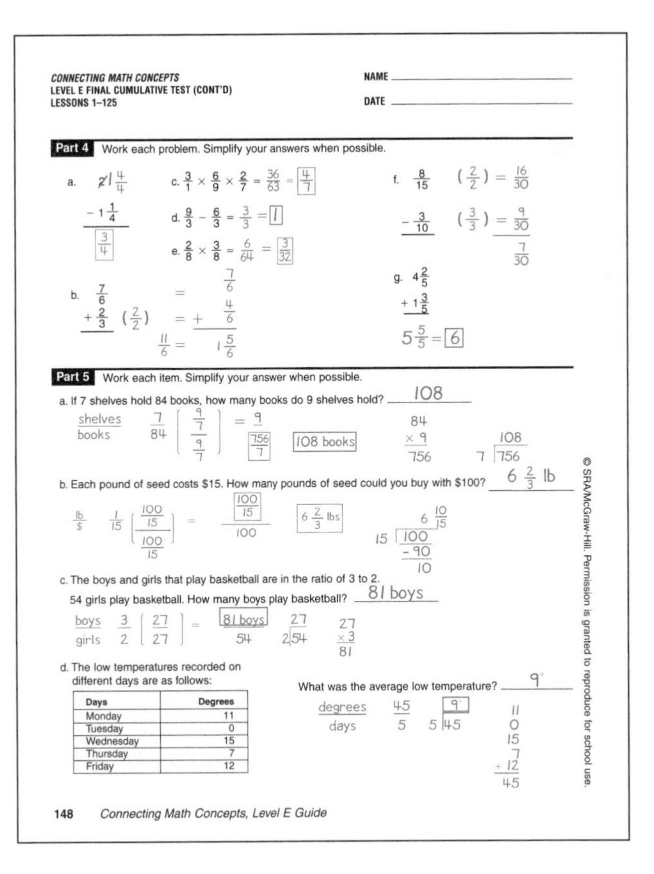

CONNECTING MATH CONCEPTS
LEVEL E FINAL CUMULATIVE TEST (CONT'D)
LESSONS 1–125

NAME ______________________

DATE ______________________

Part 4 Work each problem. Simplify your answers when possible.

a. $2\frac{1}{4} - 1\frac{1}{4} = \frac{3}{4}$

b. $\frac{7}{6} + \frac{2}{3}\left(\frac{2}{2}\right) = \frac{7}{6} + \frac{4}{6} = \frac{11}{6} = 1\frac{5}{6}$

c. $\frac{3}{1} \times \frac{6}{9} \times \frac{2}{7} = \frac{36}{63} = \frac{4}{7}$

d. $\frac{9}{3} - \frac{6}{3} = \frac{3}{3} = 1$

e. $\frac{2}{8} \times \frac{3}{8} = \frac{6}{64} = \frac{3}{32}$

f. $\frac{8}{15}\left(\frac{2}{2}\right) = \frac{16}{30}$; $-\frac{3}{10}\left(\frac{3}{3}\right) = \frac{9}{30}$; $\frac{7}{30}$

g. $4\frac{2}{5} + 1\frac{3}{5} = 5\frac{5}{5} = 6$

Part 5 Work each item. Simplify your answer when possible.

a. If 7 shelves hold 84 books, how many books do 9 shelves hold? 108

shelves/books $\frac{7}{84}\left(\frac{9}{7}\right) = \frac{9}{756/7}$ = 108 books; 84 × 9 = 756; 756 ÷ 7 = 108

b. Each pound of seed costs $15. How many pounds of seed could you buy with $100? $6\frac{2}{3}$ lb

$\frac{lb}{\$}\ \frac{1}{15}\left(\frac{100/15}{100/15}\right) = \frac{100/15}{100}$; $6\frac{2}{3}$ lbs; 15 ⟌100 = $6\frac{10}{15}$ (− 90, 10)

c. The boys and girls that play basketball are in the ratio of 3 to 2. 54 girls play basketball. How many boys play basketball? 81 boys

boys/girls $\frac{3}{2}\left(\frac{27}{27}\right) = \frac{81 \text{ boys}}{54}$; 2 ⟌54 = 27; 27 × 3 = 81

d. The low temperatures recorded on different days are as follows:

Days	Degrees
Monday	11
Tuesday	0
Wednesday	15
Thursday	7
Friday	12

What was the average low temperature? 9°

degrees/days $\frac{45}{5}$ = 9; 5 ⟌45; 11 + 0 + 15 + 7 + 12 = 45

© SRA/McGraw-Hill. Permission is granted to reproduce for school use.

CONNECTING MATH CONCEPTS
LEVEL E FINAL CUMULATIVE TEST (CONT'D)
LESSONS 1–125

NAME ______________________

DATE ______________________

Part 6 Simplify each fraction. Rewrite each fraction that is more than 1 as a whole number or a mixed number.

a. $\frac{20}{24} = \frac{5}{6}$ b. $\frac{50}{5} = 10$ c. $\frac{28}{25} = 1\frac{3}{25}$ d. $\frac{21}{42} = \frac{1}{2}$ e. $\frac{48}{7} = 6\frac{6}{7}$

Part 7 Complete the table. The sample has been worked.

	Mixed Number	Fraction	Decimal
Sample	$7\frac{218}{1000}$	$\frac{7218}{1000}$	7.218
a.	$2\frac{46}{100}$	$\frac{246}{100}$	2.46
b.	$1\frac{17}{1000}$	$\frac{1017}{1000}$	1.017
c.	$8\frac{4}{100}$	$\frac{804}{100}$	8.04

Part 8 Work each item. Simplify answers when possible.

a. What is $\frac{3}{8}$ of 92? $34\frac{1}{2}$

$\frac{3}{8} \times \frac{92}{1} = \frac{276}{8} = 34\frac{1}{2}$; 92 × 3 = 276; 8 ⟌276 = $34\frac{4}{8}$

b. How many degrees are in $\frac{8}{9}$ of a circle? 320°

$\frac{8}{9} \times \frac{360}{1} = \frac{2880}{9} = 320°$; 360 × 8 = 2880; 9 ⟌2880 = 320

c. Which is more, 72 inches or 5 feet? 72 inches

$\frac{ft}{in}\ \frac{1}{12} = \frac{6}{72} = \frac{5}{60}$; 72 inches; 12 ⟌72 = 6; 12 × 5 = 60

d. Which is more, $\frac{6}{5}$ or $\frac{4}{3}$? $\frac{4}{3}$

$\frac{6}{5}\left(\frac{3}{3}\right) = \frac{18}{15}$; $\frac{4}{3}\left(\frac{5}{5}\right) = \frac{20}{15}$; $\frac{6}{5} < \frac{4}{3}$

e. Which is more, $\frac{10}{12}$ or $\frac{38}{48}$? $\frac{10}{12}$

$\frac{10}{12}\left(\frac{4}{4}\right) = \frac{40}{48}$; $\frac{38}{48} = \frac{38}{48}$; $\frac{10}{12} > \frac{38}{48}$

© SRA/McGraw-Hill. Permission is granted to reproduce for school use.

CONNECTING MATH CONCEPTS
LEVEL E FINAL CUMULATIVE TEST (CONT'D)
LESSONS 1–125

NAME ______________________

DATE ______________________

Part 9

For each item, write the decimal numbers in order of size. Write the largest value on top and the smallest value on the bottom. If the values are equal, write them on the same line.

a. .999, 1.009, 1.9 — 1.9; 1.009; .999

b. 27.3, 2.73, 7.37 — 27.30; 7.37; 2.73

c. 5.700, 5.7, 5.71 — 5.71; 5.700, 5.700

Part 10 Figure out the perimeter and area of each figure. Remember the unit name.

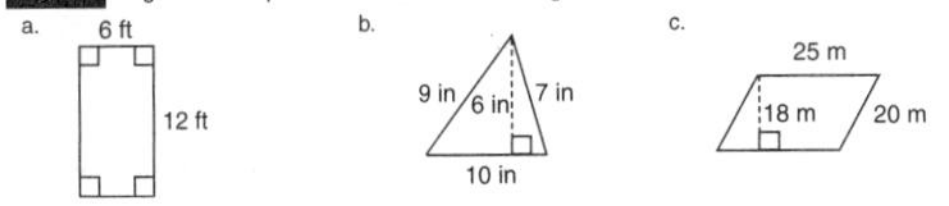

a. (rectangle, 6 ft by 12 ft) Perimeter 36 feet; Area 72 square ft

12 + 12 + 6 + 6 = 36; Area □ = b × h; Area = 6 × 12; 72 sq ft

b. (triangle, sides 9 in, 7 in, base 10 in, height 6 in) Perimeter 26 in; Area 30 sq in

9 + 7 + 10 = 26 in; Area △ = $\frac{b \times h}{2}$; Area = $\frac{10 \times 6}{2} = \frac{60}{2}$ = 30 sq in

c. (parallelogram, 25 m, 20 m, height 18 m) Perimeter 90 m; Area 450 sq m

20 + 20 + 25 + 25 = 90 m; Area □ = b × h; Area = 25 × 18; 450 sq m; 25 × 18 = 200 + 250 = 450

© SRA/McGraw-Hill. Permission is granted to reproduce for school use.

CONNECTING MATH CONCEPTS
LEVEL E FINAL CUMULATIVE TEST (CONT'D)
LESSONS 1–125

NAME ________________
DATE ________________

Part 11 Answer each question.

a. 75% of the cars in the lot are white. There are 24 cars that are not white.

1. How many white cars are in the lot? 72 white cars

2. How many cars are in the lot altogether? 96 cars

	W	NW	T
	75	25	100
	100	100	100

W	75	72
NW	25	24
T	100	96

b. Andrew collected $\frac{7}{5}$ times as much money as Ben collected. Ben collected $25.

1. How much money did Andrew collect? $35

2. How much more money did Andrew collect than Ben collected? $10

Dif	2	10
B	5	25
A	7	35

c. The sale price is 80% of the regular price. The regular price is $25.

1. How much is the sale price? $20

2. How much less than the regular price is the sale price? $5

Dif	20	5
S	80	20
R	100	25

Part 12 For each bag, write the fraction for your chances of drawing a circle.

a. $\frac{3}{6}$ b. $\frac{3}{4}$ c. $\frac{1}{5}$ d. $\frac{5}{5}$

© SRA/McGraw-Hill. Permission is granted to reproduce for school use.

CONNECTING MATH CONCEPTS
LEVEL E FINAL CUMULATIVE TEST (CONT'D)
LESSONS 1–125

NAME ________________
DATE ________________

Part 13 Work each item.

a. The apartment building is 62 feet taller than the church. The apartment building is 104 feet tall. How tall is the church? 42 feet

b. A boat set sail with 275 passengers on board. At the first stop, 52 passengers got off and 37 passengers got on. At the second stop, 28 passengers got on and 12 passengers got off. How many passengers were left on board? 276 passengers

c. Yesterday, Linda earned some money. Today, she earned another $52. In all, she earned $105 for the two days. How much did she earn yesterday? $53

Part 14 Complete each equation. If the fractions shown are equivalent, write a simple equation below.

a. $\frac{3}{8}\left(\frac{5}{5}\right) = \frac{15}{40}$ b. $\frac{7}{2}\left(\frac{9}{9}\right) = \frac{63}{18}$ c. $\frac{9}{5}\left(\frac{5}{4}\right) = \frac{45}{20}$

$\frac{3}{8} = \frac{15}{40}$ $\frac{7}{2} = \frac{63}{18}$

© SRA/McGraw-Hill. Permission is granted to reproduce for school use.

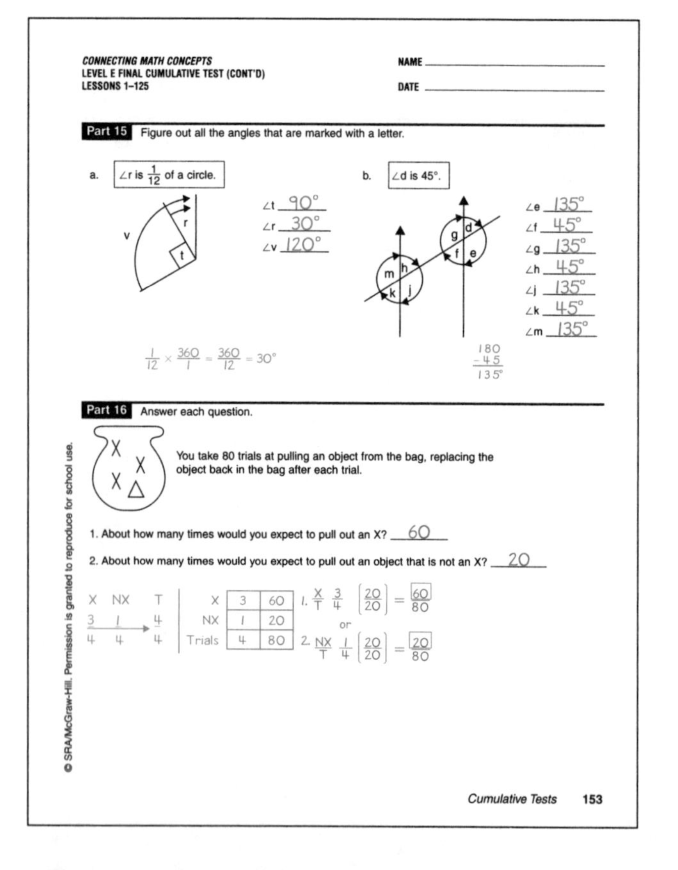
CONNECTING MATH CONCEPTS
LEVEL E FINAL CUMULATIVE TEST (CONT'D)
LESSONS 1–125

NAME ________________
DATE ________________

Part 15 Figure out all the angles that are marked with a letter.

a. ∠r is $\frac{1}{12}$ of a circle. ∠t 90° ∠r 30° ∠v 120°

b. ∠d is 45°. ∠e 135° ∠f 45° ∠g 135° ∠h 45° ∠j 135° ∠k 45° ∠m 135°

Part 16 Answer each question.

You take 80 trials at pulling an object from the bag, replacing the object back in the bag after each trial.

1. About how many times would you expect to pull out an X? 60

2. About how many times would you expect to pull out an object that is not an X? 20

© SRA/McGraw-Hill. Permission is granted to reproduce for school use.

CONNECTING MATH CONCEPTS
LEVEL E FINAL CUMULATIVE TEST (CONT'D)
LESSONS 1–125

NAME ________________
DATE ________________

Part 17 Complete the table. The sample problem has been worked.

		$\frac{\square}{100}$	%	Decimal
Sample	$\frac{23}{10}$	$\frac{230}{100}$	23%	2.35
a.	$\frac{4}{5}$	$\frac{80}{100}$	80%	.80
b.	$\frac{7}{2}$	$\frac{350}{100}$	350%	3.50
c.	$\frac{20}{50}$	$\frac{40}{100}$	40%	.40
d.	$\frac{6}{8}$	$\frac{75}{100}$	75%	.75

Part 18 Complete the table.

	Mixed number	Fraction
a.	$5\frac{8}{10}$	$\frac{58}{10}$
b.	$16\frac{3}{4}$	$\frac{67}{4}$
c.	$3\frac{3}{6}$	$\frac{21}{6}$
d.	$10\frac{3}{5}$	$\frac{503}{5}$

Part 19 Rewrite each problem as a column problem and work it.

a. 14.08 − .975 = 13.105 b. 8 + 12.92 + 105.9 = 126.82 c. 48 − 25.4 = 22.6

© SRA/McGraw-Hill. Permission is granted to reproduce for school use.

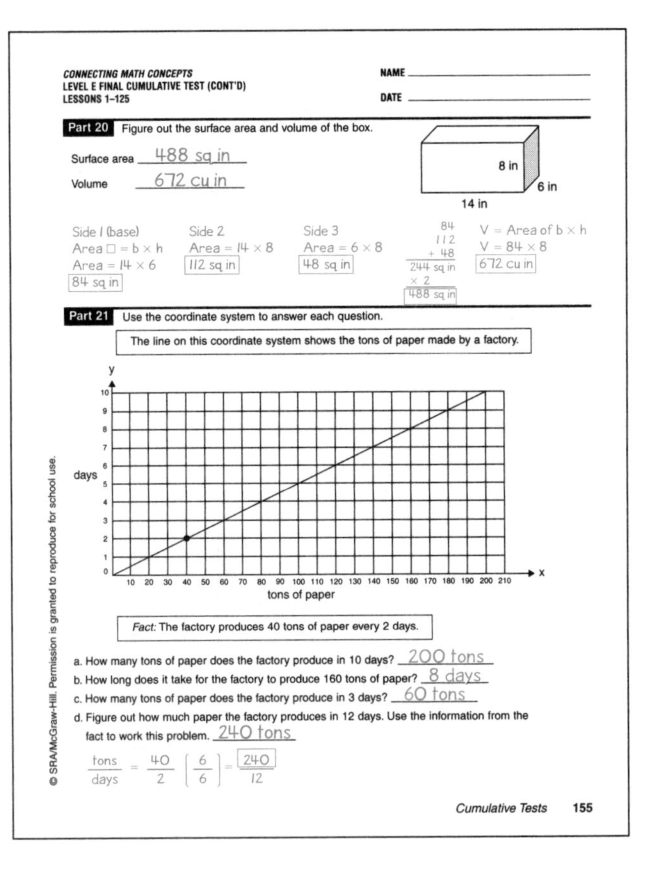

CONNECTING MATH CONCEPTS
LEVEL E FINAL CUMULATIVE TEST (CONT'D)
LESSONS 1–125

NAME ________
DATE ________

Part 20 Figure out the surface area and volume of the box.

Surface area 488 sq in

Volume 672 cu in

Side 1 (base)
Area □ = b × h
Area = 14 × 6
84 sq in

Side 2
Area = 14 × 8
112 sq in

Side 3
Area = 6 × 8
48 sq in

84
112
+ 48
244 sq in
× 2
488 sq in

V = Area of b × h
V = 84 × 8
672 cu in

Part 21 Use the coordinate system to answer each question.

The line on this coordinate system shows the tons of paper made by a factory.

Fact: The factory produces 40 tons of paper every 2 days.

a. How many tons of paper does the factory produce in 10 days? 200 tons

b. How long does it take for the factory to produce 160 tons of paper? 8 days

c. How many tons of paper does the factory produce in 3 days? 60 tons

d. Figure out how much paper the factory produces in 12 days. Use the information from the fact to work this problem. 240 tons

$\frac{tons}{days} = \frac{40}{2}\left(\frac{6}{6}\right) = \frac{240}{12}$

© SRA/McGraw-Hill. Permission is granted to reproduce for school use.

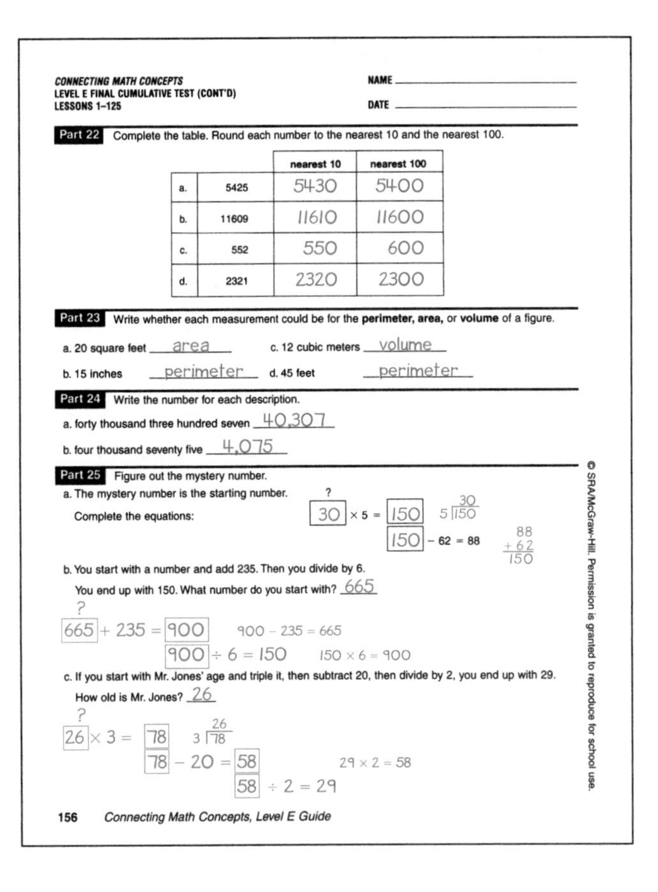

CONNECTING MATH CONCEPTS
LEVEL E FINAL CUMULATIVE TEST (CONT'D)
LESSONS 1–125

NAME ________
DATE ________

Part 22 Complete the table. Round each number to the nearest 10 and the nearest 100.

		nearest 10	nearest 100
a.	5425	5430	5400
b.	11609	11610	11600
c.	552	550	600
d.	2321	2320	2300

Part 23 Write whether each measurement could be for the **perimeter, area,** or **volume** of a figure.

a. 20 square feet area
b. 15 inches perimeter
c. 12 cubic meters volume
d. 45 feet perimeter

Part 24 Write the number for each description.

a. forty thousand three hundred seven 40,307

b. four thousand seventy five 4,075

Part 25 Figure out the mystery number.

a. The mystery number is the starting number.

Complete the equations:

?
30 × 5 = 150 (30 / 5)150)
150 − 62 = 88 (88 + 62 = 150)

b. You start with a number and add 235. Then you divide by 6. You end up with 150. What number do you start with? 665

?
665 + 235 = 900 (900 − 235 = 665)
900 ÷ 6 = 150 (150 × 6 = 900)

c. If you start with Mr. Jones' age and triple it, then subtract 20, then divide by 2, you end up with 29. How old is Mr. Jones? 26

?
26 × 3 = 78 (26 / 3)78)
78 − 20 = 58 (29 × 2 = 58)
58 ÷ 2 = 29

© SRA/McGraw-Hill. Permission is granted to reproduce for school use.

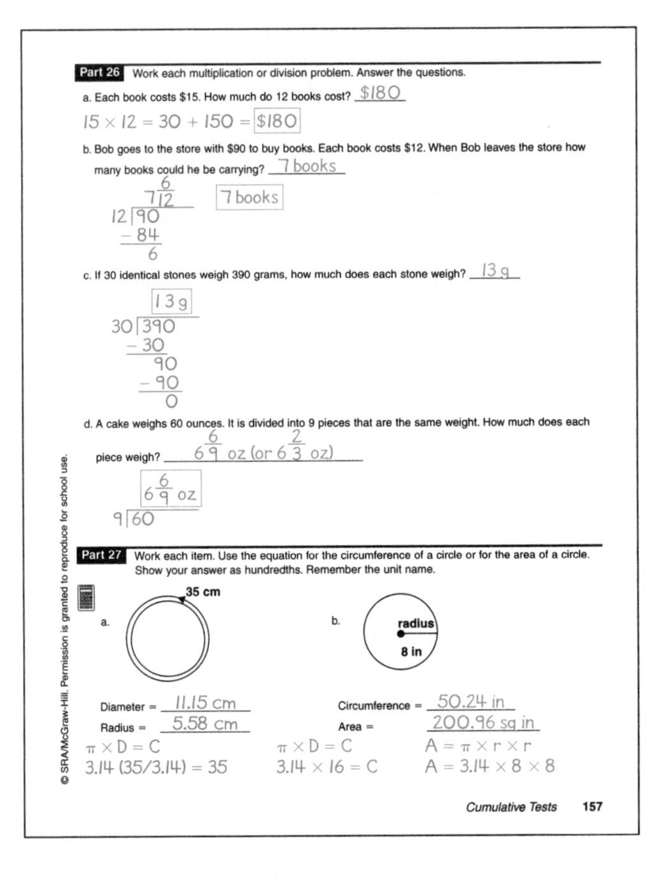

Part 26 Work each multiplication or division problem. Answer the questions.

a. Each book costs $15. How much do 12 books cost? $180

15 × 12 = 30 + 150 = $180

b. Bob goes to the store with $90 to buy books. Each book costs $12. When Bob leaves the store how many books could he be carrying? 7 books

12)90 = 7 r6; 90 − 84 = 6 — 7 books

c. If 30 identical stones weigh 390 grams, how much does each stone weigh? 13 g

30)390 = 13 g; 390 − 30 = 90; 90 − 90 = 0

d. A cake weighs 60 ounces. It is divided into 9 pieces that are the same weight. How much does each piece weigh? $6\frac{6}{9}$ oz (or $6\frac{2}{3}$ oz)

9)60 = $6\frac{6}{9}$ oz

Part 27 Work each item. Use the equation for the circumference of a circle or for the area of a circle. Show your answer as hundredths. Remember the unit name.

a. Diameter = 11.15 cm
Radius = 5.58 cm
π × D = C
3.14 (35/3.14) = 35

b. Circumference = 50.24 in
Area = 200.96 sq in
π × D = C
3.14 × 16 = C
A = π × r × r
A = 3.14 × 8 × 8

© SRA/McGraw-Hill. Permission is granted to reproduce for school use.

Remedy Summary CMC E

	Name	Cumulative Test 1														
		Check parts not passed														
		1	2	3	4	5	6	7	8	9	10	11	12	13	14	15
1.																
2.																
3.																
4.																
5.																
6.																
7.																
8.																
9.																
10.																
11.																
12.																
13.																
14.																
15.																
16.																
17.																
18.																
19.																
20.																
21.																
22.																
23.																
24.																
25.																
26.																
27.																
28.																
29.																
30.																

Copyright © SRA/McGraw-Hill. Permission is granted to reproduce for school use.

	Name	Cumulative Test 2 Check parts not passed													
		1	2	3	4	5	6	7	8	9	10	11	12	13	14
1.															
2.															
3.															
4.															
5.															
6.															
7.															
8.															
9.															
10.															
11.															
12.															
13.															
14.															
15.															
16.															
17.															
18.															
19.															
20.															
21.															
22.															
23.															
24.															
25.															
26.															
27.															
28.															
29.															
30.															

Copyright © SRA/McGraw-Hill. Permission is granted to reproduce for school use.

	Name	Cumulative Test 3																
		Check parts not passed																
		1	2	3	4	5	6	7	8	9	10	11	12	13	14	15	16	17
1.																		
2.																		
3.																		
4.																		
5.																		
6.																		
7.																		
8.																		
9.																		
10.																		
11.																		
12.																		
13.																		
14.																		
15.																		
16.																		
17.																		
18.																		
19.																		
20.																		
21.																		
22.																		
23.																		
24.																		
25.																		
26.																		
27.																		
28.																		
29.																		
30.																		

Copyright © SRA/McGraw-Hill. Permission is granted to reproduce for school use.

Remedy Summary CMC E

	Name	Final Cumulative Test																										
		Check parts not passed																										
		1	2	3	4	5	6	7	8	9	10	11	12	13	14	15	16	17	18	19	20	21	22	23	24	25	26	27
1.																												
2.																												
3.																												
4.																												
5.																												
6.																												
7.																												
8.																												
9.																												
10.																												
11.																												
12.																												
13.																												
14.																												
15.																												
16.																												
17.																												
18.																												
19.																												
20.																												
21.																												
22.																												
23.																												
24.																												
25.																												
26.																												
27.																												
28.																												
29.																												
30.																												

Copyright © SRA/McGraw-Hill. Permission is granted to reproduce for school use.

Appendix B

Objectives

WHOLE NUMBER OPERATIONS

	Objectives	Lessons
Column Multiplication	Work multiplication problems that have a tens number. Problems are of the form: $\begin{array}{r} 18 \\ \times\ 50 \\ \hline \end{array}$.	2
	Work a mixed set of multiplication problems.	3
	Solve multiplication problems that involve two 2-digit values. Problems are of the form: $\begin{array}{r} 53 \\ \times\ 42 \\ \hline \end{array}$.	5, 6
	Work column-multiplication problems that involve carrying for both the ones digit and tens digit of the multiplier.	7–10
	Copy column multiplication problems and work them.	15
Short Division	Complete division problems to show the correct fact number and the remainder.	4–7
	Work division problems that have a single-digit answer and a remainder.	8, 9, 11–13, 19
	Work short-division problems in which each digit of the dividend is a multiple of the divisor.	21
	Work short-division problems in which not all digits of the dividend are multiples of the divisor.	22–24
	Work short-division problems in which the divisor may be larger than the first digit of the dividend.	25–28
	Work short-division problems, some of which have zero as the middle digit of the answer.	29, 31
	Rewrite the answer to a division problem as a mixed number.	32–35
	Work short-division problems and write the answers as mixed numbers.	36, 37
Long Division	Complete division problems by multiplying, subtracting, and writing the remainder as a fraction.	43–46
	Work partially-completed division problems that have 2-digit divisors; for example: $42\overline{)389}$ with 9 above.	46, 47
	Complete division problems, some of which have a 2-digit divisor and some of which have a 1-digit divisor.	48
	Complete division problems in which the whole-number part of the initial answer is either correct or too large.	49, 51–53, 57
	Correct answers to division problems that have a remainder that is too large.	58, 59, 61
	Rework long division problems in which the whole-number part of the answer shown is either too large or too small.	62–65

	Objectives	Lessons
Long Division (cont.)	Work division problems by saying the estimation problem for the tens.	66, 67
	Work division problems (for example: **68⟌364**) by using rounding and estimating.	68, 69, 71, 72
	Work division problems in which the estimation problem does not give the correct quotient.	86, 89
	Work long division problems that have 2-digit answers.	97–99
	Work long division problems that have 1- or 2-digit answers.	101–103
	Work a set of division problems that have 1-digit and 2-digit divisors.	104, 105

CALCULATOR SKILLS

	Objectives	Lessons
	Use a calculator to work problems involving addition, subtraction and multiplication.	3
	Work division problems of the form: **4⟌616** using a calculator.	4
	Use a calculator to figure out missing numbers in number families.	8, 9
	Use a calculator to determine if numbers are prime numbers.	21, 22
	Use a calculator to find the two prime factors of a larger composite number.	24, 25
	Use a calculator to figure out the decimal value for any fraction or mixed number.	41, 42, 80
	Use a calculator to figure out the fraction that equals 1 for equivalent fraction problems of the form: $\frac{5}{7}\left(-\right) = \frac{185}{259}$.	43–45

NUMBER RELATIONSHIPS

	Objectives	Lessons
Fractions/Whole Numbers	Write division problems and answers for fractions that equal whole numbers.	8, 9, 11
	Write equations that show a fraction and the whole number it equals. Problems are of the form: $\frac{■}{7} = 6$.	14, 17, 18
	Complete an equation to show various fractions that equal a whole number.	25–27
	Complete equations to show the whole number a fraction equals.	23, 24, 30
Fractions/Decimals/ Mixed Numbers	Write fractions for mixed numbers.	19–21
	Complete a table to show decimal values and equivalent fractions.	22, 23
	Write equations that show a mixed number and the fraction it equals.	23, 24

	Objectives	Lessons
Fractions/Decimals/ Mixed Numbers (cont.)	Complete a table to show decimal values and the corresponding mixed numbers.	24, 25
	Write decimal values for fractions that have denominators of 10, 100, and 1000.	28–31
	Write fractions with denominators of 10, 100, or 1000 for decimal values.	32, 33
	Complete a table to show decimal values and equivalent fractions with denominators of 10, 100, or 1000.	34
	Complete a table to show decimal numbers and mixed numbers for fractions with denominators of 10 or 100.	37, 38
	Rewrite fractions as mixed numbers.	39, 41
	Complete a table to show fractions with denominators of 10 or 100 and equivalent decimals and mixed numbers.	39, 41, 42
	Complete equations that show a fraction or mixed number and the decimal value it equals.	40
	Complete a table to show fractions and equivalent mixed numbers.	44, 45
	Complete inequality statements involving decimal values and fractions.	103
Fractions/Decimals/ Percents	Complete a table to show hundredths fractions and their equivalent decimal and percent values.	92–94
	Write equations to show the decimal value for a specified percent value.	95
	Write equations to show percents that equal specified decimal values.	96
	Write equations for a mixed set of percent, decimal, and fractional values.	97, 98
	Rewrite fractions as hundredths.	99
	Write equations that show fractions and equivalent percent values.	101, 103

OPERATIONAL RELATIONSHIPS

Inverse Operations	Write division problems for multiplication problems of the form: **9 × ■ = 63**.	1–3
	Rewrite and solve problems of the form: **4 × ■ = 816**.	4
	Complete multiplication and division facts that have zero.	11
	Check answers to addition problems by subtracting.	11, 12
	Check answers to subtraction problems by adding.	13
	Check answers to addition and subtraction problems by using the opposite operation.	14

	Objectives	Lessons
Fractions/Division/ Multiplication	Complete rows of a table to show the whole number a fraction equals and the corresponding division fact.	12, 13
	Complete a table to show the division fact for a fraction that equals a whole number.	17, 18
	Complete a table that has multiplication problems and corresponding fraction equations.	19, 21, 22
	Write the missing middle value as a fraction for multiplication problems of the form: **3 (■) = 369**.	45–51
	Complete equations of the form: **5 (■) = 6**.	102

PLACE VALUE AND ROUNDING

	Objectives	Lessons
Whole Numbers	Rewrite equations of the form: **18 = 10 + 8**.	1, 2
	Complete equations to show place-value addition for 2-digit numbers (for example: **56 = 50 + 6**).	2–4
	Write place-value addition equations for 3-digit numerals (for example: **357 = 300 + 50 + 7**).	5
	Write place-value addition equations for 2-digit and 3-digit numerals.	6
	Round 2-digit values to the nearest ten.	66, 67
	Identify the place of digits through millions (7-digit numerals).	71, 72
	Identify the value of arrowed digits through millions (7-digit numerals).	73, 74
	Identify the value of arrowed digits by subtraction.	75
	Round values to the nearest thousand, hundred, or ten.	76, 77
	Follow directions to round numerals to the nearest ten through nearest million.	78, 79
	Use rounding to estimate the answers to problems.	81, 82
	Express numbers that are multiples of 10, 100, or 1000 as factors.	94
Decimals	Read and write decimal values that end in tenths, hundredths, and thousandths.	17, 18
	Write decimal values for tenths, hundredths, and thousandths, some of which have zero(s) before the last digit.	19–21
	Simplify decimal values that end in zero(s).	35, 36
	Round decimal values to tenths or hundredths.	90, 91
	Round decimal values to tenths, hundredths, or thousandths.	92
	Order decimal values.	102–104
	Convert amounts for cents into amounts for dollars and cents.	108, 109

FRACTIONS	Objectives	Lessons
Analysis	Write fractions for pictures, then circle fractions that are more than 1.	1, 2
	Identify fractions that are more than 1.	2
	Write fractions from descriptions, then circle fractions that are more than 1.	3–6
	Write fractions for values shown on a number line.	5, 6
	Write fractions for whole numbers from descriptions.	7–9
	Write equations from descriptions that give information about a fraction and the whole number it equals.	10, 11
	Classify fractions as more than 1, less than 1, or equal to 1.	10, 11
	Write fractions for whole numbers on a number line.	12
	Write fractions for whole numbers on an undivided number line.	13–15
	Write fractions from descriptions, some of which tell the number of whole units. (For example: The bottom number of the fraction is 5. The fraction equals 3 whole units.)	16
	Write fractions from descriptions.	19
	Identify numerators of fractions.	28
Addition/ Subtraction (Like Denominators)	Identify and solve problems involving addition and subtraction of fractions that do not need to be rewritten.	4–7
	Work column problems that add or subtract like-denominator fractions.	61, 62
Addition/ Subtraction (Unlike Denominators)	Work addition and subtraction problems that have a whole number and a fraction; for example: $\frac{15}{4} + 1$; $9 - \frac{3}{12}$.	29, 31
	Work column addition and subtraction problems that have a whole number and a fraction.	63, 64
	Work column addition and subtraction problems that have either a whole number and a fraction or two fractions with the same denominator.	65
	Work problem pairs to show the least common multiple.	65–67
	Work addition and subtraction problems that have two fractions with unlike denominators.	67, 68, 71
	Work unlike-denominator problems, some of which require rewriting only one of the fractions.	69, 70
Multiplication	Multiply two fractions.	9, 11
	Identify the fraction problems in a mixed set (addition, subtraction, multiplication) that can be worked as written and work them.	12, 13, 15, 16

	Objectives	Lessons
Multiplication (cont.)	Determine whether the answer to a fraction-multiplication problem is more or less than the starting value in the problem.	31, 32, 34, 35
	Work a set of addition, subtraction and multiplication problems that have a whole number and a fraction.	32–34
	Work fraction-multiplication problems in which the starting and ending values equal whole numbers.	36, 37
	Work fraction-multiplication problems and indicate whether the starting value or ending value is greater.	38, 39, 41
	Solve multiplication problems by interpreting the phrase "a fraction **of** a value" as "a fraction **times** a value."	71–73
	Work column problems involving addition, subtraction, and multiplication of fractions.	73, 74
	Rewrite and work row problems involving fraction operations as column problems.	75, 78
Equivalence	Write equations to show fractions that are equivalent.	14, 15
	Work fraction-multiplication problems to determine whether two fractions are equivalent.	16
	Figure out the fraction that equals 1 for a given pair of equivalent-fraction pictures.	17
	Write equations for equivalent fractions and figure out the fraction that equals 1.	18, 19
	Use multiplication to determine whether pairs of fractions are equivalent.	21–23
	Solve equivalent-fraction problems of the form: $\frac{3}{7}(-) = \frac{15}{\blacksquare}$.	24–26
	Use a calculator to figure out the fraction that equals 1 for equivalent-fraction problems of the form: $\frac{5}{7}(-) = \frac{185}{259}$.	43–45
	Use the sign $=$ or $\neq$ to indicate whether pairs of fractions are equivalent.	44
	Work equivalent-fraction problems with fractions that have 3-digit values; for example: $\frac{11}{10} = \frac{264}{\square}$.	46–48
	Use division to determine whether pairs of fractions are equivalent.	48, 49
	Complete equations to determine whether two fractions are equivalent.	54–56
	Work equivalent-fraction problems by expressing the fraction that equals 1 as a fraction over a fraction.	55–58
	Work a mixed set of equivalent-fraction problems, some of which involve a complex fraction equal to 1.	59, 60

	Objectives	Lessons
Equivalence (cont.)	Complete a series of equivalent fractions by referring to the first fraction in the series (for example: $\boxed{\frac{2}{3}} = \frac{■}{18} = \frac{10}{■} = \frac{4}{■}$).	59, 61, 62
	Work equivalent-fraction problems in which one of the values is 1; for example: $\frac{3}{270} = \frac{1}{\square}$.	90
	Rewrite inequality statements for items that show more than one value on a side.	101, 102
Comparison	Convert two fractions into whole numbers and identify the greater fraction.	25, 26
	Compare fractions, not all of which equal whole numbers.	27
	Compare fractions using $>$, $<$, or $=$.	28, 29
	Complete inequality statements involving whole numbers and fractions.	90, 91
	Compare fractions with unlike denominators.	111, 112
Simplification	Use prime factors to simplify fractions.	31
	Simplify fractions, some of which result in a numerator of 1.	32, 33, 35–37
	Simplify fractions, some of which equal a whole number.	38
	Use prime-factor analysis to determine whether fractions can be simplified.	41, 42
	Simplify fractions and write mixed numbers for fractions that are more than 1.	43
	Simplify fractions in which the numerator and denominator are multiples of 10, 100, or 1000.	95, 96, 98
	Simplify equivalent fractions in which the numerator and denominator end with one or more zeros.	99, 100

WHOLE NUMBER PROPERTIES

	Objectives	Lessons
Prime Numbers	Use a calculator to determine if numbers are prime numbers.	21, 22
	Multiply prime factors.	23
	Show the prime factors for composite values.	24
	Use a calculator to find the two prime factors of a larger composite number.	24, 25
	Write equations for composite values to show only prime factors.	25, 28, 29
	Rewrite equations to show prime factors for two composite factors.	26, 27
	Show the prime factors for composite values.	44

	Objectives	Lessons
Odd/Even Numbers	Determine whether numbers are odd or even by dividing by 2.	91, 92
	Refer to the last digit of larger numbers to determine whether they are odd or even.	93

MENTAL ARITHMETIC

Objectives	Lessons
Work single-digit division problems mentally (for example: $3\overline{)23}$ ■).	16–18
Convert mixed numbers into fractions using mental math.	22
Use mental math to solve subtraction problems that have a difference of less than 10.	38, 39
Work single-digit division problems mentally and write the remainder as a fraction.	41
Work problems mentally that require rewriting fractions as mixed numbers.	42, 43
Determine the missing value for orally-presented problems; for example: 7 times some fraction equals 9. What's the fraction?	52-54, 61
Work problems of the form: $\mathbf{4x = 7; x =}$ ■.	62-64
Work problems of the form: $\mathbf{4x = 7; 1x =}$ ■.	65, 66
Identify the missing factor for orally presented problems that tell about more than one object and ask about 1.	77

MIXED NUMBER OPERATIONS

Objectives	Lessons
Work column problems that add or subtract mixed numbers having like-denominator fractions.	74, 75
Work addition and subtraction problems that have a whole number and a mixed number.	76, 77
Simplify mixed numbers that have fractions that equal 1.	79
Work column problems that add mixed numbers having like-denominator fractions and simplify the answers.	80, 81
Work subtraction problems in which the minuend is a whole number and the subtrahend is a mixed number.	84, 85
Work column problems that add and subtract whole numbers and mixed numbers.	86, 87
Work addition and subtraction problems involving mixed numbers that are in a ratio-table context.	88, 89

NUMBER FAMILIES AND EXTENSIONS

	Objectives	Lessons
Whole Number Operations	Write column problems to find missing numbers in number families.	1–4
	Translate addition-subtraction problems into number-family problems and solve.	15–17
	Analyze and solve addition-subtraction equations that do not have the missing value after the equal sign.	90–92
Number-Family Tables	Compute the missing number in each row of a 3-by-3 table.	5–7
	Compute the missing number in each column of a 3-by-3 table.	7
	Figure out missing numbers in 3-by-3 tables by working rows and columns, respectively.	8
	Work the same 3-by-3 table twice, first using the columns as number families, then using the rows as number families.	9
	Work the same 3-by-3 table twice, first using the rows as number families, then using the columns as number families.	11, 12
	Complete a 3-by-3 table by first working rows with two numbers, then columns that have two numbers.	13–16
	Complete a 3-by-3 table.	33
Fraction Number Families	Complete fraction number families that show a fraction and a big number of 1; for example: $\frac{■}{■}\ \frac{5}{8} \longrightarrow 1$.	46, 47
	Complete fraction number families of the form: $\frac{3}{■}\ \frac{7}{■} \longrightarrow \frac{■}{■}$.	51
	Make fraction number families for statements of the form: M is $\frac{2}{5}$ of 1.	74, 75
	Make number families for statements of the form: J is $\frac{3}{4}$ of B.	76
	Make fraction number families for sentences that compare two values.	77–79
	Make fraction number families for sentences that compare and sentences that classify.	84–86
	Make fraction number families for sentences that refer to parts of a whole group.	93
	Write fraction number families for sentences that tell about percents or about fractions.	112, 113
	Make fraction number families based on illustrations of Xs in a bag.	113

DECIMAL OPERATIONS

	Objectives	Lessons
Addition/ Subtraction	Write and solve column addition and subtraction problems involving dollar-and-cent amounts.	31
	Write row problems involving dollar-and-cent values as column problems.	73
	Add decimal values.	85
	Subtract decimal values.	86
	Add and subtract decimal values.	87
	Add and subtract whole numbers and decimal values.	89
Multiplication/ Division	Work problems that multiply a dollar-and-cent amount by a whole number.	75
	Work a mixed set of problems involving dollar-and-cent amounts.	78
	Multiply a whole number and a decimal value.	99, 101
	Work multiplication problems that have two decimal values.	102
	Multiply decimal values.	103–105
	Work division problems that have a decimal value in the dividend.	123

COORDINATE SYSTEM

	Objectives	Lessons
Points and Lines	Write the X and Y values for points shown on the coordinate system.	49, 51
	Graph points on the coordinate system given their X and Y values.	52, 53
	Complete a table to show X and Y values of points shown on a coordinate system.	54, 55
	Identify incorrectly-plotted points on a coordinate system.	56, 57
	Relate a line on the coordinate system to values in a table.	56–58
Functions	Complete a function table that indicates X values for points on a line, and graph those points.	114, 115
	Figure out a function and complete a function table.	117
	Generate possible functions for a given set of X and Y values and complete a function table.	118

PROBLEM SOLVING

	Objectives	Lessons
Addition/ Subtraction	Make number families for comparison sentences.	12, 13
	Use number families to solve addition and subtraction comparison word problems.	14–16
	Use number families to solve word problems that tell what happened first and next.	18, 19, 21–23
	Work number-family problems that refer to **in, out,** and **end up**.	34–36

	Objectives	Lessons
Addition/ Subtraction (cont.)	Use number families to solve comparison word problems that ask about the difference number.	45
	Work number-family problems that tell about **goals** and **difference**.	87–89
	Make vertical number families for word problems that tell about either **in** or **out**.	93–95
	Work a mixed set of word problems which require horizontal or vertical number families.	96, 97
Number-Family Tables	Answer questions by referring to a 3-by-3 table.	1
	Answer questions about comparative amounts by referring to a 3-by-3 table.	2–4
	Complete a 3-by-3 table and answer questions by referring to the table.	17
	Use comparison facts to figure out numbers needed in a 3-by-3 table.	26–29
	Construct and use a 3-by-3 table with column and row headings.	33–35
	Construct a 3-by-3 table using a comparison fact to figure out a needed number.	36–39
Multi-Step Problems	Work number-family problems that give more than one number for **in** and/or **out**.	37, 38
	Work word problems that imply number families with more than one value for **in** or **out**.	39, 41–44
	Work word problems that have two vertical number families (one for **in** and one for **out**).	45–48
	Work number-family problems involving dollar amounts and change.	81–83
	Work a mixed set of word problems that require vertical number families.	84
	Work horizontal goal problems that require vertical number families for **goal, now,** or both.	96–98
	Work average problems by dividing.	111, 112
Fraction Number Families	Construct fraction number families to solve word problems. (For example: $\frac{3}{5}$ of the children were girls. What fraction of the children were boys?)	47–49
	Use fraction number families to solve word problems that tell about numbers and ask about fractions. (For example: 7 of the berries are ripe. 2 are not ripe. What fraction of the berries are not ripe?)	51, 52
	Work a mixed set of fraction-number-family problems.	53, 54

	Objectives	Lessons
Ratios and Proportions (Equations)	Write and solve ratio equations for word problems.	27–32
	Solve word problems and write the answers as a number and a unit name.	40
	Work picture problems that show ratios and proportions.	42, 43
	Work proportion problems that involve 3- and 4-digit numbers.	49–51
	Answer questions by referring to complex ratios.	58–60
	Solve proportion problems, some of which require multiplying by a complex fraction equal to 1.	61–63
	Use facts to complete a table that shows equivalent ratios.	63–66
	Graph a line on the coordinate system for a set of equivalent ratios and answer questions based on the line.	71–73, 76, 77
	Work a set of problems that tell about more than 1 and ask a question.	78, 79
	Work a mixed set of word problems that require multiplication, division, or a ratio equation.	89, 101
	Work proportion word problems that have numbers that end in zeros.	101
	Compute averages.	108, 109
	Work a mixed set of multiplication and proportion problems that tell about 1 and ask about more than 1.	121–123
Ratios and Proportions (Tables)	Complete ratio tables.	52–55
	Solve word problems using ratio tables.	56–59, 61–63
	Work ratio-table problems that give information for fraction number families.	64–66
	Work ratio-table problems, some of which require fraction number families.	67–69
	Use facts to complete a table that shows equivalent ratios and check work by graphing points on the coordinate system.	68, 69
	Work ratio-table problems that have a comparison statement involving fractions. For example: The sand weighed $\frac{2}{5}$ as much as the cement.	82–84
	Work a mixed set of ratio-table problems, some of which compare.	87, 88
	Work ratio-table problems in which the second column contains two mixed numbers.	91, 92
	Make fraction number families and ratio tables for problems that do not provide fraction information.	94, 95

	Objectives	Lessons
Ratios and Proportions (Tables) (cont.)	Discriminate between problems that require a ratio table and those that require only a ratio equation.	105, 106
	Work ratio-table problems that involve percents.	106–109
	Use a ratio table to work word problems that give two or three names.	107
	Work ratio-table problems that compare percents.	110, 111
	Work a mixed set of ratio-table problems that include fractions and percents.	114
Multiplication/ Division	Work word problems of the form: 4 cakes = 7 pounds, 1 cake = ■.	71, 72
	Identify the missing factor for problems that tell about more than one object and ask about 1. For example: 3 toys weigh 16 ounces. What does 1 toy weigh?	73, 76
	Work multiplication word problems that tell about 1 and ask about more than 1.	81
	Work multiplication and division word problems.	82–85
	Work a mixed set of multiplication and division problems that use the words **each** and **per**.	87, 88
	Work problems that describe the division of a quantity into equal-sized parts.	98–100
	Solve word problems that refer to even and odd numbers.	103, 104
	Work word problems that require decimal multiplication.	106, 107
	Work division problems in which the answer refers to non-divisible entities.	115, 116
	Work word problems that require division of a dollar amount.	124
Inverse Operations	Work 2-step word problems that give the starting number and two operations.	104
	Use inverse operations to solve pairs of equations and figure out the starting number.	105–108
	Use inverse operations to solve word problems.	109–111
	Work word problems that generate a series of inverse-operation equations.	112, 114
	Work story problems that involve inverse operations.	124, 125
Measurement	Complete a series of equivalent fractions, based on equivalent measures.	105, 106
	Work problems that compare different units of measurement.	107–109, 111

PROBABILITY	Objectives	Lessons
	Write fractions that represent the probability of pulling an X from a bag.	112
	Use information presented as a fraction to generate a set of objects.	113, 114
	Relate the composition of a set to the number of trials required to give each member one chance of being selected.	114
	Work ratio-table problems that involve probability.	115, 116, 118, 119
	Determine which set of objects provides the best chance of drawing a winner.	124

GEOMETRY

Perimeter and Area	Figure out the lengths of sides in quadrilaterals with parallel sides.	56, 57
	Compute perimeters of polygons.	58, 59, 61
	Work area-of-rectangle problems shown on the coordinate system using the equation: squares = $x \times y$.	62–65
	Work area and perimeter problems for rectangles shown on the coordinate system.	66, 68–70, 72
	Work area-of-triangle problems shown on the coordinate system.	74, 75
	Work area problems for rectangles and triangles that are not shown on the coordinate system.	76, 77
	Work area-of-parallelogram problems shown on the coordinate system.	79, 80
	Work area and perimeter problems for parallelograms shown on the coordinate system.	81, 82
	Work area and perimeter problems for parallelograms that are not shown on the coordinate system.	83, 85
	Work area problems for triangles and parallelograms that are not shown on the coordinate system.	86
	Find the area of non-right triangles shown on the coordinate system by constructing parallelograms.	96
	Find the area and perimeter of non-right triangles that are not shown on the coordinate system.	97
	Find the area and perimeter of parallelograms, rectangles and triangles.	98
Circles	Figure out the relationship between the diameter and circumference of a circle.	91
	Use the equation $\pi \times \mathbf{D} = \mathbf{C}$ to figure out the circumference of a circle.	92
	Use the equation $\pi \times \mathbf{D} = \mathbf{C}$ to figure out the circumference or diameter of a circle.	93–95

	Objectives	Lessons
Circles (cont.)	Use the equation $\pi \times \mathbf{D} = \mathbf{C}$ to figure out the circumference or radius of a circle.	111, 112
	Use the equation $\pi \times \mathbf{D} = \mathbf{C}$ to figure out the circumference, radius, or diameter of a circle.	113
	Use the equation $\mathbf{A} = \pi \times \mathbf{r} \times \mathbf{r}$ to figure out the area of a circle.	113, 114
	Find the circumference and the area of circles.	115, 117
Surface Area	Compute the surface area of a rectangular prism.	94–96
	Find the surface area of a rectangular prism from a non-exploded diagram.	97, 98
	Find the surface area of a pyramid with a rectangular base.	99–101
	Find the surface area of a pyramid that has a triangular base.	102, 103
Volume	Find the volume of rectangular prisms.	104, 105
	Find the volume of a triangular prism.	106, 109
	Find the volume of rectangular and triangular prisms.	107
	Find the surface area and volume of a rectangular prism.	108
Angles and Lines	Indicate whether pairs of lines are parallel or not parallel.	55
	Answer questions about the number of degrees in angles.	71
	Make number families to solve angle problems involving an angle that is divided into two smaller angles.	72, 73
	Work problems requiring conversion of a fraction of a circle into degrees.	74, 75
	Use a fact about a fraction of a circle to make a number family and work problems involving three angles.	77–79
	Make number families to solve angle problems involving complementary and supplementary angles.	81, 82
	Identify corresponding angles.	83
	Figure out the degrees in corresponding and supplementary angles.	84–86
	Figure out the degrees in four angles that are formed by two intersecting lines.	88, 89
	Figure out the rule for vertically opposite angles formed by two intersecting lines.	91
	Apply the rule for vertically opposite angles to figure out corresponding sets of angles at parallel lines.	92, 93
	Use a protractor to measure degrees in an angle.	118

Objectives	Lessons
Do the groundwork for building a model of the solar system.	116
Use ratio numbers to complete a table about the solar system and make a scale model.	117
Complete a circle graph based on a table that shows amounts of time a person spent on various activities.	118
Construct a circle graph to show use of time.	119
Gather data on favorite colors and complete a table that shows tallies, numbers, and degrees.	119
Construct a bar graph and circle graph to display percents for various geometric shapes selected as favorites by 20 different people.	120
Construct a bar graph to display the average percents of 10 student surveys conducted in lesson 120.	121
Compare the ratio of surface area to volume for cubes that are relatively large and small.	122
Determine the contents of a bag based on experimental data and expected outcomes.	123
Figure out the threshold of efficiency for a square (the size at which the perimeter and area have the same number of units).	124
Conduct an experiment and display the results as a frequency distribution.	125

Skills Profile

Student's Name ______________________ Grade or year in school ________

Teacher's name ______________________________

Starting lesson ______________________ Date ________

Last lesson Completed __________ Date __________ Number of days absent ______

Summary of In-program Test Performance

	Part 1	Part 2	Part 3	Part 4	Part 5	Part 6	Part 7	Part 8	Part 9	Part 10	Part 11	Part 12
Test 1	+ −	+ −	+ −	+ −	+ −	+ −						
Test 2	+ −	+ −	+ −	+ −	+ −	+ −	+ −	+ −	+ −	+ −	+ −	
Test 3	+ −	+ −	+ −	+ −	+ −	+ −	+ −	+ −	+ −	+ −		
Test 4	+ −	+ −	+ −	+ −	+ −	+ −	+ −	+ −	+ −			
Test 5	+ −	+ −	+ −	+ −	+ −	+ −	+ −					
Test 6	+ −	+ −	+ −	+ −	+ −							
Test 7	+ −	+ −	+ −	+ −	+ −	+ −	+ −	+ −				
Test 8	+ −	+ −	+ −	+ −	+ −	+ −	+ −	+ −	+ −	+ −		
Test 9	+ −	+ −	+ −	+ −	+ −	+ −	+ −	+ −	+ −			
Test 10	+ −	+ −	+ −	+ −	+ −	+ −	+ −	+ −	+ −	+ −	+ −	
Test 11	+ −	+ −	+ −	+ −	+ −	+ −	+ −	+ −	+ −	+ −	+ −	+ −
Test 12	+ −	+ −	+ −	+ −	+ −	+ −	+ −	+ −	+ −			

Final Test Score ______ %

The charts on pages 187 to 198 may be reproduced to make a skills profile for each student. The charts summarize the skills presented in *Connecting Math Concepts, Level E* and provide space for indicating the date on which the student completes the lessons in which the skills are taught.

© SRA/McGraw-Hill. Permission is granted to reproduce for school use.

Skills Profile–Page 2

Name ______________________

Skills	Taught in these Lessons	Date Lessons Completed
WHOLE NUMBER OPERATIONS		
Column Multiplication		
Works multiplication problems that have a tens number. Problems are of the form: $\begin{array}{r} 18 \\ \times 50 \\ \hline \end{array}$	2	✓
Works a mixed set of multiplication problems.	3	✓
Solves multiplication problems that involve two 2-digit values. Problems are of the form: $\begin{array}{r} 53 \\ \times 42 \\ \hline \end{array}$.	5, 6	✓
Works column-multiplication problems that involve carrying for both the ones digit and tens digit of the multiplier.	7–10	✓
Copies column multiplication problems and works them.	15	✓
Short Division		
Completes division problems to show the correct fact number and the remainder.	4–7	✓
Works division problems that have a single-digit answer and a remainder.	8–19	✓
Works short-division problems in which each digit of the dividend is a multiple of the divisor.	21	✓
Works short-division problems in which not all digits of the dividend are multiples of the divisor.	22–24	✓
Works short-division problems in which the divisor may be larger than the first digit of the dividend.	25–28	✓
Works short-division problems, some of which have zero as the middle digit of the answer.	29, 31	✓
Rewrites the answer to a division problem as a mixed number.	32–35	✓
Works short-division problems and writes the answers as mixed numbers.	36, 37	✓

Skills	Taught in these Lessons	Date Lessons Completed
Long Division		
Completes division problems by multiplying, subtracting, and writing the remainder as a fraction.	43–46	
Works partially-completed division problems that have 2-digit divisors; for example: $42\overline{)389}$ with 9 in the quotient.	46, 47	
Completes division problems, some of which have a 2-digit divisor and some of which have a 1-digit divisor.	48	
Completes division problems in which the whole-number part of the initial answer is either correct or too large.	49–57	
Corrects answers to division problems that have a remainder that is too large.	58–61	
Reworks long division problems in which the whole-number part of the answer shown is either too large or too small.	62–65	
Works division problems by saying the estimation problem for the tens.	66, 67	
Works division problems (for example: $68\overline{)364}$ by using rounding and estimating.	68–72	
Works division problems in which the estimation problem does not give the correct quotient.	86, 89	
Works long division problems that have 2-digit answers.	97–99	
Works long division problems that have 1- or 2-digit answers.	101–103	
Works a set of division problems that have 1-digit and 2-digit divisors.	104, 105	
Calculator Skills		
Uses a calculator to work problems involving addition, subtraction and multiplication.	3	✓

© SRA/McGraw-Hill. Permission is granted to reproduce for school use.

Name ______________________________

Skills	Taught in these Lessons	Date Lessons Completed
Works division problems of the form: using a $4\overline{)616}$ calculator.	4	✓
Uses a calculator to figure out missing numbers in number families.	8, 9	✓
Uses a calculator to determine if numbers are prime numbers.	21, 22	
Uses a calculator to find the two prime factors of a larger composite number.	24, 25	
Uses a calculator to figure out the decimal value for any fraction or mixed number.	41–80	
Uses a calculator to figure out the fraction that equals 1 for equivalent fraction problems of the form: $\frac{5}{7}\left(-\right) = \frac{185}{259}$.	43–45	
NUMBER RELATIONSHIPS **Fractions/Whole Numbers**		
Writes division problems and answers for fractions that equal whole numbers.	8–11	✓
Writes equations that show a fraction and the whole number it equals. Problems are of the form: $\frac{\blacksquare}{7} = 6$.	14–18	✓
Completes an equation to show various fractions that equal a whole number.	25–27	✓
Completes equations to show the whole number a fraction equals.	23–30	✓
Fractions/Decimals/Mixed Numbers		
Writes fractions for mixed numbers.	19–21	✓
Completes a table to show decimal values and equivalent fractions.	22, 23	✓
Writes equations that show a mixed number and the fraction it equals.	23, 24	✓

Skills	Taught in these Lessons	Date Lessons Completed
Completes a table to show decimal values and the corresponding mixed numbers.	24, 25	
Writes decimal values for fractions that have denominators of 10, 100, and 1000.	28–31	
Writes fractions with denominators of 10, 100, or 1000 for decimal values.	32, 33	
Completes a table to show decimal values and equivalent fractions with denominators of 10, 100, or 1000.	34	
Completes a table to show decimal numbers and mixed numbers for fractions with denominators of 10 or 100.	37, 38	
Rewrites fractions as mixed numbers.	39, 41	✓
Completes a table to show fractions with denominators of 10 or 100 and equivalent decimals and mixed numbers.	39–42	
Completes equations that show a fraction or mixed number and the decimal value it equals.	40	
Completes a table to show fractions and equivalent mixed numbers.	44, 45	
Completes inequality statements involving decimal values and fractions.	103	
Completes a table to show hundredths fractions and their equivalent decimal and percent values.	92–94	
Writes equations to show the decimal value for a specified percent value.	95	
Writes equations to show percents that equal specified decimal values.	96	
Writes equations for a mixed set of percent, decimal, and fractional values.	97, 98	

$1\frac{3}{4}$

 © SRA/McGraw-Hill. Permission is granted to reproduce for school use.

Name ______________________________

Skills	Taught in these Lessons	Date Lessons Completed
Rewrites fractions as hundredths.	99	
Writes equations that show fractions and equivalent percent values.	101, 103	
OPERATIONAL RELATIONSHIPS **Inverse Operations**		
Writes division problems for multiplication problems of the form: 9 × ■ = 63.	1–3	✓
Rewrites and solves problems of the form: 4 × ■ = 816.	4	✓
Completes multiplication and division facts that have zero.	11	✓
Checks answers to addition problems by subtracting.	11, 12	✓
Checks answers to subtraction problems by adding.	13	✓
Checks answers to addition and subtraction problems by using the opposite operation.	14	✓
Fractions/Division/Multiplication		
Completes rows of a table to show the whole number a fraction equals and the corresponding division fact.	12, 13	✓
Completes a table to show the division fact for a fraction that equals a whole number.	17, 18	✓
Completes a table that has multiplication problems and corresponding fraction equations.	19–22	✓
Writes the missing middle value as a fraction for multiplication problems of the form: 3 (■) = 369.	45–51	
Completes equations of the form: 5 (■) = 6.	102	
PLACE VALUE AND ROUNDING **Whole Numbers**		
Rewrites equations of the form: 18 = 10 + 8.	1, 2	✓
Completes equations to show place-value addition for 2-digit numbers (for example: 56 = 50 + 6).	2–4	✓

Skills	Taught in these Lessons	Date Lessons Completed
Writes place-value addition equations for 3-digit numerals (for example: 357 = 300 + 50 + 7).	5	✓
Writes place-value addition equations for 2-digit and 3-digit numerals.	6	✓
Rounds 2-digit values to the nearest ten.	66, 67	✓
Identifies the place of digits through millions (7-digit numerals).	71, 72	
Identifies the value of arrowed digits through millions (7-digit numerals).	73, 74	
Identifies the value of arrowed digits by subtraction.	75	
Rounds values to the nearest thousand, hundred, or ten.	76, 77	
Follows directions to round numerals to the nearest ten through nearest million.	78, 79	
Uses rounding to estimate the answers to problems.	81, 82	
Expresses numbers that are multiples of 10, 100, or 1000 as factors.	94	
Decimals		
Reads and write decimal values that end in tenths, hundredths, and thousandths.	17, 18	
Writes decimal values for tenths, hundredths, and thousandths, some of which have zero(s) before the last digit.	19–21	
Simplifies decimal values that end in zero(s).	35, 36	
Rounds decimal values to tenths or hundredths.	90, 91	
Rounds decimal values to tenths, hundredths, or thousandths.	92	
Orders decimal values.	102–104	
Converts amounts for cents into amounts for dollars and cents.	108, 109	

© SRA/McGraw-Hill. Permission is granted to reproduce for school use.

Name ____________________

Skills	Taught in these Lessons	Date Lessons Completed
FRACTIONS		
Analysis		
Writes fractions for pictures, then circles fractions that are more than 1.	1, 2	✓
Identifies fractions that are more than 1.	2	✓
Writes fractions from descriptions, then circle fractions that are more than 1.	3–6	✓
Writes fractions for values shown on a number line.	5, 6	✓
Writes fractions for whole numbers from descriptions.	7–9	✓
Writes equations from descriptions that give information about a fraction and the whole number it equals.	10, 11	✓
Classifies fractions as more than 1, less than 1, or equal to 1.	10, 11	✓
Writes fractions for whole numbers on a number line.	12	✓
Writes fractions for whole numbers on an undivided number line.	13–15	✓
Writes fractions from descriptions, some of which tell the number of whole units. (For example: The bottom number of the fraction is 5. The fraction equals 3 whole units.)	16	✓
Writes fractions from descriptions.	19	✓
Identifies numerators of fractions.	28	✓
Addition/Subtraction (Like Demoninators)		
Identifies and solves problems involving addition and subtraction of fractions that do not need to be rewritten.	4–7	✓
Works column problems that add or subtract like-denominator fractions.	61, 62	✓

Skills	Taught in these Lessons	Date Lessons Completed
Addition/Subtraction (Unlike Denominators)		
Works addition and subtraction problems that have a whole number and a fraction, for example: $\frac{15}{4} + 1$; $9 - \frac{3}{12}$.	29, 31	
Works column addition and subtraction problems that have a whole number and a fraction.	63, 64	
Works column addition and subtraction problems that have either a whole number and a fraction or two fractions with the same denominator.	65	
Works problem pairs to show the least common multiple.	65–67	
Works addition and subtraction problems that have two fractions with unlike denominators.	67–71	
Works unlike-denominator problems, some of which require rewriting only one of the fractions.	69, 70	
Multiplication		
Multiplies two fractions.	9, 11	✓
Identifies the fraction problems in a mixed set (addition, subtraction, multiplication) that can be worked as written and works them.	12–16	✓
Determines whether the answer to a fraction-multiplication problem is more or less than the starting value in the problem.	31–35	
Works a set of addition, subtraction and multiplication problems that have a whole number and a fraction.	32–34	
Works fraction-multiplication problems in which the starting and ending values equal whole numbers.	36, 37	

© SRA/McGraw-Hill. Permission is granted to reproduce for school use.

Name ______________________________

Skills	Taught in these Lessons	Date Lessons Completed
Works fraction-multiplication problems and indicate whether the starting value or ending value is greater.	38–41	
Solves multiplication problems by interpreting the phrase "a fraction **of** a value" as "a fraction **times** a value."	71–73	
Works column problems involving addition, subtraction, and multiplication of fractions.	73, 74	
Rewrites and work row problems involving fraction operations as column problems.	75, 78	
Equivalence		
Writes equations to show fractions that are equivalent.	14, 15	
Works fraction-multiplication problems to determine whether two fractions are equivalent.	16	
Figures out the fraction that equals 1 for a given pair of equivalent-fraction pictures.	17	
Writes equations for equivalent fractions and figure out the fraction that equals 1.	18, 19	
Uses multiplication to determine whether pairs of fractions are equivalent.	21–23	
Solves equivalent-fraction problems of the form: $\frac{3}{7}\left(-\right) = \frac{15}{\blacksquare}$.	24–26	
Uses a calculator to figure out the fraction that equals 1 for equivalent-fraction problems of the form: $\frac{5}{7}\left(-\right) = \frac{185}{259}$.	43–45	
Uses the sign $=$ or $\neq$ to indicate whether pairs of fractions are equivalent.	44	

Skills	Taught in these Lessons	Date Lessons Completed
Works equivalent-fraction problems with fractions that have 3-digit values; for example: $\frac{11}{10} = \frac{264}{\square}$.	46–48	
Uses division to determine whether pairs of fractions are equivalent.	48, 49	
Completes equations to determine whether two fractions are equivalent.	54–56	
Works equivalent-fraction problems by expressing the fraction that equals 1 as a fraction over a fraction.	55–58	
Works a mixed set of equivalent-fraction problems, some of which involve a complex fraction equal to 1.	59, 60	
Completes a series of equivalent fractions by referring to the first fraction in the series (for example: $\boxed{\frac{2}{3}} = \frac{\blacksquare}{18} = \frac{10}{\blacksquare} = \frac{4}{\blacksquare}$).	59–62	
Works equivalent-fraction problems in which one of the values is 1; for example: $\frac{3}{270} = \frac{1}{\square}$.	90	
Rewrites inequality statements for items that show more than one value on a side.	101, 102	
Comparison		
Converts two fractions into whole numbers and identifies the greater fraction.	25, 26	
Compares fractions, not all of which equal whole numbers.	27	
Compares fractions using $>$, $<$, or $=$.	28, 29	
Completes inequality statements involving whole numbers and fractions.	90, 91	
Compares fractions with unlike denominators.	111, 112	

© SRA/McGraw-Hill. Permission is granted to reproduce for school use.

Name ______________________

Skills	Taught in these Lessons	Date Lessons Completed
Simplification Uses prime factors to simplify fractions.	31	
Simplifies fractions, some of which result in a numerator of 1.	32–37	
Simplifies fractions, some of which equal a whole number.	38	
Uses prime-factor analysis to determine whether fractions can be simplified.	41, 42	
Simplifies fractions and write mixed numbers for fractions that are more than 1.	43	
Simplifies fractions in which the numerator and denominator are multiples of 10, 100, or 1000.	95–98	
Simplifies equivalent fractions in which the numerator and denominator end with one or more zeros.	99, 100	
WHOLE NUMBER PROPERTIES Prime Numbers Uses a calculator to determine if numbers are prime numbers.	21, 22	
Multiplies prime factors.	23	
Shows the prime factors for composite values.	24	
Uses a calculator to find the two prime factors of a larger composite number.	24, 25	
Writes equations for composite values to show only prime factors.	25–29	
Rewrites equations to show prime factors for two composite factors.	26, 27	
Shows the prime factors for composite values.	44	
Odd/Even Numbers Determines whether numbers are odd or even by dividing by 2.	91, 92	

Skills	Taught in these Lessons	Date Lessons Completed
Refers to the last digit of larger numbers to determine whether they are odd or even.	93	
Mental Arithmetic Works single-digit division problems mentally (for example: $3\overline{)23}$ ■).	16–18	
Converts mixed numbers into fractions using mental math.	22	
Uses mental math to solve subtraction problems that have a difference of less than 10.	38, 39	
Works single-digit division problems mentally and write the remainder as a fraction.	41	
Works problems mentally that require rewriting fractions as mixed numbers.	42, 43	
Determines the missing value for orally-presented problems; for example: 7 times some fraction equals 9. What's the fraction?	52-61	
Works problems of the form: $4x = 7$; $x = $ ■.	62–64	
Works problems of the form: $4x = 7$; $1x = $ ■.	65, 66	
Identifies the missing factor for orally presented problems that tell about more than one object and ask about 1.	77	
MIXED NUMBER OPERATIONS Works column problems that add or subtract mixed numbers having like-denominator fractions.	74, 75	
Works addition and subtraction problems that have a whole number and a mixed number.	76, 77	
Simplifies mixed numbers that have fractions that equal 1.	79	

© SRA/McGraw-Hill. Permission is granted to reproduce for school use.

Name ______________________________

Skills	Taught in these Lessons	Date Lessons Completed
Works column problems that add mixed numbers having like-denominator fractions and simplifies the answers.	80, 81	
Works subtraction problems in which the minuend is a whole number and the subtrahend is a mixed number.	84, 85	
Works column problems that add and subtract whole numbers and mixed numbers.	86, 87	
Works addition and subtraction problems involving mixed numbers that are in a ratio-table context.	88, 89	
NUMBER FAMILIES AND EXTENSIONS		
Whole Number Operations		
Writes column problems to find missing numbers in number families.	1–4	
Translates addition-subtraction problems into number-family problems and solves.	15–17	
Analyzes and solves addition-subtraction equations that do not have the missing value after the equal sign.	90–92	
Number-Family Tables		
Computes the missing number in each row of a 3-by-3 table.	5–7	
Computes the missing number in each column of a 3-by-3 table.	7	
Figures out missing numbers in 3-by-3 tables by working rows and columns, respectively.	8	
Works the same 3-by-3 table twice, first using the columns as number families, then using the rows as number families.	9	
Works the same 3-by-3 table twice, first using the rows as number families, then using the columns as number families.	11, 12	

Skills	Taught in these Lessons	Date Lessons Completed
Completes a 3-by-3 table by first working rows with two numbers, then columns that have two numbers.	13–16	
Completes a 3-by-3 table.	33	
Fraction Number Families		
Completes fraction number families that show a fraction and a big number of 1; for example: $\frac{\blacksquare}{\blacksquare}\ \frac{5}{8} \longrightarrow 1$.	46, 47	
Completes fraction number families of the form: $\frac{3}{\blacksquare}\ \frac{7}{\blacksquare} \longrightarrow \frac{\blacksquare}{\blacksquare}$.	51	
Makes fraction number families for statements of the form: M is $\frac{2}{5}$ of 1.	74, 75	
Makes number families for statements of the form: J is $\frac{3}{4}$ of B.	76	
Makes fraction number families for sentences that compare two values.	77–79	
Makes fraction number families for sentences that compare and sentences that classify.	84–86	
Makes fraction number families for sentences that refer to parts of a whole group.	93	
Writes fraction number families for sentences that tell about percents or about fractions.	112, 113	
Makes fraction number families based on illustrations of Xs in a bag.	113	
DECIMAL OPERATIONS		
Addition/Subtraction		
Writes and solves column addition and subtraction problems involving dollar-and-cent amounts.	31	
Writes row problems involving dollar-and-cent values as column problems.	73	

© SRA/McGraw-Hill. Permission is granted to reproduce for school use.

Name ____________________

Skills	Taught in these Lessons	Date Lessons Completed
Adds decimal values.	85	
Subtracts decimal values.	86	
Adds and subtracts decimal values.	87	
Adds and subtracts whole numbers and decimal values.	89	
Multiplication/Division Works problems that multiply a dollar-and-cent amount by a whole number.	75	
Works a mixed set of problems involving dollar-and-cent amounts.	78	
Multiplies a whole number and a decimal value.	99, 101	
Works multiplication problems that have two decimal values.	102	
Multiplies decimal values.	103–105	
Works division problems that have a decimal value in the dividend.	123	
COORDINATE SYSTEM **Points and Lines** Writes the X and Y values for points shown on the coordinate system.	49, 51	
Graphs points on the coordinate system given their X and Y values.	52, 53	
Completes a table to show X and Y values of points shown on a coordinate system.	54, 55	
Identifies incorrectly-plotted points on a coordinate system.	56, 57	
Relates a line on the coordinate system to values in a table.	56–58	
Functions Completes a function table that indicates X values for points on a line, and graphs those points.	114, 115	
Figures out a function and completes a function table.	117	
Generates possible functions for a given set of X and Y values and completes a function table.	118	

Skills	Taught in these Lessons	Date Lessons Completed
PROBLEM SOLVING **Addition/Subtraction** Makes number families for comparison sentences.	12, 13	
Uses number families to solve addition and subtraction comparison word problems.	14–16	
Uses number families to solve word problems that tell what happened first and next.	18–23	
Works number-family problems that refer to **in, out,** and **end up**.	34–36	
Uses number families to solve comparison word problems that ask about the difference number.	45	
Works number-family problems that tell about **goals** and **difference**.	87–89	
Makes vertical number families for word problems that tell about either **in** or **out**.	93–95	
Works a mixed set of word problems which require horizontal or vertical number families.	96, 97	
Number-Family Tables Answers questions by referring to a 3-by-3 table.	1	
Answers questions about comparative amounts by referring to a 3-by-3 table.	2–4	
Completes a 3-by-3 table and answer questions by referring to the table.	17	
Uses comparison facts to figure out numbers needed in a 3-by-3 table.	26–29	
Constructs and uses a 3-by-3 table with column and row headings.	33–35	
Constructs a 3-by-3 table using a comparison fact to figure out a needed number.	36–39	
Multi-Step Problems Works number-family problems that give more than one number for **in** and/or **out**.	37, 38	

© SRA/McGraw-Hill. Permission is granted to reproduce for school use.

Name ______________________________

Skills	Taught in these Lessons	Date Lessons Completed
Works word problems that imply number families with more than one value for **in** or **out**.	39–44	
Works word problems that have two vertical number families (one for **in** and one for **out**).	45–48	
Works number-family problems involving dollar amounts and change.	81–83	
Works a mixed set of word problems that require vertical number families.	84	
Works horizontal goal problems that require vertical number families for **goal, now** or **both**.	96–98	
Works average problems by dividing.	111, 112	
Fraction Number Families		
Constructs fraction number families to solve word problems. (For example: $\frac{3}{5}$ of the children were girls. What fraction of the children were boys?)	47–49	
Uses fraction number families to solve word problems that tell about numbers and ask about fractions. (For example: 7 of the berries are ripe. 2 are not ripe. What fraction of the berries are not ripe?)	51, 52	
Works a mixed set of fraction-number-family problems.	53, 54	
Ratios and Proportions (Equations)		
Writes and solves ratio equations for word problems.	27–32	
Solves word problems and writes the answers as a number and a unit name.	40	
Works picture problems that show ratios and proportions.	42, 43	

Skills	Taught in these Lessons	Date Lessons Completed
Works proportion problems that involve 3- and 4-digit numbers.	49–51	
Answers questions by referring to complex ratios.	58–60	
Solves proportion problems, some of which require multiplying by a complex fraction equal to 1.	61–63	
Uses facts to complete a table that shows equivalent ratios.	63–66	
Graphs a line on the coordinate system for a set of equivalent ratios and answers questions based on the line.	71–77	
Works a set of problems that tell about more than 1 and ask a question.	78, 79	
Works a mixed set of word problems that require multiplication, division, or a ratio equation.	89, 101	
Works proportion word problems that have numbers that end in zeros.	101	
Computes averages.	108, 109	
Works a mixed set of multiplication and proportion problems that tell about 1 and ask about more than 1.	121–123	
Ratios and Proportions (Tables)		
Completes ratio tables.	52–55	
Solves word problems using ratio tables.	56–63	
Works ratio-table problems that give information for fraction number families.	64–66	
Works ratio-table problems, some of which require fraction number families.	67–69	
Uses facts to complete a table that shows equivalent ratios and check work by graphing points on the coordinate system.	68, 69	

© SRA/McGraw-Hill. Permission is granted to reproduce for school use.

Name ______________________

Skills	Taught in these Lessons	Date Lessons Completed
Works ratio-table problems that have a comparison statement involving fractions. For example: The sand weighed $\frac{2}{5}$ as much as the cement.	82–84	
Works a mixed set of ratio-table problems, some of which compare.	87, 88	
Works ratio-table problems in which the second column contains two mixed numbers.	91, 92	
Makes fraction number families and ratio tables for problems that do not provide fraction information.	94, 95	
Discriminates between problems that require a ratio table and those that require only a ratio equation.	105, 106	
Works ratio-table problems that involve percents.	106–109	
Uses a ratio table to work word problems that give two or three names.	107	
Works ratio-table problems that compare percents.	110, 111	
Works a mixed set of ratio-table problems that include fractions and percents.	114	
Multiplication/Division		
Works word problems of the form: 4 cakes = 7 pounds, 1 cake = ■.	71, 72	
Identifies the missing factor for problems that tell about more than one object and ask about 1. For example: 3 toys weigh 16 ounces. What does 1 toy weigh?	73, 76	
Works multiplication word problems that tell about 1 and ask about more than 1.	81	
Works multiplication and division word problems.	82–85	

Skills	Taught in these Lessons	Date Lessons Completed
Works a mixed set of multiplication and division problems that use the words **each** and **per**.	87, 88	
Works problems that describe the division of a quantity into equal-sized parts.	98–100	
Solves word problems that refer to even and odd numbers.	103, 104	
Works word problems that require decimal multiplication.	106, 107	
Works division problems in which the answer refers to non-divisible entities.	115, 116	
Works word problems that require division of a dollar amount.	124	
Inverse Operations		
Works 2-step word problems that give the starting number and two operations.	104	
Uses inverse operations to solve pairs of equations and figure out the starting number.	105–108	
Uses inverse operations to solve word problems.	109–111	
Works word problems that generate a series of inverse-operation equations.	112, 114	
Works story problems that involve inverse operations.	124, 125	
Measurement		
Completes a series of equivalent fractions, based on equivalent measures.	105, 106	
Works problems that compare different units of measurement.	107–111	
PROBABILITY		
Writes fractions that represent the probability of pulling an X from a bag.	112	
Uses information presented as a fraction to generate a set of objects.	113, 114	

© SRA/McGraw-Hill. Permission is granted to reproduce for school use.

Name ______________________

Skills	Taught in these Lessons	Date Lessons Completed
Relates the composition of a set to the number of trials required to give each member one chance of being selected.	114	
Works ratio-table problems that involve probability.	115–119	
Determines which set of objects provides the best chance of drawing a winner.	124	
GEOMETRY **Perimeter and Area**		
Figures out the lengths of sides in quadrilaterals with parallel sides.	56, 57	
Computes perimeters of polygons.	58–61	
Works area-of-rectangle problems shown on the coordinate system using the equation: squares = $x \times y$.	62–65	
Works area and perimeter problems for rectangles shown on the coordinate system.	66, 68	
Works area and perimeter problems for rectangles shown on the coordinate system.	69–72	
Works area-of-triangle problems shown on the coordinate system.	74, 75	
Works area problems for rectangles and triangles that are not shown on the coordinate system.	76, 77	
Works area-of-parallelogram problems shown on the coordinate system.	79, 80	
Works area and perimeter problems for parallelograms shown on the coordinate system.	81, 82	
Works area and perimeter problems for parallelograms that are not shown on the coordinate system.	83, 85	
Works area problems for triangles and parallelograms that are not shown on the coordinate system.	86	

Skills	Taught in these Lessons	Date Lessons Completed
Finds the area of non-right triangles shown on the coordinate system by constructing parallelograms.	96	
Finds the area and perimeter of non-right triangles that are not shown on the coordinate system.	97	
Finds the area and perimeter of parallelograms, rectangles and triangles.	98	
Circles		
Figures out the relationship between the diameter and circumference of a circle.	91	
Uses the equation $\pi \times \mathbf{D} = \mathbf{C}$ to figure out the circumference of a circle.	92	
Uses the equation $\pi \times \mathbf{D} = \mathbf{C}$ to figure out the circumference or diameter of a circle.	93–95	
Uses the equation $\pi \times \mathbf{D} = \mathbf{C}$ to figure out the circumference or radius of a circle.	111, 112	
Uses the equation $\pi \times \mathbf{D} = \mathbf{C}$ to figure out the circumference, radius, or diameter of a circle.	113	
Uses the equation $\mathbf{A} = \pi \times \mathbf{r} \times \mathbf{r}$ to figure out the area of a circle.	113, 114	
Finds the circumference and the area of circles.	115, 117	
Surface Area		
Computes the surface area of a rectangular prism.	94–96	
Finds the surface area of a rectangular prism from a non-exploded diagram.	97, 98	
Finds the surface area of a pyramid with a rectangular base.	99–101	
Finds the surface area of a pyramid that has a triangular base.	102, 103	

© SRA/McGraw-Hill. Permission is granted to reproduce for school use.

Name ______________________

Skills	Taught in these Lessons	Date Lessons Completed
Volume		
Finds the volume of rectangular prisms.	104, 105	
Finds the volume of a triangular prism.	106, 109	
Finds the volume of rectangular and triangular prisms.	107	
Finds the surface area and volume of a rectangular prism.	108	
Angles and Lines		
Indicates whether pairs of lines are parallel or not parallel.	55	
Answers questions about the number of degrees in angles.	71	
Makes number families to solve angle problems involving an angle that is divided into two smaller angles.	72, 73	
Works problems requiring conversion of a fraction of a circle into degrees.	74, 75	
Uses a fact about a fraction of a circle to make a number family and work problems involving three angles.	77–79	
Makes number families to solve angle problems involving complementary and supplementary angles.	81, 82	
Identifies corresponding angles.	83	
Figures out the degrees in corresponding and supplementary angles.	84–86	
Figures out the degrees in four angles that are formed by two intersecting lines.	88, 89	
Figures out the rule for vertically opposite angles formed by two intersecting lines.	91	
Applies the rule for vertically opposite angles to figure out corresponding sets of angles at parallel lines.	92, 93	
Uses a protractor to measure degrees in an angle.	118	

Skills	Taught in these Lessons	Date Lessons Completed
PROJECTS		
Does the groundwork for building a model of the solar system.	116	
Uses ratio numbers to complete a table about the solar system and makes a scale model.	117	
Completes a circle graph based on a table that shows amounts of time a person spent on various activities.	118	
Constructs a circle graph to show use of time.	119	
Gathers data on favorite colors and complete a table that shows tallies, numbers, and degrees.	119	
Constructs a bar graph and circle graph to display percents for various geometric shapes selected as favorites by 20 different people.	120	
Constructs a bar graph to display the average percents of 10 student surveys conducted in lesson 120.	121	
Compares the ratio of surface area to volume for cubes that are relatively large and small.	122	
Determines the contents of a bag based on experimental data and expected outcomes.	123	
Figures out the threshold of efficiency for a square (the size at which the perimeter and area have the same number of units).	124	
Conducts an experiment and display the results as a frequency distribution.	125	

© SRA/McGraw-Hill. Permission is granted to reproduce for school use.

Remedy Summary—Group Summary of Test Performance

Note: Test remedies are specified in the *Answer Key.* Percent Summary is also specified in the *Answer Key.*

Name	Test 1							Test 2												Test 3										
	Check parts not passed						Total %	Check parts not passed											Total %	Check parts not passed										Total %
	1	2	3	4	5	6		1	2	3	4	5	6	7	8	9	10	11		1	2	3	4	5	6	7	8	9	10	
1.																														
2.																														
3.																														
4.																														
5.																														
6.																														
7.																														
8.																														
9.																														
10.																														
11.																														
12.																														
13.																														
14.																														
15.																														
16.																														
17.																														
18.																														
19.																														
20.																														
21.																														
22.																														
23.																														
24.																														
25.																														
26.																														
27.																														
28.																														
29.																														
30.																														
Number of students Not Passed = NP																														
Total number of students = T																														
Remedy needed if NP/T = 25% or more																														

© SRA/McGraw-Hill. Permission is granted to reproduce for school use.

	Test 4										Test 5								Test 6					
	Check parts not passed									Total %	Check parts not passed							Total %	Check parts not passed					Total %
Name	1	2	3	4	5	6	7	8	9		1	2	3	4	5	6	7		1	2	3	4	5	
1.																								
2.																								
3.																								
4.																								
5.																								
6.																								
7.																								
8.																								
9.																								
10.																								
11.																								
12.																								
13.																								
14.																								
15.																								
16.																								
17.																								
18.																								
19.																								
20.																								
21.																								
22.																								
23.																								
24.																								
25.																								
26.																								
27.																								
28.																								
29.																								
30.																								
Number of students Not Passed = NP																								
Total number of students = T																								
Remedy needed if NP/T = 25% or more																								

© SRA/McGraw-Hill. Permission is granted to reproduce for school use.

Remedy Summary—Group Summary of Test Performance

Name	Test 7									Test 8											Test 9									
	Check parts not passed								Total %	Check parts not passed										Total %	Check parts not passed									Total %
	1	2	3	4	5	6	7	8		1	2	3	4	5	6	7	8	9	10		1	2	3	4	5	6	7	8	9	
1.																														
2.																														
3.																														
4.																														
5.																														
6.																														
7.																														
8.																														
9.																														
10.																														
11.																														
12.																														
13.																														
14.																														
15.																														
16.																														
17.																														
18.																														
19.																														
20.																														
21.																														
22.																														
23.																														
24.																														
25.																														
26.																														
27.																														
28.																														
29.																														
30.																														
Number of students Not Passed = NP																														
Total number of students = T																														
Remedy needed if NP/T = 25% or more																														

© SRA/McGraw-Hill. Permission is granted to reproduce for school use.

Remedy Summary—Group Summary of Test Performance

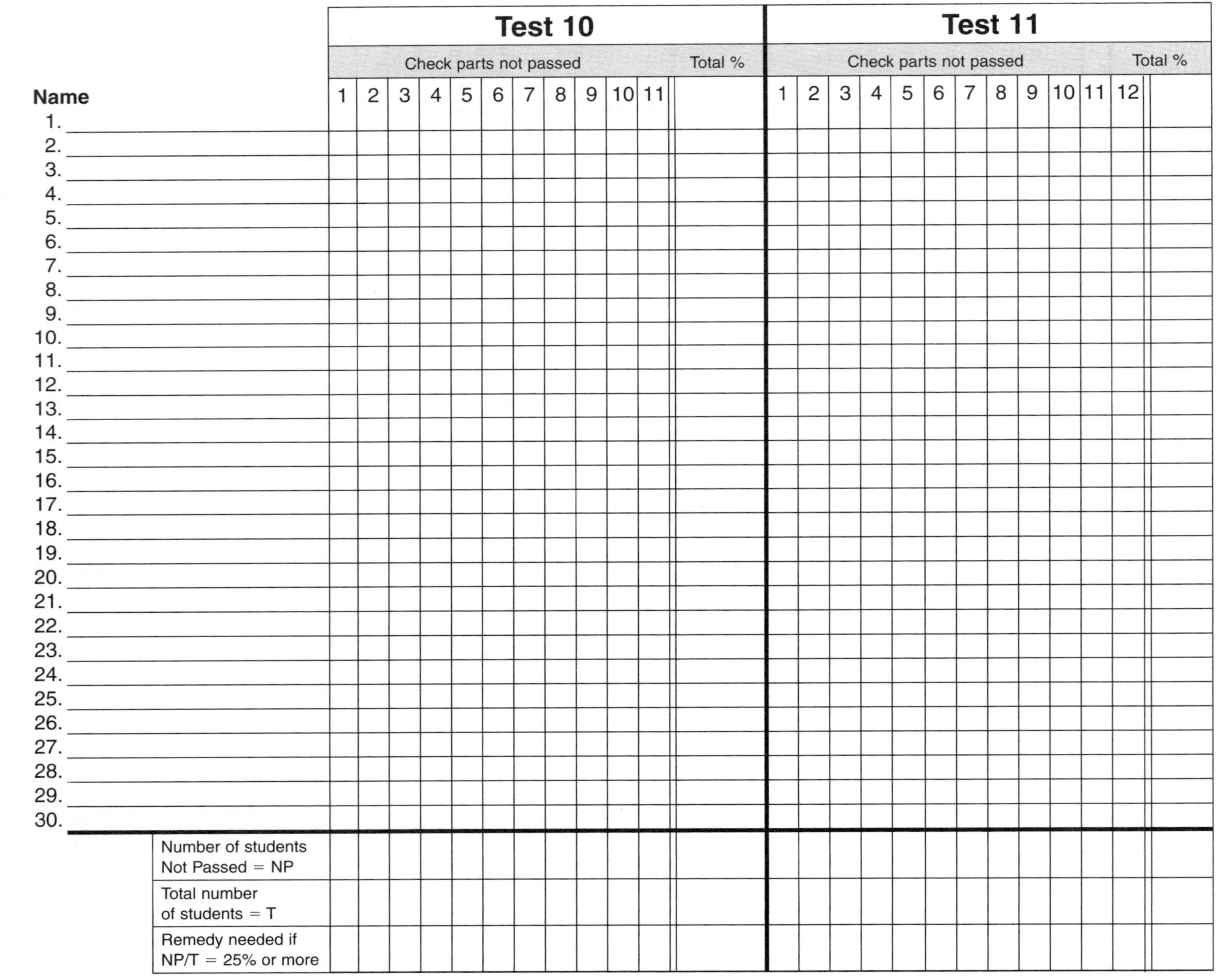

	Test 10												Test 11												
	Check parts not passed											Total %	Check parts not passed												Total %
Name	1	2	3	4	5	6	7	8	9	10	11		1	2	3	4	5	6	7	8	9	10	11	12	
1.																									
2.																									
3.																									
4.																									
5.																									
6.																									
7.																									
8.																									
9.																									
10.																									
11.																									
12.																									
13.																									
14.																									
15.																									
16.																									
17.																									
18.																									
19.																									
20.																									
21.																									
22.																									
23.																									
24.																									
25.																									
26.																									
27.																									
28.																									
29.																									
30.																									
Number of students Not Passed = NP																									
Total number of students = T																									
Remedy needed if NP/T = 25% or more																									

© SRA/McGraw-Hill. Permission is granted to reproduce for school use.

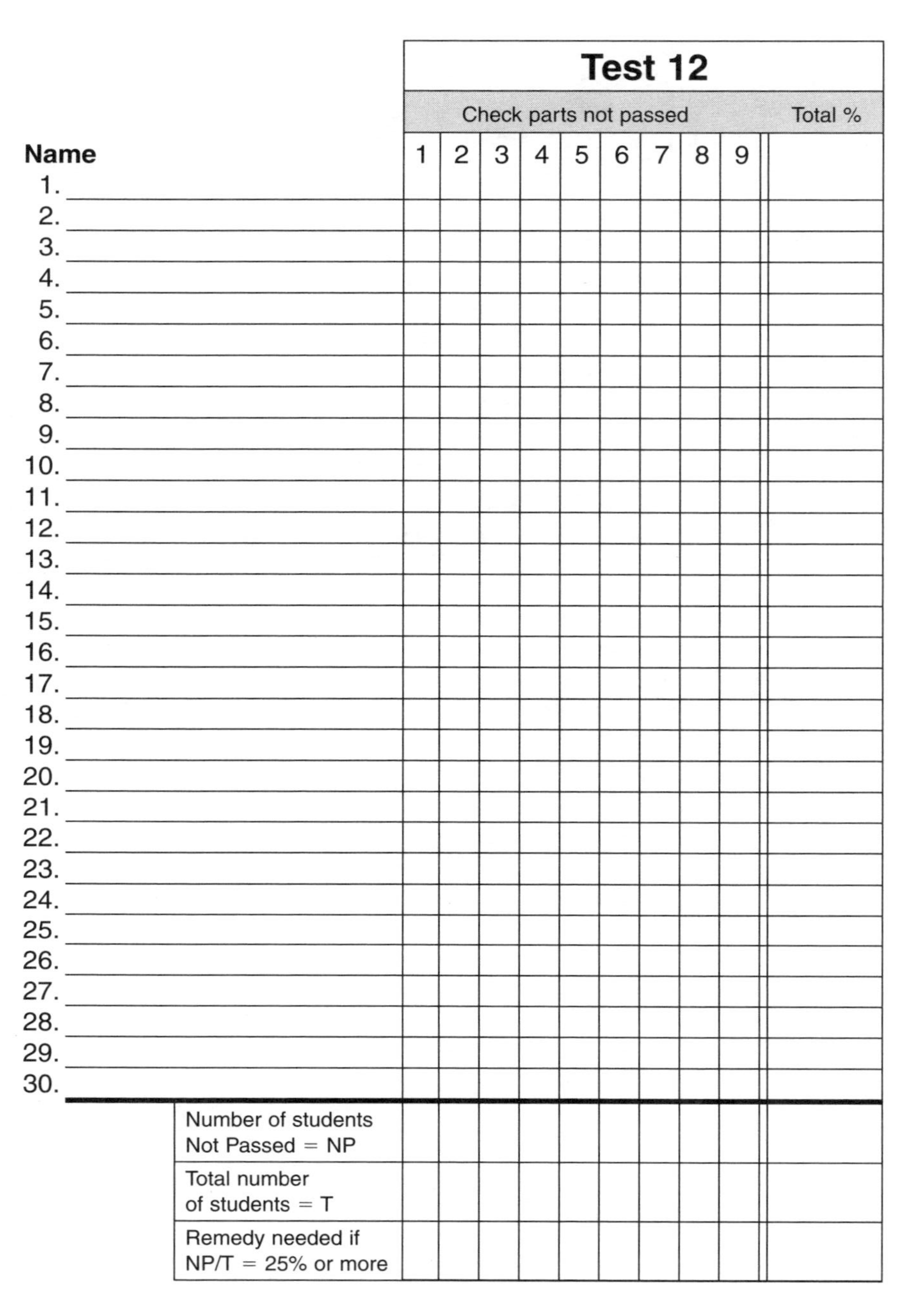

Test 12

Name	Check parts not passed									Total %
	1	2	3	4	5	6	7	8	9	
1.										
2.										
3.										
4.										
5.										
6.										
7.										
8.										
9.										
10.										
11.										
12.										
13.										
14.										
15.										
16.										
17.										
18.										
19.										
20.										
21.										
22.										
23.										
24.										
25.										
26.										
27.										
28.										
29.										
30.										
Number of students Not Passed = NP										
Total number of students = T										
Remedy needed if NP/T = 25% or more										

© SRA/McGraw-Hill. Permission is granted to reproduce for school use.